STP 1309

Thermal and Mechanical Test Methods and Behavior of Continuous-Fiber Ceramic Composites

Michael G. Jenkins, Edgar Lara-Curzio, Stephen T. Gonczy, Noel E. Ashbaugh, and Larry P. Zawada, Editors

ASTM Publication Code Number (PCN):
04-013090-30

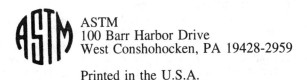

ASTM
100 Barr Harbor Drive
West Conshohocken, PA 19428-2959

Printed in the U.S.A.

ISBN: 0-8031-2033-8
PCN: 04-013090-30

Photocopy Rights

Peer Review Policy

Each paper published in this volume was evaluated by two peer reviewers and at least one of the Editors. The authors addressed all of the reviewers' comments to the satisfaction of both the technical editor(s) and the ASTM Committee on Publications.

To make technical information available as quickly as possible, the peer-reviewed papers in this publication were prepared "camera-ready" as submitted by the authors.

The quality of the papers in this publication reflects not only the obvious efforts of the authors and the technical editor(s), but also the work of these peer reviewers. The ASTM Committee on Publications acknowledges with appreciation their dedication and contribution of time and effort on behalf of ASTM.

Printed in Philadelphia, PA
March 1997

Foreword

This publication, *Thermal and Mechanical Test Methods and Behavior of Continuous-Fiber Ceramic Composites,* contains papers presented at the symposium of the same name held in Cocoa Beach, Florida on 8-9 Jan. 1996. The symposium was sponsored by ASTM Committee C28 on Advanced Ceramics, ASTM Committee E08 on Fatigue and Fracture, and the American Ceramic Society, Engineering Ceramics Division. Michael G. Jenkins, University of Washington, Edgar Lara-Curzio, Oak Ridge National Laboratory, Stephen T. Gonczy, Gateway Materials Technology, Noel E. Ashbaugh, University of Dayton Research Institute, and Larry P. Zawada, Wright Laboratory, presided as symposium cochairmen and are also the editors of the resulting publication.

Contents

Overview

In the ten years since its establishment in 1986, ASTM Committee C28 on Advanced Ceramics has provided a major forum for promoting standardized terminology, guides, classifications, practices, and test methods for advanced (namely, structural, fine, and technical) ceramics. Similarly, for the past 30 or more years, ASTM Committee E08 on Fatigue and Fracture and its predecessors have been involved in fracture and fatigue activities, both in developing standards and transferring information primarily for metallic materials, but also in advanced and newly emerging materials such as advanced ceramics. The American Ceramic Society for over 100 years has promoted, educated, disseminated, and conferred on a variety of topics related to ceramic materials including processing, manufacturing, characterizing, and utilizing.

This publication and the Symposium on Thermal and Mechanical Test Methods and Behavior of Continuous-Fiber Ceramic Composites, which was held in Cocoa Beach, Florida, 8–9 Jan. 1996, were cosponsored by these organizations to continue all their past efforts. Twenty-six papers were presented at the symposium, and this publication contains nineteen peer-reviewed articles on a special subset of advanced ceramics: continuous-fiber ceramic composites.

The advancement of technology is often limited by the availability and understanding of materials. In today's technology, the U.S. Government is currently supporting programs such Enabling Propulsion Materials and the Continuous Fiber Ceramic Composite (CFCCs) programs that target specific new materials such as CFCCs for a broad range of applications from chemical processing to stationary heat engines to power generation to aerospace vehicles. Such applications require that still-emerging materials such as CFCCs be refined, processed, characterized, and manufactured in sufficient volume for successful widespread use under the proposed aggressive thermal/mechanical operating conditions. Concurrently, as the materials are refined, designers must have access to material properties and performance databases to integrate the material systems into their advanced engineering concepts. Without extensive materials characterization, producers of materials cannot evaluate relative process improvements nor can designers have confidence in the performance of the material for a particular application.

Developing and verifying appropriate test methods as well as generating design data for advanced materials is expensive and time-consuming. High-temperature ceramic composites cost more to process than monolithic ceramics because of both the cost of constituent materials in addition to extra, labor-intensive fabrication steps. Equipment for testing at elevated temperatures is highly specialized and expensive. Unique and novel test methods must be developed to take into account thermal stresses, stress gradients, measurement capabilities, gripping methods, environmental effects, statistical considerations, and limited material quantities. It is therefore imperative that test methods be carefully developed, standardized, verified, and used so that accurate data are generated, and duplication of test data can be minimized in test programs.

The papers in this STP provide current results of research and development programs on continuous-fiber ceramic composites. The papers are divided into five categories:

(1) Room-Temperature Test Results/Methods,
(2) High-Temperature Test Results/Methods,

(3) Nondestructive Characterization,
(4) Modeling and Processing, and
(5) Testing of Tubes.

In the different sections, various types of continuous-fiber ceramic composites including those processed with chemically infiltrated, polymer-impregnated, sintered, melt-infiltrated, or viscous glass-infiltrated matrices are addressed. The Room-Temperature Test Results/ Methods section includes papers on the influence of various test parameters on the tensile behavior, high-strain rate effects on tensile behavior, shear properties, and unloading-reloading sequences and their effects. The section on High-Temperature Test Results/Methods includes papers on the effect of hold times on fatigue behavior, high-temperautre crack growth, tensile and fatigue at a particular temperature, fatigue crack growth, creep rupture behavior, and retained tensile properties after exposure to elevated temperatures. In the Nondestructive Characterization section, the characterization of damage progression using an integrated testing system, an infrared-based method for determining thermal properties and defects, and measurements of orthotropic properties using impulse resonance are addressed. In the section on Modeling and Processing, papers are included on optimal design of laminates, modeling of creep response, and the secondary processing effects of abrasive water jet cutting. The section on Testing of Tubes includes burner rig testing of a hoop subelement.

With this symposium and the resulting STP, ASTM has made another stride forward by providing a wealth of information on continuous-fiber ceramic composites that will assist the research, processing, and design community in better understanding the behavior of these materials. This information will also be invaluable as test methods continue to be developed and verified for continuous-fiber ceramic matrix composites.

Michael G. Jenkins
Department of Mechanical Engineering
University of Washington, Seattle, WA;
Symposium cochair and coeditor.

Edgar Lara-Curzio
Metals and Ceramics Division
Oak Ridge National Laboratory,
Oak Ridge, TN;
Symposium cochair and coeditor.

Stephen T. Gonczy
Gateway Materials Technology,
Mt. Prospect, IL;
Symposium cochair and coeditor.

Noel E. Ashbaugh
University of Dayton Research Institute
University of Dayton, Dayton OH;
Symposium cochair and coeditor.

Larry P. Zawada
Materials Directorate
Wright Laboratory,
Wright-Patterson AFB, OH;
Symposium cochair and coeditor.

Room-Temperature Test Results/Methods

John P. Piccola, Jr.,[1] Michael G. Jenkins,[2] and Edgar Lara-Curzio[3]

INFLUENCE OF TEST MODE, TEST RATE, SPECIMEN GEOMETRY, AND BENDING ON TENSILE MECHANICAL BEHAVIOR OF A CONTINUOUS FIBER CERAMIC COMPOSITE

REFERENCE: Piccola, J. P., Jr., Jenkins, M. G., and Lara-Curzio, E., "**Influence of Test Mode, Test Rate, Specimen Geometry, and Bending on Tensile Mechanical Behavior of a Continuous Fiber Ceramic Composite**," Thermal and Mechanical Test Methods and Behavior of Continuous-Fiber Ceramic Composites, ASTM STP 1309, Michael G. Jenkins, Stephen T. Gonczy, Edgar Lara-Curzio, Noel E. Ashbaugh, and Larry P. Zawada, Eds., American Society for Testing and Materials, 1997.

ABSTRACT: ASTM Test Method for Monotonic Tensile Strength Testing of Continuous Fiber-Reinforced Advanced Ceramics with Solid Rectangular Cross-Section Specimens at Ambient Temperatures (C 1275) was used to investigate the effects of test mode (load versus displacement), test rate (fast versus slow), specimen geometry (straight-sided versus reduced-gage section), specimen volume (long/thin versus short/fat), and bending in tension for a twelve-ply, two-dimensional, plain weave SiC fiber reinforced / SiC matrix continuous fibre ceramic composite. Although it appeared that "graceful failure" is sometimes accentuated by displacement control at slow rates, a two-way analysis of variance (ANOVA) with replication at the 95% significance level of all the test results showed that there was no significance of test rate, test mode or specimen geometry for proportional limit stress. Similarly, for ultimate tensile strength there was no significance of test rate or test mode although there was a significance of specimen geometry. Finally, for this two dimensional, plain weave fiber architecture there was no significance of test rate, test mode, or specimen geometry (including straight-sided specimens) on fracture location. Proportional limit stress decreased with increasing bending while ultimate tensile strength appeared independent of bending.

KEYWORDS: continuous fiber ceramic composite, tension test, bending, test rate, test mode, specimen volume, proportional limit stress, ultimate tensile strength

---

Continuous fiber ceramic composites (CFCCs) are a relatively new area of composite research. Additional and extensive investigations of

---

[1]Structural analyst, seats, Boeing Commercial Airplane Group, Seattle, WA 98124-2207.

[2]Assistant professor, Department of Mechanical Engineering, University of Washington, Seattle, WA 98195-2600.

[3]Development staff member, Metals and Ceramics Division, Oak Ridge National Laboratory, Oak Ridge, TN 37831-6064.

various types of CFCCs and other ceramic matrix composites are required before industry adopts CFCCs on a widespread scale [1]. A primary advantage of CFCCs is their inherent damage tolerance (i.e. the increased ability of the material to absorb energy without catastrophic fracture, also known as "toughness"), thereby overcoming the brittleness often associated with ceramics, while maintaining the high-temperature performance of their monolithic counterparts [2,3].

A broad range of industrial sectors have the potential for implementing CFCCs [1] because of the economic and energy considerations. Chemical processing, refining operations, power generation, and heat engines all can benefit from the use of CFCC components such as filters, substrates, piping, tanks, burners, heat pipes, tubes, combustor liners, vanes, and nozzles.

These potential applications have justified the need for additional experimental [4-6] and analytical research [7-9] of CFCCs. However, many of these studies have involved unidirectional composites with glass matrices [4]. Brittle matrix composites reinforced in multiple directions have only recently begun receiving attention [2,5,6]. Experimental work has demonstrated the effect of matrix cracking and the debonding layer between the fibers and the matrix on the strength of the composite [10]. Analytical modeling of these conditions has been performed along with models of the stress-strain behavior [7]. More extensive systematic studies are still lacking to determine the effects on the mechanical properties and performance of such common test parameters as test mode/rate, specimen geometry/volume, and nonuniform stresses (i.e., bending).

A primary motivation for this study was to produce fundamental information the mechanical properties and performance of a two-dimensionally-reinforced CFCC. Additionally, certain recommendations and requirements of the recently introduced test standard ASTM Test Method for Monotonic Tensile Strength Testing of Continuous Fiber-Reinforced Advanced Ceramics with Solid Rectangular Cross-Section Specimens at Ambient Temperatures (C 1275) still require clarification. Thus, a further motivation for this study was to characterize various testing parameters such as test mode, test rate, specimen geometry, etc. and their subsequent effects on the tensile mechanical behavior of a two-dimensional (2D), woven SiC fiber-reinforced / SiC matrix CFCC.

The material is briefly described. An overview of the experimental procedure follows. Test results are presented in terms of stress-strain response, proportional limit stress, ultimate tensile strength and modulus of toughness. The effect of bending on proportional limit stress and ultimate tensile strength is discussed. Fracture location and its relation to specimen geometry is also evaluated. Finally, an analysis of variation (ANOVA) is used to justify pooling of the test results.

TEST MATERIAL

Material Description

A commercial CFCC (SuperTemp from B.F. Goodrich Aerospace, Brecksville, Ohio) was the focus of this study. The 2D-reinforcement was a plain woven cloth of ~1800 denier fiber bundles (~500 fibers/bundle) composed of a ceramic grade (Nicalon™) Si-C-O fiber. The fiber preform was fabricated by layering twelve plies of cloth with the warp of the fibers along the longitudinal direction of the test specimens.

The matrix was processed as follows. In the initial step, chemical vapor infiltration (CVI) was used to deposit a ~0.3 μm interfacial layer of pyrolytic carbon onto the fiber preform. In the final step, methyltrichlorosilane was decomposed, infiltrating the preforms by CVI until all the surface microporosity was filled, thus preventing further CVI of the interior of the material while forming a crystalline β-SiC matrix. The remaining microporosity (~20 to 25 vol%) was primarily located within the internal fiber bundles. The porosity was estimated from bulk density measurements, actual fiber volume fractions, and theoretical density of the CFCC calculated densities of constituent materials. Approximate volume fractions of fibers and matrix were 35% and 40%, respectively.

Tensile Specimens

Simple, straight-sided and reduced gage section (i.e., dog bone) flat specimens were fabricated by an undisclosed process (presumably diamond-grit cutting and grinding) into four different test specimen geometries designated RG1, RG2, RG3, and SS (Fig. 1). The twelve-ply specimens were ~3.7 mm thick.

Tapered (5°) end tabs [6] consisted of an E-glass fiber/epoxy matrix composite were used to protect the specimens from being damaged at the area within the hydraulic grips. Such damage can be in the form of premature splitting due to the contact of the grip surface with the specimen. The ratio of the resin to curing agent was chosen to produce an adhesive with a shear strength greater than ~9.4 MPa, the maximum interfacial shear stress anticipated at the interface of the tab and specimen, so as to prevent delamination at the end tab and subsequent damage to the specimen.

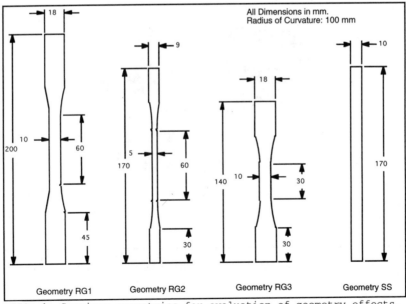

FIG. 1--Specimen geometries for evaluation of geometry effects.

EXPERIMENTAL PROCEDURE

All thirty-two tests were conducted at ambient temperatures (20 to 22°C, 55 to 65 %RH) per ASTM C 1275 on a commercial, single-actuator, electromechanical materials test system (100-kN capacity) having both load and cross-head displacement control capabilities. A digital controller with related software managed all input and output signals.

Commercial, hydraulically-actuated specimen grips were independently activated and could maintain an adjustable grip force on the specimen grip face without backlash. The actual grip faces were coated with a roughened, sputtered WC coating to prevent slippage at the specimen/grip interface. Grips were attached to the load frame via a fixed, but adjustable, commercially available alignment system.

In compliance with ASTM C 1275 verification of load train alignment was performed before and after the series of tests to assure less than 5 percent bending (PB as described in Eq. 1 below) at an average strain of 500×10^{-6} m/m in the alignment specimen. A steel alignment specimen was employed, 200 mm in length with a 35-mm long reduced gage section and a 6 by 6 mm cross section. Four longitudinal strain gages, equispaced around the circumference, were adhered on two separate longitudinal planes for a total of eight strain gages. Proper load train alignment helps to reduce the introduction of bending moments (and nonuniform stresses) into the specimen during a tension test.

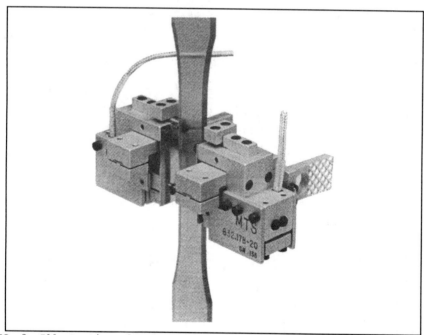

FIG. 2--Illustration of a dual extensometer mounted on a polymer specimen. For tests of CFCCs the extensometer was mounted on the specimen faces.

Separate, continuous strain readings were recorded for two opposing faces of the specimen using a dual-arm, strain-gage based extensometer, Axis A and Axis B, over gage lengths of 25 mm and a range of $+50000 \times 10^{-6}$ to -20000×10^{-6} m/m strain (Fig. 2). Percent bending (in this case, out of plane bending only) was calculated as:

$$PB = 100 \frac{(\varepsilon_A - \varepsilon_B)}{(\varepsilon_A + \varepsilon_B)} \tag{1}$$

where PB is percent bending, ε_A is the strain from Axis A, and ε_B is the strain from Axis B.

A preliminary tension test of one specimen (RG1 geometry) resulted in an ultimate strength of ~250 MPa and a strain at fracture of ~6000 x 10^{-6} m/m. These values were used to approximate times to failure for various test mode and test rate combinations (Table 1). To study the effect of test rate an order of magnitude difference was chosen between the minimum and maximum test rates. Similar rates were chosen to compare differences in test mode. Therefore, establishing times to failure for each geometry was necessary to compare strength and strain results. The final load (500 and 50 N/s) and crosshead displacement rates (0.03 and 0.003 mm/s) were chosen to produce failure times of ~20 and ~200 s.

TABLE 1--Estimated times to failure for various test modes and rates

| Geometry | Displacement Control | | Load Control | |
	0.003 mm/s	0.03 mm/s	50 N/s	500 N/s
RG1, V1=L2*W2	240 s	24 s	180 s	18 s
RG2, V2=L2*W1	340 s	34 s	90 s	9 s
RG3, V2=L1*W2	124 s	12 s	180 s	18 s
SS, V1=L2*W2	180 s	18 s	180 s	18 s

Note: RG (reduced gage), SS (straight sided), volume gage sections, V1 and V2 are computed with: L1 = 30 mm, L2 = 60 mm, W1 = 5 mm, W2 = 10 mm.

RESULTS

Stress-strain Relation

Stress-strain response is the primary means for gathering and analyzing data. The stress-strain response of the test material in this study was generally linear up to the proportional limit stress, σ_O. The proportional limit stress was followed by a nonlinear stress-strain response up to the ultimate tensile strength with stress increasing at a much slower rate than in the linear region. In most cases the stress at fracture corresponded to the ultimate tensile strength. In addition to the proportional limit stress, the elastic modulus, E, ultimate tensile strength, S_U, fracture strength, S_F, and corresponding strain values (ε_O, ε_U, and ε_F), along with the modulus of toughness, U_T, can be represented on a stress-strain curve (Fig. 3). Actual curves of stress versus strain with superposed curves of percent bending versus strain for two specimens of the same geometry are shown in Fig. 4. Two specimens (i.e., one test with replication) were tested at each combination of geometry, test mode, and test rate.

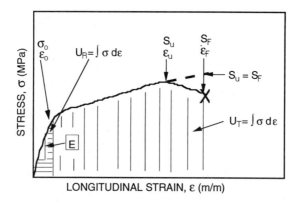

FIG. 3--Generic stress-strain curve and related mechanical properties (ASTM C 1275).

Elastic Modulus

For consistency, elastic modulus for each test was calculated from the slope of the linear, least-squares regression of the stress-strain curve from 0 to 15 MPa. The upper stress value of 15 MPa was used as it represented the least value of the onset of non linearity observed in previous tests. Therefore, it was assumed that all test exhibited a linear region from 0 to 15 MPa. Test results for elastic modulus have been reported previously [6].

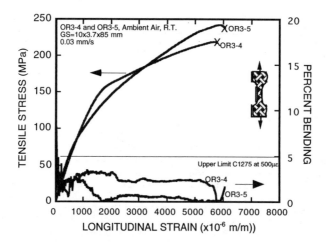

FIG. 4--Actual stress-strain and percent bending-strain curves.

Proportional Limit Stress

ASTM C 1275 recommends two methods for determining the proportional limit (PL) stress (i.e., PL is the stress at an offset strain and PL is stress at a prescribed strain). However, out of five different methods applied to the test data [6], for reasons of consistency, objectivity and numerical efficiency, the proportional limit stress in this study was calculated as follows:

$$\sigma = PL = \sigma_o \text{ when } \frac{(\sigma_i - \sigma)}{\sigma} x100 \geq 10\% \tag{2}$$

where σ_i is the stress calculated from the elastic modulus, E, and the corresponding strain, ε_i, at the ith datum such that $\sigma_i = E\varepsilon_i$, and σ is the actual stress at the ith strain. The proportional limit is the point at which the difference between the actual stress and the calculated stress is equal to or greater than 10%. It can be argued that the proportional limit is the most important design parameter for CFCCs because it defines the stress or strain at the onset of nonlinearity. When specimen geometries are grouped (Fig. 5a) specimen RG1 has the most consistent proportional limit values regardless of test rate or control with specimen RG2 having the overall greatest average value. Comparing test mode and test rate (Fig. 5b) shows that displacement control often results in greater proportional limits than load control.

Ultimate Tensile Strength

In the case of ultimate tensile strength, S_U, both the specimen geometry and test mode/rate relations show fairly consistent results (Fig. 6). The ultimate tensile strength is an important parameter when comparing most materials and can be used intuitively to compare and select a material for "engineering" design. At the ultimate tensile strength, the load is carried almost entirely by the fibers and therefore often coincides with the fracture strength, S_F, of the composite. Although the load is carried by the fibers at S_U, an accurate measure of the in situ fiber strength is difficult since physical and chemical degradation may occur during fabrication [12].

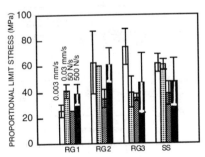

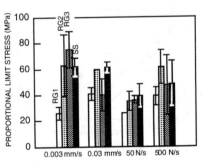

a) Specimen geometry effect on σ_o b) Test mode/rate effect on σ_o

FIG. 5--Effect of test parameters on the proportional limit stress (error bars represent the upper and lower range of the data).

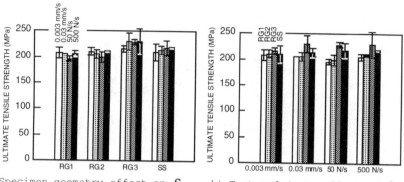

a) Specimen geometry effect on S_U b) Test mode/rate effect on S_U

FIG. 6--Effect of test parameters on the ultimate tensile strength (error bars represent the upper and lower range of the data).

Effect of Percent Bending, PB

The use of a dual-arm extensometer made it possible to calculate the amount of out-of-plane bending in each specimen during each test. PB was calculated to determine the effect of the nonuniformity of uniaxial tensile stress on the calculated material properties. Figure 7 contains all data points represented as a scatter plot to illustrate the effect of percent bending on proportional limit stress and ultimate tensile strength. Data points in Fig. 7 are grouped well around the 1 to 5 PB range. Proportional limit stress (~matrix cracking stress), as expected for the fracture stress of a brittle matrix, decreases with increasing percent bending. Ultimate tensile strengths of 200 to 250 MPa show little effect of increasing percent bending, as expected for the fiber-dominated ultimate tensile strength. Note that trend lines in Fig. 7 are guides for the eye and not curve fits.

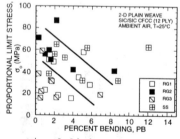
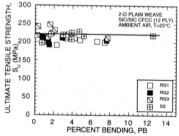

a) Proportional limit stress   b) Ultimate tensile strength

FIG 7--Strength as a function of percent bending (a) proportional limit stress and (b) ultimate tensile strength. Note that trend lines are guides for the eye and not curve fits.

<u>Modulus of Toughness and Failure Location</u>

    Figure 8 illustrates the scatter for the modulus of toughness
(i.e., the total energy absorbed during the tensile deformation and
failure of the material), U_T, in relation to the fracture location, l_f,
of each specimen. U_T seemed to be more consistent as fracture occurred
nearer to the midpoint of the specimen, which is consistent with
$U_T = f(\varepsilon)$. U_T as defined mathematically (total area under the tensile
stress-strain curve) can be approximated by numerical integration such
that:

$$U_T = \int_0^{\varepsilon_f} \sigma \, d\varepsilon \approx \sum_{i=2}^{n} \frac{\sigma_i + \sigma_{i-1}}{2}(\varepsilon_i - \varepsilon_{i-1}) \tag{3}$$

where ε_f is the strain at fracture and σ and ε are the stress and
strains from the stress-strain curves, respectively, i is the individual
σ and ε data pair, and n is the total number of data pairs.

DISCUSSION

<u>Analysis of Variance</u>

    Because of the limited number of replicate tests a statistical
analysis of the data was performed to identify the effects of test mode,
test rate, and specimen geometry. Specifically, a two-way analysis of
variance (ANOVA) with replication [13, 14] capable of evaluating more
than one hypothesis simultaneously was performed to determine the effect

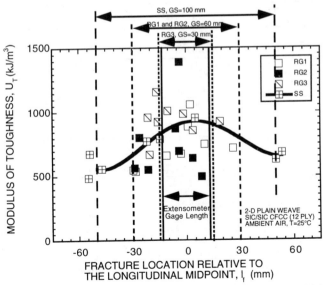

FIG 8--Modulus of toughness for each geometry with respect to fracture
location

of load rate, displacement rate, or load/displacement mode, within a given geometry and between the four test specimen geometries at a 95% significance level. In addition, the rate and mode effects for geometry to geometry results for proportional limit stress and ultimate strength of the test were analyzed.

Table 2 shows a summary for the ANOVA for test mode/rate and specimen geometry for proportional limit stress and ultimate tensile strength. Under the Source of Variation column, the row labeled Interaction is important to check before drawing conclusions on the main effects (test mode/rate and geometry). If the interaction is not significant (i.e., no interactions are present) the tests on the main effects are interpretable. A significant interaction would suggest that the data should be analyzed in a different manner. If no interactions are present then more general comparisons can be made rather than separate comparisons. In this study, there are no interactions present (i.e., F < F crit). Since F < F crit for both the row and column categories then neither load rate or geometry display statistically significant interaction for either stress or strain.

The P-value can also be used to interpret the ANOVA results. The P-value is the probability (i.e., significance level) that the null hypothesis is true (i.e., the means for each sample set are equal). If the P-value is less than the imposed level of significance, $\alpha = 0.05$, then the null hypothesis of the means being equal is not supported and the effect of the source of variation is "real" at the 95% (i.e., $1-\alpha$) significance level.

TABLE 2--<u>ANOVA for "pooled" results for test mode/rate and geometry</u>

Source of Variation	Test Property	SS[a]	df[b]	MS[c]	F[d]	P-value[e]	F crit[f]
Test Mode/ Rate	σ_O	654.86	3	218.29	0.73	0.55	3.24
	S_U	191.28	3	63.76	0.60	0.62	3.24
Geometry	σ_O	2274.81	3	758.27	2.52	0.09	3.24
	S_U	2481.51	3	827.17	7.79	0.0019	3.24
Interaction	σ_O	3121.86	9	346.87	1.15	0.38	2.54
	S_U	726.17	9	80.69	0.76	0.65	2.54
Within	σ_O	4813.31	16	300.83	...	...	...
	S_U	1698.21	16	106.14	...	...	...
Total	σ_O	10864.84	31	...	...	...	...
	S_U	5097.181	31	...	...	...	...

[a]SS = sum of squares; [b]df = degrees of freedom; [c]MS = mean sum of squares; [d]F = F statistic; [e]P-value = probability (i.e., significance level) that null hypothesis is true (i.e., means for each sample set are equal); [f]F-crit = critical value of F statistic for significance level of $\alpha = 0.05$.

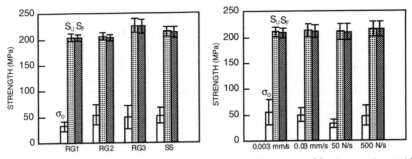

a) Geometry effect on strength   b)Test mode/rate effect on strength

FIG 9--Pooled data for strength values with relation to (a) geometry and (b) test mode/rate. (error bars represent the range of data)

In summary, the salient aspects of the ANOVA are:

1.   For the proportional limit stress, there was no significance of test rate, there was no significance of test mode, and there was no significance for geometry.

2.   For the ultimate strength, there was no significance of test rate, there was no significance of test mode, and there was a significance for geometry.

An additional ANOVA was performed to determine the effect of specimen geometry on the fracture location with the following result:

3.   For fracture location, there was no significance of test rate, there was no significance of test mode, and there was no significance for geometry.

"Pooled" Data

Data was similarly "pooled" graphically for the proportional limit stress, ultimate tensile strength, and fracture strength following the statistical analysis (Fig. 9).
From Fig. 9, no distinct trends can be seen that indicate an effect of test rate/mode on these material properties. However, although Geometry RG3 stands out as having the greatest ultimate tensile strength, this may be due to the actual ratio of gage length to gage width (30 mm / 10 mm = 3) being less than the ratio of 4 normally recommended for tension test specimens. Averaging the mechanical properties for *all* tests reveals that the elastic modulus was 136 ± 10 GPa, the proportional limit stress was 47 ± 20 MPa, ultimate tensile strength was 213 ± 13 MPa, and fracture strength was also 212 ± 13 MPa. Studies show [6] that there was no more or less correlation when comparing material properties in terms of strain than when compared to stress.

CONCLUSIONS

As noted in the Introduction, one of the primary objectives of this study was to clarify various requirements and recommendations of ASTM C 1275. A summary of these clarifications is shown in Table 3.

In addition, basic information about the tensile mechanical behavior of a CFCC was also obtained. One must be careful in interpreting this information. Both stress-strain curves and bar charts seemed to indicate that, faster loading rates resulted in greater ultimate tensile strengths [15]. In addition, there also seemed to be a lower fracture strength under displacement control than for load control as a result of the increasing compliance of cumulative damage in displacement control, whereas under load control the test machine continued to "pull" the specimen. As for geometry effects, the strength of the material seemed to be affected by the volume of the gage section, that is, a smaller volume showed greater strength values. The variation of S_U with geometry indicates that, as expected, ultimate tensile strength rested on the strength of the fibers

TABLE 3--<u>Recommendations for certain aspects of ASTM C 1275</u>

ASTM C 1275	This Study	Recommendation
1. Strain measurement		
Mechanical attachment of extensometer	Difficult to use such extensometers due to rough surface	Other extensometer types are allowed
2. Geometry		
Any geometry is acceptable, contoured preferred	Geometry effect with contoured RG3 producing the greatest S_U, possibly due to gage length effects	Contoured specimens only with geometry effects accounted for by choosing specimens to avoid these effects
3. End tabs		
Recommended for straight-sided specimens	Used on each specimen geometry	Use on all face-loaded specimens to prevent grip-related failures
4. Bending Effects		
<5 PB at 500×10^{-6} m/m for load train alignment	<5 PB at 500×10^{-6} m/m for load train alignment (bending in specimens sometimes >5 PB)	Continue <5 PB at 500×10^{-6} m/m
5. Test mode/rate		
Rapid rate (<30 s to failure) and displacement mode recommended	No effect for either test mode or rate	Continue to report specifics regarding test mode and rate
6. Proportional Limit		
Recommends two methods (stress at offset strain and stress at a fixed strain)	Tried five methods as discussed in Ref [6] including those of the standard, chose method of Eq. 2	Add additional recommended methods

However, the statistical analysis does not allow subjectivity and as indicated by the ANOVA there were no effects of test rate or test mode at the 95% significance level for either proportional limit stress or ultimate tensile strength. The ANOVA did support the observation of geometry effect in which the ultimate strength was affected by geometry at the 95% significance level. For fracture location, there was no significance at the 95% level of test rate, test mode, or geometry. Finally, proportional limit stress decreased with increasing bending while ultimate tensile strength appeared independent of bending.

ACKNOWLEDGMENTS

Research sponsored by the U.S. Department of Energy, Assistant Secretary for Conservation and Renewable Energy, Office of Industrial Technologies, as part of the CFCC Program under Contract DE-AC05-84OR21400 with Martin Marietta Systems, Inc.

REFERENCES

[1]   Karnitz, M. A., Craig, D. A., and Richlen, S. L., _Ceramic Bulletin,_ Vol. 70, No. 3, 1991, pp. 430-435.

[2]   Inghels, E. and Lamon, J., _Journal of Materials Science,_ Vol. 26, 1991, pp. 5403-5410.

[3]   Donald, I. W. and McMillan, P. W., _Journal of Materials Science,_ Vol. 11, 1976, pp. 949-972.

[4]   Cao, H. C., Bischoff, E., Sbaizero, O., Ruhle, M., and Evans, A. G, _Journal of the American Ceramic Society,_ Vol. 73, No. 6, 1990, pp. 1691-1599.

[5]   Jenkins, M. G., Piccola, J. P. Jr., Mello, M. D., Lara-Curzio, E., and Wereszczak, A. A., _Ceramic Engineering and Science Proceedings,_ Vol. 15, No. 4, 1994, pp. 209-218

[6]   Piccola, J.P. Jr., "Effects of Test Parameters on Tensile Mechanical Behavior of a Continuous Fiber Ceramic Composite (CFCC)," Master of science thesis, University of Washington, 1994

[7]   Aveston J., and Kelly, A., _Journal of Materials Science,_ Vol. 8, 1973, pp. 352-362.

[8]   Curtin, W. A., _Journal of the American Ceramic Society,_ Vol. 74, No. 11, 1991, pp. 2837-2845.

[9]   Curtin, W. A., _Journal of the American Ceramic Society,_ Vol. 77, No. 4, 1994, pp. 1075-1078.

[10]   Marshall, D. B., and Evans, A. G., _Journal of the American Ceramic Society,_ Vol. 68, No. 5, 1985, pp. 225-231

[11]   Sankar, J., Kelkar, A. D., and Vaidyanathan, R., North Carolina A & T State University Final Report, ORNL/SUB/88-SC423, Oak Ridge National Laboratory, Oak Ridge, TN, Sept. 1993

[12]   Davidge, R. W., and Briggs, A., _Journal of Materials Science,_ Vol. 24, 1989, pp. 2815-2819

[13]   Walpole, R. E., and Myers, R. H., _Probability and Statistics for Engineers and Scientists,_ MacMillan Publishing, Co., 1989.

[14]   Fisher, R. A., _Statistical Methods of Experimental Design and Scientific Inference,_ Oxford University Press, Oxford, U.K., 1990.

[15]   Worthem, D. W., "Flat Tensile Specimen Design for Advanced Composites," NASA CR-185621, NASA Lewis Research Center, Cleveland, OH, 1990.

José M. Sánchez,[1] Iñigo Puente,[2] Reyes Elizalde,[1] Antonio Martín,[2] José M. Martínez,[1] Adrian M. Daniel,[1] Manuel Fuentes,[1] Colin P. Beesley[3]

EFFECT OF HIGH STRAIN RATE ON THE TENSILE BEHAVIOR OF NICALON™/CAS CONTINUOUS-FIBER CERAMIC COMPOSITES

REFERENCE: Sánchez, J. M., Puente, I., Elizalde, R., Martín, A., Martínez, J. M., Daniel, A. M., Fuentes, M., and Beesley, C. P., **"Effect of High Strain Rate on the Tensile Behavior of Nicalon™/CAS Continuous-Fiber Ceramic Composites,"** Thermal and Mechanical Test Methods and Behavior of Continuous-Fiber Ceramic Composites, ASTM STP 1309, Michael G. Jenkins, Stephen T. Gonczy, Edgar Lara-Curzio, Noel E. Ashbaugh, and Larry P. Zawada, Eds., American Society for Testing and Materials, 1997.

ABSTRACT: The tensile properties of CAS/SiC $[(0/90)_3]_s$ ceramic matrix composites have been measured as a function of strain rate up to 100 s^{-1}. Novel test methods, including the use of piezoelectric transducers as load cells, strain gauges, and high sampling rate data acquisition systems, were set up to ensure accurate measurement of load and strain. Dynamic effects were taken into account when analyzing the stress-strain raw data. It has been observed that the average fracture strength and the average strain energy density are higher with increasing strain rate. This trend is related to the mode of fracture and the damage observed in the composite at different strain rates.

KEYWORDS: Nicalon™ fibers; calcium aluminum silicate matrix; cross-ply structure; tension test; high strain rate; dynamic effects; toughness; failure mechanisms

Continuous fiber ceramic composites (CFCCs) are intended for applications in which they will be subjected to wide variations in strain rate (that is, aeroengine components). The industrial application of these materials requires a better understanding of the tensile properties at high strain rates and their dependence with the typical failure micromechanisms. The strain rate sensitivity of monolithic ceramics under compressive stresses (up to $\dot{\varepsilon} = 10^3$ s^{-1}) has been characterized in previous works,

---

[1] Research scientists and professor, respectively, Centro de Estudios e Investigaciones Técnicas de Guipúzcoa (C.E.I.T.), P.O. Box 1555, 20080, San Sebastián, Spain.
[2] Research scientists, Escuela Superior de Ingenieros Industriales, Universidad de Navarra, P.O. Box 1674, 20080, San Sebastián, Spain.
[3] Manager, Rolls Royce plc, Composites and Ceramics Group, P.O. Box 31, 20080, Derby, DE24 8BJ, UK.

showing that these materials exhibit considerable strain rate sensitivity [1]. CFCCs have also been tested under high strain rate compressive stresses and found that their strain rate sensitivity is well in excess of the cube-root theoretical maximum of monolithic materials [2]. In tension tests, Holmes and Sorensen [3] have studied the CFCCs mechanical behavior up to 0.01 s^{-1}. However, there is no information available in the literature for tension tests at higher strain rates.

The tensile properties (that is, the elastic modulus, matrix cracking stress, the ultimate tensile strength, the strain to fracture, and the strain energy density) of a CAS/SiC ceramic composite (calcium aluminum silicate reinforced with Nicalon™ fibers) with a $[(0/90)_3]_s$ cross-ply architecture have been measured and related to the mode of fracture and the damage induced in the composite at strain rates up to 100 s^{-1}. Tension testing at high rates requires extremely precise alignment of the test pieces along the load axis, high sampling rate data acquisition, and the use of highly sensitive strain and load sensors. For the highest applied strain rates, dynamic effects have to be taken into account. Fractographic analyses of the broken test pieces have been carried out to correlate the tensile properties with typical composite fracture mechanisms, such as matrix cracking and fiber pullout.

Experimental Procedure

Material

The material studied, provided by Rolls Royce plc, was a commercially available CFCC comprising a calcium aluminum silicate glass-ceramic matrix (CAS) reinforced with

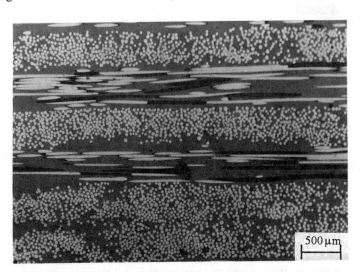

FIG. 1--Typical microstructure of $[(0/90)_3]_s$ CAS/SiC ceramic composite.

Nicalon fibers. This composite has a cross-ply symmetrical structure with twelve plies oriented alternatively at 0 and 90°, with a double thickness 90° ply in the center of the sample. A detail of this structure is shown in Fig. 1.

Tension Test Arrangement

Fifty-six tension tests were carried out using a MTS 819 servohydraulic testing machine with a maximum actuator speed of 14 m/s on 200-mm-long test pieces with a gauge length of 40 mm (gauge length width: 8 mm, thickness: 2.5 mm, shoulder radius: 30 mm). The specimens were selected at a random from a population of 120 test pieces obtained from twenty panels. The gripping system consisted of a set of flat wedges coated with tungsten carbide grains. The optimum clamping conditions to avoid sliding or test piece damage were obtained with a pump pressure of 15 MPa. Aluminum end tabs were not needed with this facility. The applied strain rates ranged from 5.10^{-4} s^{-1} to 10^2 s^{-1}.

Because of the inherent brittleness of the CAS matrix, a very precise sample alignment is required to avoid damage caused by nonaxial loading during gripping and testing. A procedure [4] based on the use of strain-gauged specimens has been set up to ensure that the bending stresses are below the matrix cracking stress.

For testing at strain rates higher than 2 s^{-1}, a new gripping arrangement was set up based on the use of a "slack adapter" (Fig. 2). This tool lets the actuator accelerate without applying load to the samples until the programmed test rate is achieved. For high acceleration purposes, the heavy hydraulic grips used in the low strain rate tests were substituted by light aluminum grips.

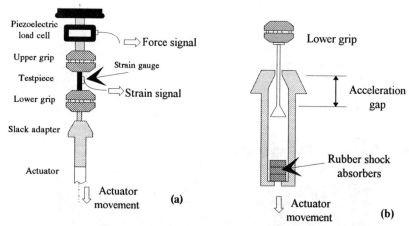

FIG. 2--(a) Experimental arrangement. (b) Detail of the slack adapter.

Strain gauges have been used not only to measure the strain at different strain rates, but to detect any bending strain during gripping and testing. For strain rates from $\dot{\varepsilon} = 2$ s^{-1} to $\dot{\varepsilon} = 100$ s^{-1}, conventional AC strain amplifiers were substituted by Nec-Sanei DC strain amplifiers with much higher sampling rates. A conventional load cell was used for load measurements at slow rates. As the test rate increased, the measurement of dynamic loads required the use of a fast response piezoelectric force link. The accuracy of the measurements at high strain rates depends on the load and strain signal amplification and data acquisition sampling. The maximum frequency response of the load and strain amplifiers used in the present work is 180 kHz; therefore, a data acquisition board of at least this sampling rate per channel is required. For the tests carried out in this study, a Keithley-Metrabite DAS-58, 1-MHz, 12-bit A/D data acquisition board was used.

Microstructural Characterization

Microstructural characterization of the as-fabricated and tested material was carried out using optical and scanning electron microscopy (SEM). Fiber volume fraction parallel to the load direction was measured by the point-counting method. The saturation matrix cracking spacings have been measured by linear intercept along the gauge length on the edge of the specimen. Mode II cracks were not considered. The fiber pullout length distributions were measured from SEM micrographs of the fracture surfaces of samples.

Results

Low Strain Rate Tensile Properties

The stress-strain experimental data were fitted by means of a β-cubic spline and linear regressions were fitted to all the possible segments of the curve with more than two points. The Young's modulus was calculated as the slope corresponding to the maximum correlation coefficient. The stress for the initiation of matrix cracking was obtained as the stress corresponding to a 2% decrease in tangent modulus [5].

TABLE 1--CAS/SiC $[(0/90)_3]_s$. *Tensile parameters corresponding to the tests carried out at 5.10^{-4} s^{-1}. Standard deviations and Weibull parameters are also included.*

	E (GPa)	σ_{mc} (MPa)	σ_{UTS} (MPa)	ε_f (%)	SED (MJ/m^3)
Average value	**119**	**62**	**246**	**0.92**	**1.51**
Stand. deviation	7	9	28	0.14	0.31
Minimum	102	49	192	0.64	0.90
Maximum	129	82	296	1.18	2.06
Weibull modulus	**21.9**	**8.25**	**10.4**	**7.5**	**5.4**
Correlation coeff.	0.99	0.94	0.99	0.97	0.98
Lower 95% C.I.	20.3	6.75	9.6	6.6	4.8
Upper 95% C.I.	23.5	9.75	11.2	8.4	6.0

The results of the 21 tension tests carried out at 5.10^{-4} s^{-1} on samples obtained from different panels are given in Table 1. The elastic modulus, matrix cracking stress, fracture strength, strain-to-fracture, and strain energy density (SED) mean values are shown together with the standard deviations and Weibull parameters. The high correlation coefficients obtained by fitting Weibull distributions to these experimental data suggest that CAS/SiC fulfills the "weakest link" model assumptions [6].

The mechanical behavior of CAS/SiC is reproducible before the onset of matrix cracking (the Weibull parameter corresponding to the elastic modulus is 21.9). However, the tensile parameters show large variations beyond the elastic regime. A study carried out to identify possible sources of material variability has shown that the dispersion in mechanical properties is reduced if only test pieces within the same panel are taken into account. Microscopical observations have proved that the global fiber volume fraction along the loading direction changes from panel to panel, and a clear correlation has been established between this parameter and the fracture strength (Fig. 3).

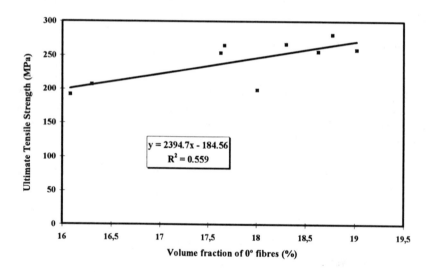

FIG. 3--Fracture strength as a function of fiber volume fraction. Results corresponding to tests carried out at 5.10^{-4} s^{-1}.

Other possible causes of material variability, such as variability in the CAS matrix composition and in the fiber spatial distribution are under investigation. This set of 21 quasistatic tests was taken as the reference against which the rest of the tests carried out at higher strain rates were compared.

High Strain Rate Tensile Properties

As the strain rate was increased, several dynamic effects were observed in the stress-strain recordings. For tests carried out at strain rates higher than 20 s^{-1}, the load signal was observed to lag behind the signal produced by the strain gauges. Because of the experimental arrangement, the strain wave propagating in the specimen, produced by the actuator stroke on the lower end of the specimen, reaches the strain sensor before the load sensor. The time delay between signals corresponds to the time required for this elastic wave to travel from the strain to the load sensor.

The elastic wave propagation speed in a solid bar [7] is:

$$v = \sqrt{\frac{E}{\rho}}$$

where E is the Young's modulus and ρ is the density of the material.

For CAS/SiC, a value of 6800 m/s is obtained. As the distance between the strain gauge and the load cell is 20 cm, it takes about $3 \cdot 10^{-5}$ s for the strain wave to travel from one sensor to another. As the sampling rate for the tests carried out at 100 s^{-1} is 180 kHz, the load signal lags behind the strain signal by six data points. Therefore, the load signal was shifted by this amount of time to match its corresponding strain signal. By following this procedure, the stress-strain curves at the different strain rates were obtained. Figure 4 shows four representative plots corresponding to tests carried out at strain rates ranging from 5.10^{-4} s^{-1} to 10^2 s^{-1}.

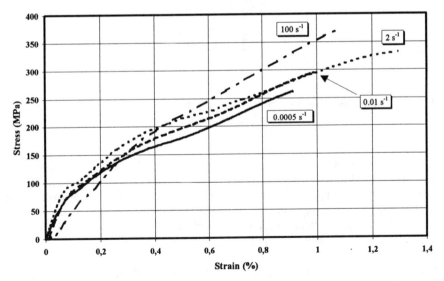

FIG. 4--CAS/SiC [(0/90)$_3$]$_s$. Typical stress-strain curves corresponding to tension tests carried out at 5.10^{-4} s^{-1}, 1.10^{-2} s^{-1}, 2 s^{-1} and 100 s^{-1}.

At strain rates higher than 20 s^{-1}, load oscillations appear in the load versus time recordings. A study of the test system natural frequencies has been carried out by recording the signal with the piezoelectric force link when the actuator is moved at 14 m/s without gripping any specimen. The natural frequencies of the test system are obtained by applying the Fourier transform to this signal. Four peaks at 4050, 6075, 10450, and 16830 Hz have been detected. The same natural frequencies appear when a CAS/SiC tension test is carried out beyond 20 s^{-1}. Therefore, it is confirmed that the distortion of the load signal is produced by the excitation of the natural frequencies of the test machine.

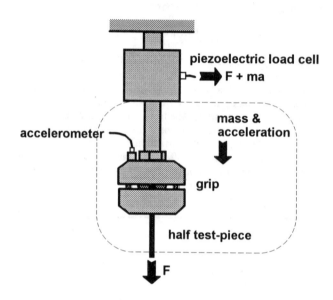

FIG. 5--Diagram showing the forces measured with the force link in a high strain rate (beyond 20 s^{-1}) tension test.

As observed in Figure 5, the signal measured by the force link has two components: the actual load applied to the specimen, and the inertia of the grip. To subtract this second component that is not applied to the specimen, a mathematical filtering procedure was intended. However, the frequency spectrum corresponding to a high strain rate test shows that the most intense natural vibration modes (4050 and 6075 Hz) are superimposed to the frequency range of the test actual signal (Fig. 6).

From these two graphs, it is concluded that mathematical filtering of the load signal is not possible as, if these frequency peaks are filtered, an important part of the test information is lost. The rest of the normal modes are less intense, and their effect on the test signal is not so important. Accelerometers together with the force link are being used to subtract the force as a result of the acceleration of the grip from the actual load on the test piece. A new test system is being set up to implement an accelerometer in the load axis of the testing machine. The results obtained with off-axis accelerometers are not useful because other vibration modes are detected.

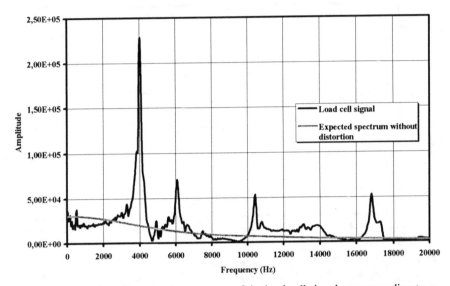

FIG. 6--Comparison between the spectrum of the load cell signal corresponding to a $100 \ s^{-1}$ test and the one expected for a test without distortion.

TABLE 2--CAS/SiC $[(0/90)_3]_s$. Tensile properties as a function of strain rate.

Strain rate	E	σ_{mc}	ε_f	σ_{UTS}	Strain Energy Density	Mean Matrix Cracking Spacing	Mean Pullout Length
(s^{-1})	(GPa)	(MPa)	(%)	(MPa)	(MJ/m^3)	(μm)	(μm)
5.10^{-4}	119	62	0.92	246	1.51	203	429
$(21)^*$	± 6	± 9	± 0.14	± 28	± 0.31		
10^{-2}	119	52	0.90	261	1.58		
$(5)^*$	± 8	± 11	± 0.28	± 52	± 0.64	...	...
2	138	56	0.81	262	1.54	164	155
$(13)^*$	± 12	± 6	± 0.30	± 47	± 0.80		
100	...	...	0.73	339	1.44	...	...
$(6)^*$			± 0.28	± 55	± 0.90		

* The number of tests carried out for each strain rate is given in parentheses.

The presence of a wave superimposed to the stress-strain data does not allow the calculation of the elastic modulus and the matrix cracking stress that are magnitudes obtained from quasistatic loading. However, the fracture strength, the strain energy density, and the strain to fracture can be easily obtained from the experimental data. The dependence of the mean values of these parameters as a function of strain rate are shown in Table 2 with their standard deviations.

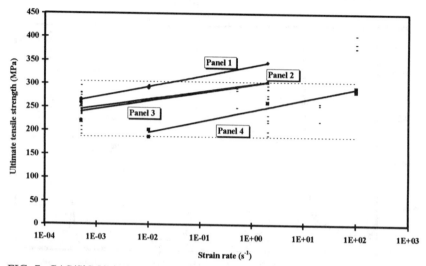

FIG. 7--CAS/SiC $[(0/90)_3]_s$. Ultimate tensile strength as a function of strain rate. The whole set of results is shown together with the 95% C.I. for the population at 5.10^{-4} s^{-1}. Logarithmic regressions are shown for test pieces of the same panel.

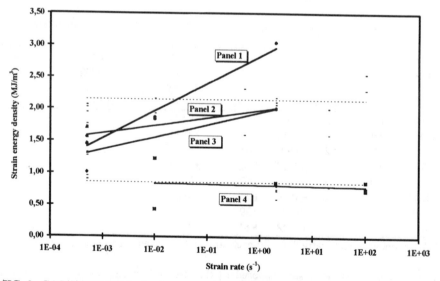

FIG. 8--CAS/SiC $[(0/90)_3]_s$. Strain energy density as a function of strain rate. The whole set of results is shown together with the 95% C.I. for the population at 5.10^{-4} s^{-1}. Logarithmic regressions are shown for test pieces of the same panel.

However, if the average values of these magnitudes are considered, a significant increase in the CAS/SiC mean fracture strength is observed as the strain rate is increased. On the contrary, the strain to fracture is observed to decrease slightly, especially for the tests carried out at 100 s^{-1}. Both effects are accounted for in the strain energy density parameter, defined as the area under the stress-strain curve. The experimental data show that the mean strain energy densities do not change appreciably within the applied strain rates range.

When only specimens within the same panel are accounted for, the material variability is reduced, and these tendencies are more clearly established. By doing so, an increase in fracture strength by testing at higher strain rates is confirmed (Fig. 7). This tendency is also observed for the strain energy density (Fig. 8). However, for the panel with the worst mechanical properties (panel 4 in Fig. 8) this behavior is not perceived.

Fractography

The main feature of macroscopic fracture at high strain rates is the presence of higher levels of damage in the test pieces. The gauge length of the specimens tested at 100 s^{-1} show a typical double fracture not observed in the quasistatic tests (Fig. 9).

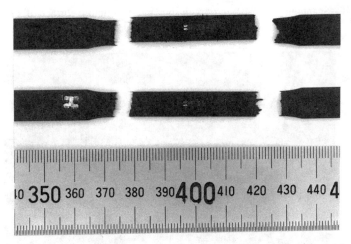

FIG. 9--Macroscopical aspect of the test pieces broken at 100 s^{-1} (units in mm).

The two parameters commonly used to characterize the fracture of CFCC, that is, pullout lengths and matrix cracking densities, have been measured for specimens tested at different strain rates. The average values of these magnitudes are summarized in Table 2.

As observed from Figures 10 and 11, a substantial decrease in the mean pullout length is observed with increasing strain rate. The tough fracture mode of CFCCs is commonly

FIG. 10--Scanning electron micrograph showing the fracture surface of a specimen tested at 5.10^{-4} s^{-1}.

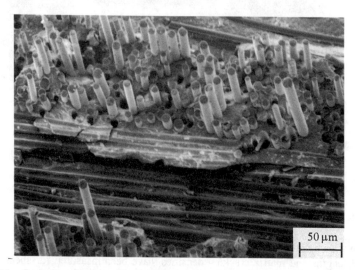

FIG. 11-- Scanning electron micrograph showing the fracture surface of a specimen tested at 2 s^{-1}. A significant decrease of the average pullout length is observed with respect to the previous micrograph.

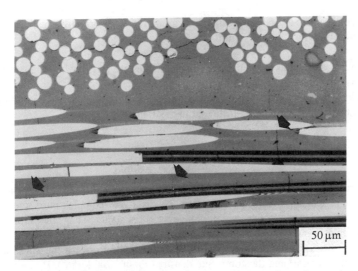

FIG. 12--Optical micrograph showing the matrix cracking spacing of a specimen tested at 5.10^{-4} s^{-1}. The solid arrows point to the observed cracks.

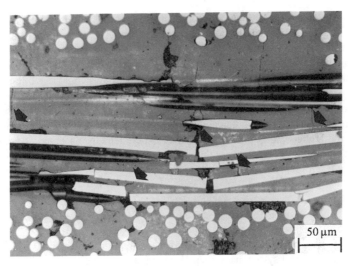

FIG. 13--Optical micrograph showing the matrix cracking spacing of a specimen tested at 2 s^{-1}. A higher crack density is observed as the strain rate increases.

related to the presence of large pullout lengths [8,9]. However, in the present study, this reduction in the pullout lengths is not related to a loss of toughness (Table 2). On the contrary, there is evidence of higher strain energy densities absorbed by testing at high strain rates, although the pullout extent is considerably reduced.

Figures 12 and 13 show that the matrix cracking densities are higher when the strain rate increases. It is also observed that, at high strain rates, most of the Nicalon fibers show multiple cracking. Therefore, it is confirmed that a larger amount of damage is produced either in the fiber or in the matrix by testing at high strain rates.

Discussion

The mechanical response of a CFCC subjected to an impact-like conditions is related to the strain wave propagation along the test piece. This is a very complex phenomenon, as the matrix and the fiber do not have the same elastic constants. Thus, the strain wave travels at different velocities in each component. A rough calculation of the average propagation speed of an elastic wave on CAS/SiC is obtained from the measured elastic modulus (about 120 GPa) and the composite density (about 2700 kg/m^3). By doing so, a value of about 6800 m/s is obtained. At slow strain rates, this wave travels along the whole gauge length 10^6 times as the tension test proceeds. Therefore, a uniform strain distribution along the gauge length is obtained.

At high strain rates, the tests last only 200 μs. During this short period of time, the strain wave travels along the gauge length about ten times. However, the area under the stress-strain curve is of the same order of magnitude as in the slow strain rate test. Thus, the strain wave amplitude must be higher for the high strain rate tests. If a larger amount of energy is localized in a small portion of material, even small flaws could reach the critical stress intensity factor either of the fiber or the matrix. This local energy density could be high enough to break the fibers in smaller flaws than those observed when the strain is uniformly distributed along the whole gauge length. This could explain the fiber multiple cracking and the higher matrix cracking densities experimentally observed. Besides, as the fibers are broken in several pieces, the average pullout length must be reduced, as observed in the fractographic analysis of the test pieces.

Conclusions

The tensile properties of a CAS/SiC CFCC have been measured up to 100 s^{-1}. Normal vibration modes of the test system have been observed above 20 s^{-1}.

A high variability of results has been obtained for the whole set of experiments. However, this dispersion is reduced if only test from the same panel are considered.

When testing at higher strain rates, the fracture strength and the strain energy density increase. Fractographic analyses have confirmed that the average pullout length decreases and the matrix cracking density increases.

Acknowledgments

The authors acknowledge Rolls-Royce plc; the Spanish "Departamento de Educación, Universidades e Investigación del Gobierno Vasco" (EC 9206 and PGV 92/17); the Spanish "Dirección General de Electrónica y Nuevas Tecnologías del Ministerio de Industria Comercio y Turismo"; and the Spanish "Comisión Interministerial de Ciencia y Tecnología" (CICYT Mat93-0348) for the financial support.

I.P., M.R.E., and A.M.D. are grateful to the "Departamento de Educación, Universidades e Investigación del Gobierno Vasco," the CICYT, and the Directorate XII of E.U., respectively, for the grants received.

References

[1] Lankford, J., "Strength of Monolithic and Fiber-Reinforced Glass Ceramics at High Rates of Loading and Elevated Temperature," Ceramic Engineering Sci. Proc., Vol. 9, Nos. 7-8, 1988, pp. 843-852.

[2] Lankford, J., "Dynamic Compressive Fracture in Fiber-reinforced Ceramic Matrix Composites," Materials Science and Engineering, Vol. A107, 1989, pp. 261-268.

[3] Sorensen, B. F., and Holmes, J. W., "Effect of Loading Rate on the Monotonic Tensile Behavior of a Continuous-Fiber-Reinforced Glass-Ceramic Matrix Composite," Journal of American Ceramic Society, Vol. 79, No. 2, 1996, pp. 313-320.

[4] Mosiman, L. G., Wallenfelt, T. L., and Larsen, C. G., "Tension/Compression Grips for Monolithic Ceramics and Ceramic Matrix Composites," in MTS internal publication, 1991.

[5] Sánchez, J. M., Elizalde, M. R., Puente, I., Martín, A., Martinez-Esnaola, J. M., and Fuentes, M., "Matrix Cracking Stress in CMCs," in Proceedings of the IV Conference in Mechanical Properties, Vitoria, Spain, 1994.

[6] Weibull, W., "A Statistical Representation of Fatigue Failures in Solids," Transactions of the Royal Institute of Technology, Stockholm, No. 47, 1949.

[7] French, A. P., "Vibrations and waves," Van Nostrand Reinhold Publishers, Berkshire, UK, 1986.

[8] Evans, A. and Marshall, D. B., "The Mechanical Behaviour of Ceramic Matrix Composites," Acta metallurgica, Vol. 37, No. 10, 1989, pp. 2567-2583.

[9] Evans, A., Domergue, J. M., Vagaggini, E., "A Methodology for Relating the Tensile Constitutive Behaviour of Ceramic Matrix Composites to Constituent Properties," in Proceedings of the 6th Conference on Composite Materials, HT-CMC1, R. Naslain, J. Lamon, and D. Doumeingts, Eds., Bordeaux, 1993.

Edgar Lara-Curzio[1] and Mattison K. Ferber[1]

SHEAR STRENGTH OF CONTINUOUS FIBER CERAMIC COMPOSITES

REFERENCE: Lara-Curzio, E. and Ferber, M. K., **"Shear Strength of Continuous Fiber Ceramic Composites,"** Thermal and Mechanical Test Methods and Behavior of Continuous-Fiber Ceramic Composites, ASTM STP 1309, Michael G. Jenkins, Stephen T. Gonczy, Edgar Lara-Curzio, Noel E. Ashbaugh, and Larry P. Zawada, Eds., American Society for Testing and Materials, 1997.

ABSTRACT: The applicability of ASTM Test Method for Shear Strength of Continuous Fiber-Reinforced Advanced Ceramics at Ambient Temperatures (C 1292) was investigated to determine the shear strength of one-dimensional and two-dimensional continuous fiber-reinforced ceramic composites. The advantages and disadvantages of the test method are addressed, and the effect of notch separation on the measured interlaminar shear strength by the compression of double-notched specimens are discussed. Experimental results are presented for the interlaminar and in-plane shear behavior of two-dimensional Nicalon™/SiC and the interlaminar shear strength of one-dimensional carbon/carbon composites both at room temperature and 1000°C. The effect of fiber coating thickness on the interlaminar shear strength of two-dimensional Nicalon™/SiC is also discussed.

KEYWORDS: shear, strength, composite, ceramic, ceramic matrix composite, test method

Because of their potential to retain strength and to exhibit tough behavior at elevated temperatures Continuous Fiber-reinforced Ceramic Composites (CFCCs) are candidate materials for numerous applications. The driving force behind the development of these materials is the promise for substantial energy, environmental and economic benefits if they are used in industrial and defense-related high temperature applications. Since CFCCs comprise a relatively new class of materials, most of the efforts toward their mechanical characterization have been concentrated in the evaluation of their behavior under tensile loading. However, CFCC components will be invariably subjected to complex states of stress during service, which makes the knowledge of their behavior under these loading conditions necessary for design purposes. Two modes of loading that will be often encountered are: in-plane and interlaminar shear. For example, the notch insensitivity of some of these materials has been found to be related to their ability to redistribute stresses around holes and notches by in-plane shear deformation [1]. At the same time, interlaminar shear stresses could limit the utilization of some laminated CFCC structures. Today many fabrication methods of 2-D CFCCs are based on the synthesis of the matrix by liquid or gaseous infiltration into a preformed stack of fiber cloth. The resulting structure usually contains interlaminar regions that are mainly matrix-rich, and with those infiltration processes in which full densification is not achievable (for example, chemical vapor infiltration), the composite will contain porosity rich interlaminar regions as well. When such structures are subjected to interlaminar shear loading, the matrix and porosity rich regions invariably become the weak links in the structure.

Unfortunately, there are no good tests for measuring the shear strength of composites [2]. The only test that comes close to inducing a uniform state of shear stress is the torsion of a thin-wall tube, a testing procedure that is not only impractical for evaluating CFCCs but also prohibitively expensive. In addition to the torsion of thin-wall tubes, several test methods have been proposed to determine the in-plane shear strength (IPSS) and interlaminar shear strength (ILSS) of composites. These include the short beam three-point bend test per the ASTM Test Method for Apparent Interlaminar Shear Strength of Parallel Fiber Composites by Short-Beam Method (D 2344), the 10°-off axis tension test [3], the ±45° tension test per Ref 4 and the ASTM Practice for In-Plane Shear Stress-Strain Response of Unidirectional Polymer Matrix Composite Materials by Tensile Test of ±45° Laminate (D 3518), the two and three rail shear tests per Refs

[1] Development Staff Members, Mechanical Characterization and Analysis Group, Metals and Ceramics Division, Oak Ridge National Laboratory, Oak Ridge, TN 37831-6069

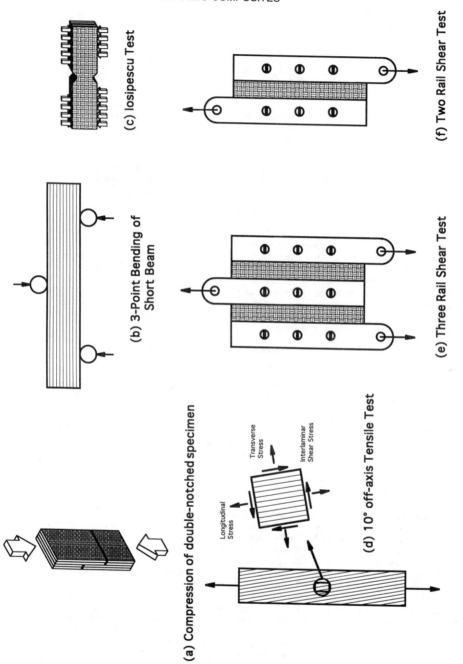

FIG. 1-- Schematic representation of different test methods for the shear strength evaluation of composites.

5 and 6 and the ASTM Guide for Testing In-Plane Shear Properties of Composite Laminates (D 4255), the torsion of flat plates[7], the Iosipescu test per the ASTM Test Method for Shear Strength Properties of Composite Materials by the V-Notched Beam Method (D 5379) and the compression/tension of double-notched specimens (DNS) [8]. Fig. 1 shows schematically some of these tests. Recently, ASTM, through Subcommittee C28.07 on Advanced Ceramic Composites, approved the ASTM Test Method for Shear Strength of Continuous Fiber-Reinforced Advanced Ceramics At Ambient Temperatures (C 1292) to determine the ILSS by means of the compression of a DNS and to determine both the IPSS and ILSS by the Iosipescu test.

The compression of a DNS was first standardized as ASTM Test Method for In-Plane Shear Strength of Reinforced Plastics (D 3846) for determining the ILSS of reinforced plastics. This test method consists in the compression of a specimen shown schematically in Fig. 1.a using a supporting jig described in the ASTM Test Method for Compressive Properties of Rigid Plastics (D 695), to provide lateral support and to prevent buckling. Although a variation of this test uses a similar specimen subjected to tensile loading, the compressive version of the test has been favored because it requires smaller specimens and because of the relatively simpler nature of the test. As a result of the asymmetric nature of the DNS, bending strains will be induced whether the specimen is loaded in tension or compression. In addition, because this test induces normal stresses on the imaginary plane between the notches and because of the stress concentrations at the root of the notches, the state of stress in the DNS will be complex and thus, far from uniform.

A comparative investigation of test methods for determining the shear strength of fiber-reinforced polymers by Chiao et al. [8] showed considerable variability in the results obtained from the compression of DNS. They calculated the intrinsic ILSS using an analysis developed by Markham and Dawson [9] and concluded that the large degree of variability was associated with a lack of consistency in preparing the notches, particularly their depth.

Using higher order beam theory, Whitney [10] derived the distribution of the interlaminar shear and normal stresses in the DNS loaded in tension. He showed that to insure that the interlaminar shear stress becomes evenly distributed over the majority of the area between the notches -rather than being isolated to the region near the notch tips- it is desirable to use specimens with small notch separations.

Dadras and McDowell [11] used a finite-difference analysis to determine the stress distribution in the DNS loaded in compression. They also conducted experimental measurements on glass- and graphite-reinforced epoxies using short specimens without a supporting fixture and found that the apparent ILSS decreased with increasing values of the ratio of the notch separation to specimen thickness (L/t). Furthermore, they found that the results were independent of the notch width. Dadras and McDowell [11] acknowledged that a fixture to provide lateral support would be required for longer specimens, although argued that such fixture could introduce undesirable lateral loading conditions. They also pointed out that specimens with short notch separations are desirable for more uniform shear stresses in the region between the notches.

Sawyer [12] determined the ILSS of two-dimensional carbon/carbon composites by the short beam three-point bend test, the Iosipescu test and the compression of DNS and modified DNS. The objective of the modified DNS, (Fig. 2) was to eliminate the bending deformation that results from the lack of symmetry of the regular DNS. Sawyer [12] found that the different test techniques produced different apparent ILSS values with the short beam flexure test yielding the highest ILSS and the Iosipescu test the lowest. In particular, the apparent ILSS obtained by the compression of the regular DNS had a parabolic dependence with notch separation and had a minimum value of 7.1 MPa for a notch separation of 6.35 mm, while the apparent ILSS obtained by the compression of the modified DNS decreased with increasing notch separation and was lower than that obtained with the regular DNS. Note that the tests with the regular DNS were conducted using a fixture to provide lateral support, whereas the modified double-notch specimens were tested without a fixture. Although the differences in the trends of the apparent ILSS with notch separation for the regular and modified DNS were not explained at the time, it is shown later in this paper that these differences may arise from frictional effects between the specimen and the supporting jig. Sawyer [12] showed using a finite-element analysis that although the shear stress distribution along the imaginary plane between the notches was comparable for both the DNS and the modified DNS specimens, the normal stresses on the imaginary plane between the two notches were larger for the modified DNS. The analysis also revealed that the shear stress distribution between the notches became more uniform for shorter notch separations as a result of the reduction in the magnitude of the stress concentration at the root of the notches. Furthermore it was shown that this reduction in the magnitude of the stress concentration resulted from the interaction of the stress fields emanating from the notches.

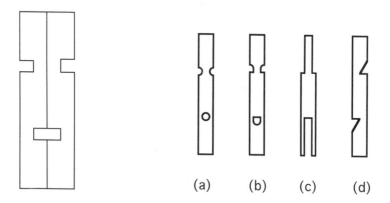

FIG. 2--Modified DNS. It is obtained by bonding face to face to regular DNS.

FIG. 3-- Alternative geometries for the double-notched specimen [14].

Sawyer [12] was able to determine the ILSS of 2-D C/C composites using the Iosipescu test. Although it was shown from finite-element calculations that this test induces the most uniform state of shear stress among the test techniques that he investigated, normal and longitudinal stresses are also induced not far from the plane between the notches, and are suspected to be the source of out-of-gauge failures [13].

Thielicke et al. [13-14] evaluated the ILSS of 2-D carbon/carbon composites and experimented as well, with variations of the DNS geometry. Figure 3 shows the specimen geometries that they investigated which include three symmetric and one un-symmetric specimens. They found from both the tensile and compressive evaluation of symmetric specimens, such as the one depicted in Fig. 3(a), that both modes of loading yielded comparable values of the apparent ILSS. Furthermore they found that under compression, comparable results were obtained among specimens with the geometries depicted in Fig. 3.a, 3.b and 3.d, regardless of notch separation (10 mm or 35 mm). For all of their tests, they did not use a fixture for lateral support.

Fang and Chou [15] determined the ILSS of Carbon/SiC, Nicalon™/SiC, and Nicalon™/CAS-II composites by the compression of DNS. They used a fixture similar to that recommended in ASTM D-695 and their 20.3-mm-long specimens were shorter than those recommended in ASTM Test Method D 3846. Experimentally they found that the apparent ILSS of Nicalon™/CAS-II had a parabolic dependence on notch separation with a minimum value of 32 MPa for a notch separation of 7.62 mm. They also observed larger scatter in the data for shorter notch separations, which was consistent with the observations of Dadras and McDowell [11] and Sawyer [12]. Fang and Chou [15] argued that the increase in the apparent ILSS for notch separations less than 7.62 mm resulted from the interaction between the stress fields emanating from the notches. Furthermore, they argued that although the stress concentration at the root of the notches was the same for specimens with notch separations larger than 7.62 mm, the apparent ILSS increased with notch separation because the percentage of localized stressed region decreased.

There has been extensive work in the analysis of the Iosipescu test [16-17] and this method has been found to be capable of providing consistent and valid shear strength characterization for a range of polymer matrix composites[18-19]. However little work has been presented of the evaluation of CFCCs using this test method[20].

The consideration of CFCCs for high temperature applications has been accompanied by a demand on part of designers for standardized data bases, making necessary an assessment of the validity of standard tests methods for CFCCs. This paper attempts to assess the applicability of ASTM Standard Test Method C 1292 to determine the shear strength of CFCCs by evaluating 2-D Nicalon™/SiC CFCCs with different fiber coating thicknesses. The ILSS was determined by means of the compression of DNS and the IPSS using the Iosipescu test. Experimental results for the ILSS of 1-D carbon/carbon CFCCs determined from the compression of DNS at room temperature and 1000°C are also included.

EXPERIMENTAL

<u>Materials</u>

The materials evaluated included 2-D Nicalon™/SiC[2] and 1-D carbon/carbon[3] CFCCs. The 2-D Nicalon™/SiC double-notched specimens used for the determination of ILSS, were obtained from 152.4 mm by 152.4 mm plates consisting of eight layers of plain-weave fiber cloth and had the dimensions summarized in Table 1. The volume fraction of these materials, which were synthesized by chemical vapor infiltration, was 45% and had a density of 2.02 g/cm³. The notches were machined in several passes with a removal rate of 30 μm/pass, using a metal-bonded diamond wheel (600 grit) specially dressed for that operation. Two sets of samples, which differed only by the thickness of the fiber carbon coating were evaluated. The first set had a nominal fiber coating thickness of 0.3 μm, whereas the second set had a 1.1-μm-thick fiber coating. The 1-D carbon/carbon double-notched specimens were prepared following similar machining practices and had the dimensions summarized in Table 2. These samples which were densified by successive infiltration and pyrolysis cycles using a pitch precursor for carbon, had a volume fraction 60% and density of 1.96 g/cm³.

For the IPSS measurements, 2-D Nicalon™/SiC Iosipescu specimens were machined to the dimensions summarized in Table 3. These specimens had a nominal 0.3-μm-thick fiber carbon coating.

<u>Test Procedures</u>

<u>ILSS Tests at Room Temperature</u>--The room temperature tests were conducted using a fixture depicted schematically in Fig. 4 and a universal testing machine[4]. The fixture was machined to tight tolerances of parallelism and perpendicularity to meet the requirements of specimen fabrication prescribed in ASTM Test Method C 1292. Details about the construction and operation of the fixture can be found elsewhere [21]. To minimize frictional effects, a 1.5-mm-thick layer of Teflon® was inserted between the specimen and the fixture. The fixture allows for the lateral clamping of the specimens and although the clamping pressure was not measured, it was minimized since it tends to reduce the stress concentration at the notches and to artificially increase the magnitude of the apparent ILSS [15]. The tests were conducted at a constant crosshead displacement rate of 0.5 mm/min and both the load and the crosshead displacement were recorded at a rate of 1Hz.

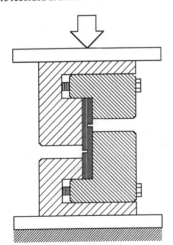

FIG. 4-- Schematic of DNS fixture for room temperature tests.

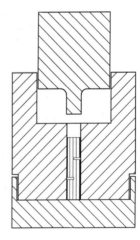

FIG. 5-- Schematic of DNS fixture for high temperature tests.

[2] BF Goodrich, Super-Temp Division. Santa Fe Springs, CA 90670.
[3] Mitsubishi, Kasei Corporation, Chiyoda-ku, Tokyo 100, Japan.
[4] Instron Model 6027, Canton MA 02021.

ILSS Tests at Elevated Temperature--The high temperature tests were conducted using a fixture shown schematically in Fig. 5. The fixture was manufactured out of machinable alumina. A thin layer (0.2 mm) of Grafoil® was inserted between the fixture and the specimen to minimize friction and accommodate the strains resulting from thermal expansion. The specimens were heated at a constant rate of 10°C/min to the test temperature of 1000°C in argon inside an alumina retort. The tests were conducted at a constant crosshead displacement rate of 0.5 mm/min and both the load and the crosshead displacement were recorded at a rate of 1Hz.

FIG. 6-- Iosipescu Fixture with NIcalon™/SiC specimens

IPSS Tests at Room Temperature--The IPSS measurements were conducted using the commercially available fixture[5] shown in Fig. 6 and a universal testing machine at a constant crosshead displacement rate of 0.5 mm/min. Extreme care was exercised to align the specimen with respect to the fixture before the test. Data pairs of load and crosshead displacement were collected at a rate of 1 Hz.

RESULTS

ILSS Tests at Room Temperature

Figure 7 shows a typical average shear stress versus crosshead displacement curve obtained from the compression of a DNS specimen. The resulting curves were slightly parabolic (that is, increasingly stiffer) up to the peak load which was followed by a sudden load drop when the specimens failed by interlaminar shear. Failure was accompanied by a large release of acoustic energy. The apparent ILSS was determined from Eq. 1, as the ratio of the peak load, P_{max}, divided by the surface area of the imaginary plane between the notches.

$$ILSS = \frac{P_{max}}{w\,L} \tag{1}$$

where w is the specimen width and L is the notch separation.

Figure 8 summarizes the apparent ILSS versus notch separation results for the 2-D Nicalon™/SiC CFCCs with 0.3- and 1.1-μm-thick carbon interphases. The error bars represent the variability from six replications for the specimens with a 0.3-μm-thick carbon interphase and three replications for the

---

[5] Wyoming Test Fixtures, Inc. Laramie, Wyoming 82010.

specimens with a 1.1-µm-thick carbon interphase. The results in Fig. 8 indicate that in both cases the apparent ILSS had a parabolic dependence with notch separation and had minimum values of 46.3 MPa ± 3.9 MPa and 16.5 MPa ± 3.6 MPa for notch separations of 6 and 5 mm, respectively. The apparent ILSS of the CFCC with a 1.1-µm-thick carbon fiber coating was less than that of the samples with a 0.3-µm-thick carbon coating. Furthermore, the data scatter was larger for samples with shorter notch separations. In the case of the specimens with 0.3-µm-thick fiber coating, failure occurred along the porosity rich interlaminar region, whereas most of the specimens with the 1.1-µm-thick fiber coating failed along the thick carbon interphase by a crack that jumped on occasion to the porosity-rich interlaminar region.

The average interlaminar shear stress versus crosshead displacement curves from the evaluation of the 1-D carbon/carbon composites were similar to those obtained from the evaluation of 2-D Nicalon™/SiC CFCCs (Fig. 7). Because of the limited number of specimens, the effect of notch separation or other geometric variables on the apparent ILSS of 1-D carbon/carbon CFCCs were not investigated. However, from the evaluation of five specimens with a notch separation of 8 mm, it was found that the apparent ILSS was 11.35 ± 2.03 MPa. The fracture surfaces of these specimens were rough, as a result of the fiber architecture as indicated by the micrograph in Fig. 9.a. In all cases failure took place along the imaginary plane between the notches. On occasion failure was initiated at the edge of the notches as shown in Fig. 9.b -rather than from their root, although in all cases the fracture plane was defined by the imaginary plane between the notches.

ILSS Tests at Elevated Temperature

The resulting load versus crosshead displacement curves for the 1-D carbon/carbon composites evaluated at 1000°C were similar to those obtained at room temperature. From the evaluation of four specimens with a notch separation of 8 mm, the apparent ILSS was found to be 9.32 ± 2.59 MPa at 1000°C. It was observed that the mode of failure was similar for specimens tested both at room and high temperature.

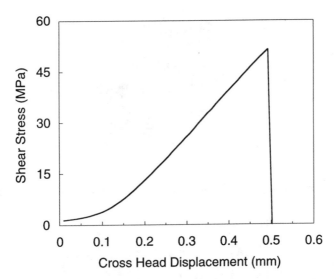

FIG. 7-- Experimental average interlaminar shear stress versus crosshead displacement from the compression of a 2-D Nicalon™/SiC CFCC double-notched specimen.

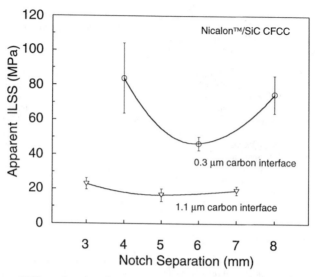

FIG. 8-- Apparent ILSS as a function of notch separation for 2-D Nicalon™/SiC CFCC with different fiber coating thicknesses.

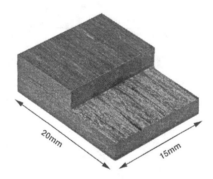

FIG. 9(a)-- Optical micrograph of fractured double-notched specimen of 1-D carbon/carbon CFCC.

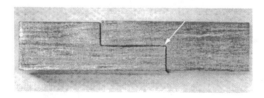

FIG. 9(b)-- Optical micrograph indicating origin of interlaminar failure crack in 1-D carbon/carbon CFCC

IPSS Tests at Room Temperature

Figure 10 shows the load versus crosshead displacement curves obtained from the IPSS evaluation of five 2-D Nicalon™/SiC CFCC specimens. The average in-plane shear strength was determined as:

$$IPSS = \frac{P_{max}}{ht} \qquad (2)$$

where P_{max} is the peak load, h is the separation between the V-notches and t is the specimen thickness. The load-displacement curves were slightly parabolic up to the peak load which was followed by a sudden load drop that accompanied the failure of the specimens. The load did not drop to zero, and the curves showed a plateau at shear stress values between 14 and 37 MPa. From the evaluation of five specimens, the IPSS was found to be 101.0 ± 4.7 MPa and as indicated by the curves in Fig. 10, the results were very reproducible. Post test examination of the specimens revealed that these failed by shear along the imaginary plane between the V-notches. Failure consisted of the fracture of the matrix and some of the fiber bundles perpendicular to the gauge plane, although the specimens remained in one piece held together by the unbroken fiber bundles as illustrated in Fig. 11.

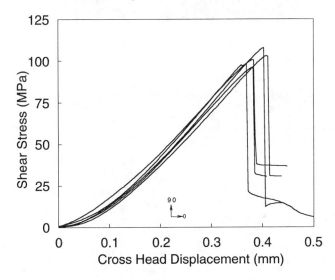

FIG. 10-- Stress versus cross-head displacement results from the IPSS testing of five 2-D Nicalon™/SiC CFCCs.

NUMERICAL ANALYSIS

Compression of DNS

A finite-element stress analysis of the compression of the DNS was conducted in an attempt to explain the experimentally observed dependence of the apparent ILSS with notch separation. A plane stress model was constructed for a hypothetical isotropic, homogeneous material using two dimensional 8-noded quadrilateral and 6-noded triangular elements. The only variable investigated was the separation between the notches and the analysis was carried out using a commercially available finite element analysis program[6]. The boundary conditions consisted of zero-lateral displacement along those portions of the specimen that were in contact with the fixture, while a constant unitary pressure was applied on the top end of the

---

[6] *COSMOS*, Structural Research and Analysis Corporation, Santa Monica, CA 90405

specimen. The notches were modeled as semi-circular, as shown in Figure 12, to be consistent with their actual shape.

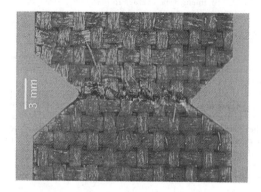

FIG. 11-- Optical micrograph of the gauge section of a 2-D Nicalon™/SiC Iosipescu specimen.

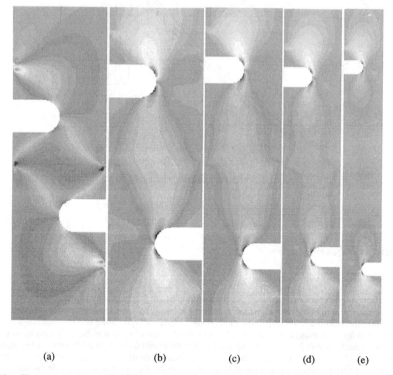

(a)   (b)   (c)   (d)   (e)

FIG. 12-- Shear stress contours for DNS with notch separations of (a) 3 mm; (b) 5 mm. (c) 7 mm; (d) 9 mm; (e) 15 mm; The ends of the specimens are not shown for clarity. To highlight the interaction between the stress fields emanating from the notches, the specimens have been drawn at different scale.

Fig. 12 (a-e) shows the in-plane shear stress distribution in DNS with different notch separations. To best illustrate the interaction of the stress fields emanating from the notches, the figures were drawn at different scale. The results show that the shear stress distribution is symmetric after sequential reflections across the two mid-planes of the specimens, and that as the distance between the notches increases, the degree of interaction between the stress fields emanating from the notches decreases. For the case when the notches are 15 mm apart, there is practically no interaction between the stress fields.

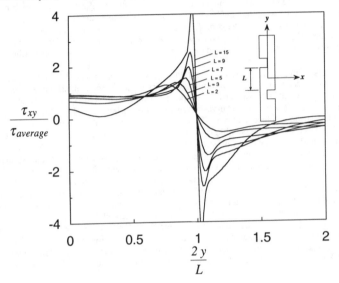

FIG. 13-- Shear stress profiles obtained from the shear stress contours in Fig. 12 for different notch separations.

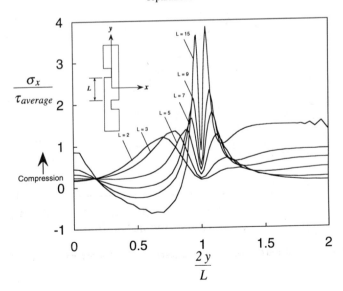

FIG. 14-- Normal stress profiles (x = 0) for different notch separations.

Stress Uniformity in the Gauge Plane--Figure 13 shows the in-plane shear stress profiles along the vertical mid-plane of the specimen obtained from the contour plots in Fig. 12. The shear stresses were normalized by the average interlaminar shear stress according to Eq. 1 and are plotted against the normalized vertical position along the mid-plane of the specimen. These results show that the magnitude of the stress concentration at the notches decreases with decreasing notch separation, and that the reduction in the magnitude of the stress concentration results from the interaction between the stress fields emanating from the notches. Moreover, as a result of the interaction between the stress fields, the shear stress distribution along the imaginary plane between the notches becomes more uniform as the notch separation is reduced. Fig. 14 shows the normalized normal stress profiles, σ_x, along the mid-plane of the specimen. It can be observed that the normal stress is compressive close to the notches where the interlaminar shear stress is largest, which may explain why stress-induced delamination does not occur in this test configuration.

Dependence of the ILSS with Notch Separation--One issue that has not been addressed but that requires attention is the definition of the conditions necessary for the onset of interlaminar shear failure. One piece of information that is provided by the shape of the experimental load versus crosshead displacement curves (Fig. 7) is that these curves are increasingly stiffer although the tests were conducted under a constant crosshead displacement rate. This observation suggests that a process involving the stable propagation of an interlaminar crack is unlikely, and that interlaminar shear failure occurs suddenly whenever the intrinsic ILSS of the material is reached locally anywhere in the gauge plane (most likely at the root of the notches where the probability of exceeding the intrinsic or characteristic ILSS is highest). Obviously, such criterion for interlaminar shear failure must be defined within the framework of theories of probabilistic failure, taking into account the multiaxial state of stress existent at the root of the notches.

If we assume for simplicity that interlaminar shear failure occurs when the intrinsic ILSS is reached (i. e. at the root of a notch), then it is possible to determine the dependence of the apparent ILSS with notch separation based on the results in Fig. 13 and on the linear elastic analysis presented in the previous section. Fig. 15 shows the dependence of the predicted ILSS with notch separation. The results in Fig. 15, which have been normalized by the predicted apparent ILSS for the specimen with a 2-mm-notch separation, show that the predicted apparent ILSS decreases with increasing notch separation in agreement with the numerical results of Markham and Dawson[9] and Dadras and McDowell[11].

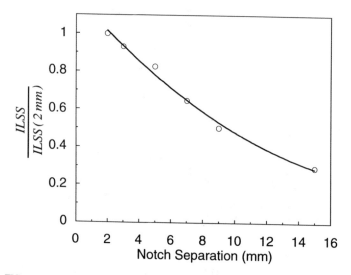

FIG. 15-- Predicted dependence of the apparent ILSS with notch separation for DNS

DISCUSSION

Compression of DNS

Although the trend predicted by the numerical analysis presented in the previous section is in agreement with the numerical results of Markham and Dawson[9] and Dadras and McDowell[11], it is in disagreement with the experimental results presented in this paper for a 2-D Nicalon™/SiC CFCCs, irrespectively of fiber coating thickness, and with the results reported by Sawyer for 2-D carbon/carbon CFCCs[12] and by Fang and Chou for 2-D Nicalon™/CAS CFCCs[15]. If we consider that the dependence of the apparent ILSS with notch separation predicted by the analysis presented in the previous section was obtained from a linear analysis, and that the materials that were evaluated in this study are perfectly elastic[7], then it is proposed that a possible explanation for the discrepancy between the results in Fig. 8 and Fig. 15 is associated with non-linear effects induced by the fixture, which evidently were not taken into account in the finite-element analysis.

Fixture Effects--To consider the effect of the fixture during the test, let us consider the following discussion. Because the analysis leading to the results in Fig. 15 is linear, then the relationship between the predicted load and the predicted crosshead displacement should also be linear, as dictated by Equation 3. In Equation 3, u is the crosshead displacement associated with P, the applied load and k is the specimen compression stiffness, assumed to be independent of notch separation.

$$P = k\,u \qquad (3)$$

However, the results in Fig. 7, showed that the experimental load versus crosshead displacement curves were increasingly stiffer in disagreement with Eq. 3. When a DNS is subjected to compression, it expands laterally as a result of Poisson's effect and the magnitude of the lateral expansion will be directly proportional to the applied compressive load. Although the finite-element stress analysis presented in the previous section did take into account the specimen's Poisson's effect, by virtue of the boundary conditions prescribed in that analysis, the specimen was constrained laterally to slide frictionless in the vertical direction by a rigid (infinitely stiff) fixture. In actuality, however, the specimen slides frictionally against an elastic fixture. If we treat the frictional interaction between the specimen and the fixture as a Coulomb problem, then the normal stress, and consequently the frictional stress between the specimen and the fixture, will be proportional to the applied compressive load. Modifying Eq. 1 to account for the frictional interaction between the specimen and the fixture, and using Eq. 3, we obtain the following relationship between the average interlaminar shear stress and the test machine crosshead displacement:

$$average\ shear\ stress = \frac{(P_{friction}(u) + k\,u)}{w\,L} \qquad (4)$$

where $P_{friction}$ is a non-linear function of the crosshead displacement. Fig. 16 shows the two contributions to the total load in Equation 4, namely a linear term associated with the elastic deformation of the specimen and a non-linear term associated with the frictional interaction between the specimen and the fixture. Based on this discussion, we could argue that the results in Fig. 8 are the superposition of: a linear elastic process that follows the trend dictated by the results in Fig. 15, and that dominates the experimental results for short notch separations, and a non-linear frictional process that dominates the experimental results at higher loads, since the load required to induce shear failure increases with larger notch separations. Equation 4 is represented schematically in Fig. 17. Despite that steps were taken to minimize friction between the specimen and the fixture by using thin sheets of Teflon® or Grafoil®, the experimental results suggest that the frictional interaction between the specimen and the fixture were still significant. Obviously further work is still required to quantify experimentally the magnitude of these effects and in the conduction of detailed numerical analyses accounting for the frictional interaction between the specimen and the fixture.

It appears that the reason why the trend of the results between the apparent ILSS and notch separation in Fig. 8 was not observed by Markham and Dawson[9] or Dadras and McDowell[11] during the evaluation of polymer-matrix composites or by Sawyer in the evaluation of 2-D carbon/carbon using the

---

[7] when loaded in compression and for stresses for which no matrix cracking occurs.

modified DNS[12], is because no supporting fixture was used to conduct those tests.   Therefore the dependence of the apparent ILSS with notch separation that they reported follows the trend in Fig. 15 in which fixture frictional effects were not accounted for.

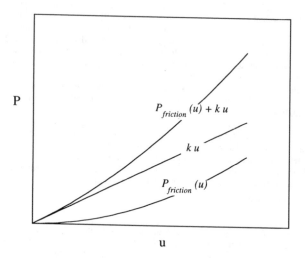

FIG. 16-- Contributions to total load from specimen elastic deformation and from frictional effects between specimen and fixture.

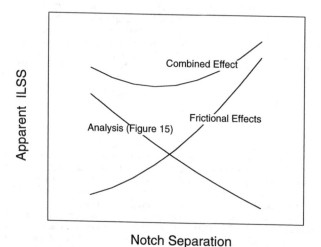

FIG. 17-- Superposition of linear and frictional effects according to Equation 4.

Effects of Interphase Thickness--The differences in the magnitude of the apparent ILSS for Nicalon™/SiC CFCCs with different fiber coating thickness resulted from the different locations in which interlaminar shear failure occurred. Specifically, the specimens with the 0.3-μm-thick fiber coating failed by shear along the porosity-rich interlaminar region whereas the thick fiber coating was the weak link in the specimens with the 1.1 μm fiber coating. These results are significant because the trend in the design of oxidation-resistant fiber coatings appears to be toward thicker fiber coatings (> 0.3 μm). Although the design of these fiber coatings is based on the assumption that they will become the element with the lowest toughness in the interfacial region to promote fiber debonding and sliding, they could also weaken the interlaminar tensile and shear macroscopic response of CFCCs.

Onset of Failure--As indicated in the previous section, it is still necessary to define the conditions for the occurrence of failure during the compression of DNS. Although in the discussion leading to the analysis of fixture frictional effects it was assumed that interlaminar shear failure occurred when the interlaminar shear stress reached the intrinsic ILSS, a more appropriate criterion should incorporate the statistics of strength and the multiaxial state of stress, particularly the effect of normal stresses on the gauge plane. The linear finite-element stress analysis presented in the previous section showed that for most conditions the normal stresses on the gauge plane were compressive which are believed to inhibit delamination. Therefore, it is expected that normal stresses will tend to artificially enhance the magnitude of the apparent ILSS.

High-Temperature Tests--The compression of the DNS test was used successfully to determine the apparent ILSS of 1-D carbon/carbon CFCCs both at room and elevated temperatures. However, the limited number of specimens did not allow for the investigation of the effect of geometric parameters, such as notch separation, on the apparent ILSS or to determine fixture effects at elevated temperature. It was found that the apparent ILSS of the 1-D carbon/carbon CFCCs with a notch separation of 8 mm decreased with temperature from 11.3 ± 2 MPa in air at room temperature to 9.3 ± 2.6 MPa at 1000°C in argon. However this trend is opposite to that reported for other 2-D carbon/carbon in which increases from 4 MPa at room temperature to 7 MPa at 2000°C in nitrogen have been reported[22]. During the evaluation of 1-D carbon/carbon CFCCs it was found that machining-induced defects at the notches served as sites for the initiation of failure. Therefore, special attention must be exercised in the preparation of specimens.

Other--Work is still needed to determine size and volume effects on the mechanical behavior of CFCCs, particularly in relation to such features as weave size, fiber architecture, etc. This observation is relevant to the results presented in this paper regarding the applicability of the compression of DNS for CFCCs. Although it was shown that the stress distribution along the gauge plane becomes more uniform as the notches are closer, a question remains as to, how close can the notches be before volume and size effects start to influence the results?. It is believed that the increase in the scatter of the apparent ILSS experimental results observed at short notch separation for the specimens with 0.3 μm-thick fiber coatings is related to the influence of volume-size effects. For example, for the 2-D Nicalon™/SiC materials investigated the typical wavelength of the weave is about 3 mm which is comparable with the 4 mm notch separation for which the largest data scatter was observed. Work is also needed to investigate the effect of notch size, notch shape and machining practices on the apparent ILSS of CFCCs, and these studies should be complemented with appropriate numerical modeling.

Iosipescu Test

The use of the Iosipescu test to determine the IPSS of 2-D Nicalon™/SiC CFCCs was successful in that valid failure modes were obtained. Because of the coarse surface features of the specimens that were evaluated it was impractical to attach strain gauges on the gauge section to determine the degree of uniformity of the strain fields. Therefore, the only information that was obtained was related to the shear strength and the mode of failure. Because of the limited number of specimens it was not possible to investigate the effect of variables such as notch shape, notch size and notch separation and obviously, these effects should be the subject of further investigation.

SUMMARY

The applicability of ASTM C-1292 *Standard Test Method for Shear Strength of Continuous Fiber-Reinforced Advanced Ceramics at Ambient Temperatures* was investigated by evaluating 2-D Nicalon™/SiC and 1-D carbon/carbon CFCCs. It was found that the apparent interlaminar shear strength, as determined by the compression of a double-notched specimen, had a parabolic dependence with notch separation. It was also found that the thickness of the fiber coating had an effect on the location of interlaminar shear failure. Specimens with thin fiber coating thicknesses (≈ 0.3 µm) failed along the porosity-rich interlaminar region, whereas specimens with thicker fiber coatings (≈ 1.1 µm) failed along the compliant thick fiber coating. The determination of the apparent ILSS of 1-D carbon/carbon composites at room temperature and at 1000°C was successful using fixtures specially designed for this purpose. Values of 11.3 ± 2 MPa at room temperature in air and at 9.3 ± 2.6 MPa at 1000°C in argon were obtained for the apparent ILSS of this material.

Although a linear finite-element stress analysis of the compression of the DNS predicted that the apparent ILSS decreases with increasing notch separation, it was shown that the experimentally observed parabolic dependence could be explained as the superposition of a linear process in which the apparent ILSS decreases with increasing notch separation and a non-linear process resulting from the frictional interaction between the specimen and the fixture. It is recognized that although the finite-element stress analysis conducted in this investigation was useful to determine the effect of notch separation on the uniformity of the shear stress between the notches and the interaction between the stress fields, it was too idealized and neglected to model the frictional interaction between the specimen and the fixture, which is suspected to be significant. Although a fixture is necessary to provide lateral support and to prevent buckling during the compression of DNS, frictional effects between the fixture and the specimen may tend to artificially increase the magnitude of the apparent ILSS.

Valid in-plane shear failures were obtained for 2-D Nicalon™/SiC by means of the Iosipescu test. The mode of failure was found to consists of matrix cracking along the plane between the V-notches and failure of some of the fiber bundles perpendicular to the gauge plane. However, in all cases the specimens remained in one piece held together by unbroken fiber bundles. Further work is still necessary to investigate the effect of geometrical parameters on the shear strength of CFCCs for the Iosipescu test.

Despite its disadvantages, the compression of DNS is still an attractive test method for the determination of ILSS because of its simplicity and the relatively small specimens used. Although ASTM C1292 provides some guidance regarding specimen dimensions, in light of the effect of notch separation on the apparent ILSS, it is recommended as a starting point, to test specimens with different notch separations and use the most conservative value. Evidently, much work is still needed to optimize the fixture and the specimen to minimize extraneous effects and in investigating such factors as notch geometry, notch size, volume effects and machining practices, for example. Ideally these studies should be complemented with appropriate numerical analyses.

ACKNOWLEDGMENTS

This research was sponsored by the U. S. Department of Energy, Assistant Secretary for Energy Efficiency and Renewable Energy, Office of Industrial Technologies, Industrial Energy Efficiency Division and Continuous Fiber Ceramic Composites Program, under contract DE-AC05-96OR22464 with Lockheed Martin Energy Research Corporation.

Table 1-- DNS dimensions

	Dimension	Value (mm)
q	Specimen length	30.00
L	Distance ÷ notches	3.0, 4.0 5.0, 6.0 7.0, 8.0
w	Specimen width	15.00
d	Notch width	0.50
t	Thickness	≈ 3.3

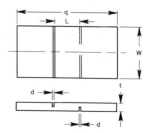

FIG. 18-- Schematic of DNS and nomenclature for dimensions in Tables 1 and 2.

Table 2-- DNS dimensions

	Dimension	Value (mm)
q	Specimen length	30.00
L	Distance ÷ notches	8.00
w	Specimen width	15.00
d	Notch width	0.50
t	Thickness	≈ 6.0

Table 3-- Iosipescu specimen dimensions

	Dimension	Value
L	Specimen length	76.00 mm
h	Distance ÷ Notches	11.00 mm
W	Specimen width	19.00 mm
R	Notch Radius	1.30 mm
θ	Notch Angle	90.0 °
t	Thickness	≈ 3.3 mm

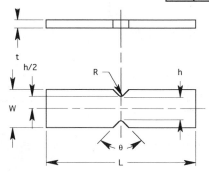

FIG. 19-- Schematic of Iosipescu specimen and nomenclature for dimensions in Table 3.

REFERENCES

[1] Genin, G. M. and Hutchinson, J. W., "Composite Laminates in Plane Stress: Constitutive Modeling and Stress Redistribution due to Matrix Cracking," in High-Temperature Ceramic Matrix Composites, Proceedings of the Second International Conference on in High-Temperature Ceramic Matrix Composites, Ceramic Transactions, Vol. 57, The American Ceramic Society, Westerville, OH.

[2] Lara-Curzio, E., Ferber, M. K., and Jenkins, M. G.," Methodologies for the Thermo-mechanical Characterization of Continuous Fiber-Reinforced Ceramic Matrix Composites: A Review of Test Methods," 39th-International SAMPE Symposium, Society for the Advancement of Material Process and Engineering, 1994, pp. 1780-1789.

[3] Chamis, C. C., and Sinclair, J. H., "Ten-deg Off-axis Test for Shear Properties in Fiber Composites," Experimental Mechanics, Sept. 1977, pp. 339-346.

[4] Rosen, B. W., "A Simple Procedure for Experimental Determination of the Longitudinal Shear Modulus of Unidirectional Composites," Journal of Composite Materials, Vol. 6, 1972, pp.552-444.

[5] Whitney, J. M., Stansbarger, D. L. and Howell, H. B., "Analysis of the Rail Shear Test: Application and Limitations," Journal of Composite Materials, Vol. 5, 1971, pp. 24-34.

[6] Sims, D. F., "In-Plane Shear Stress-Strain Response of Unidirectional Composite Materials," Journal of Composite Materials, Vol. 7, 1973, pp. 124-128.

[7] Kurtz, R. D., and Sun, C. T., "Composite Shear Moduli and Strengths from Torsion of Thick Laminates," in Composite Materials: Testing and Design (Ninth Volume), ASTM STP 1059, S. P. Garbo, Ed. American Society for Testing and Materials, West Conshohocken, PA, 1990, pp. 508-520.

[8] Chiao, C., Moore, R. L., and Chiao, T. T.," Measurement of Shear Properties of Fiber Composites: Evaluation of Test Methods," Composites, July 1977, pp. 161-169.

[9] Markham, F., and Dawson, D., "Interlaminar Shear Strength of Fiber-reinforced Composites," Composites, July 1975, pp. 173-77.

[10] Whitney, M., "Stress Analysis of the Double Notch Shear Specimen," in Proceedings of the American Society for Composites, 4th Technical Conference, Oct. 1989, Blacksburg, VA.

[11] Dadras, D., and McDowell, J. S., "Analytical and Experimental Evaluation of Double-notch Shear Specimens of Orthotropic Materials," Experimental Mechanics, June 1990, pp. 184-189.

[12] Sawyer, W., "Investigation of Test Techniques for Measuring Interlaminar Shear Strength of 2-D Carbon-Carbon Composites," NASA TM100647, Sept. 1988.

[13] Thielicke, B., Soltesz, U., and Maschke, H-G., "Determination of the Interlaminar Shear Strength of C/C Composites by the Compression-Shear Tests," Presented at the 8th CIMTEC-World Congress and Forum on New Materials, Florence Italy, 29 June- 4 July, 1994, Paper SIII-8:L12.

[14] Thielicke, B., Maschke, H-G., and Soltesz, U., "Experimental and Numerical Investigations of the Applicability of the Iosipescu-test for Determining the Interlaminar Shear Strength (ILSS) of a Carbon-Carbon Composite, " Presented at the 6th European Conference on Composite Materials, Bordeaux, France 10-24 Sept. 1993, High Temperature Ceramic Matrix Composites, HT-CMC1, R. Naslain, J. Lamon and D. Doumeingts, Ed. Woodhead Publishing Limited.

[15] Fang, N. and Chou, T-W., "Characterization of Interlaminar Shear Strength of Ceramic Matrix Composites," Journal of the American Ceramic Society, Vol. 76, No. 10, 1993, pp. 2539-48.

[16] Mo, H. H., Tsai, Y., Morton, J. and Farley, G. L., "Numerical Analysis of the Iosipescu Specimen for Composite Materials," Composites Science and Technology, Vol. 45, 1993, pp. 115-28.

[17] Lee, S. and Munro, M., "Evaluation of Testing Techniques for the Iosipescu Shear Test for Advanced Composite Materials," Journal of Composite Materials, Vol. 24, 1990, pp. 419-40.

[18] Adams, D. F., "The Iosipescu Shear Test Method as Used for Testing Polymers and Composite Materials," Polymer Composites, Vol. 11, No. 5, 1990, pp. 286-290.

[19] Wilson, D. W., "Evaluation of the V-notched Beam Shear Test Through an Interlaboratory Study," Journal of Composites Technology and Research, Vol. 12, No. 3, 1990, pp. 131-8.

[20] Brondsted, P., Heredia, F., E., and Evans, A. G., "In-Plane Shear Properties of 2-D Ceramic Matrix Composites," Journal of the American Ceramic Society, Vol. 77, No. 10, 1994, pp. 2569-74.

[21] Lara-Curzio, E. and Ferber, M. K., "A Test Fixture for the Determination of Interlaminar Shear Strength of Composites," submitted to Journal of Testing and Evaluation, 1995.

[22] Thielicke, B., Soltesz, U., and Unnasch, H., "The Interlaminar Shear Strength (ILSS) of a Laminated C/C Composite at Temperatures up to 2000°C," Presented at the European Conference on Composites Testing and Standardization, 13-15 Sept., 1994. Hamburg, Germany, ECCM-CTS2, P. J. Hogg, K. Schulte and H. Wittich, Ed., Woodhead Publishing Limited

Marc Steen[1] and José-Lorenzo Vallés[1]

UNLOADING-RELOADING SEQUENCES AND THE ANALYSIS OF MECHANICAL TEST RESULTS FOR CONTINUOUS FIBER CERAMIC COMPOSITES

REFERENCE: Steen, M. and Vallés, J. L., **"Unloading-Reloading Sequences and the Analysis of Mechanical Test Results,"** Thermal and Mechanical Test Methods and Behavior of Continuous-Fiber Ceramic Composites, ASTM STP 1309, Michael G. Jenkins, Stephen T. Gonczy, Edgar Lara-Curzio, Noel E. Ashbaugh, and Larry P. Zawada, Eds., American Society for Testing and Materials, 1997.

ABSTRACT: The introduction of intermittent unloading - reloading cycles during mechanical testing is an extremely powerful tool to assist in the interpretation of the mechanical response of a material to the imposed loading conditions. This technique has a potential as a probing method in material characterization which has been vastly underestimated, particularly in the case of continuous-fiber ceramic composites (CFCCs), where, in addition to helping in the description of damage development, it can yield important information on fiber-matrix interfacial phenomena as well. The present contribution highlights the results obtained from the incorporation of unloading-reloading cycles during uniaxial strength, creep and fatigue tests on selected 2D woven CFCCs at room and elevated temperatures. Some implications for the modeling of the mechanical behavior are indicated.

KEYWORDS: continuous-fiber ceramic composites, unloading-reloading cycles, hysteresis, residual stress, damage accumulation, creep, fatigue, ratchetting

INTRODUCTION

Intermittent unloading-reloading cycles during a mechanical test can be used as a tool to "probe" the instantaneous material response. In the past, this method has mainly been used to characterize the evolution of damage in a uniaxially loaded test piece made of a homogeneous and isotropic material through the evolution of the elastic modulus. This was framed in the theory of continuum damage mechanics with the scalar damage parameter D defined as

[1] Research Officers, Institute for Advanced Materials, Joint Research Centre, European Commission, P.O.Box 2, NL-1755 ZG Petten, the Netherlands.

$$D = 1 - (E/E_0) \tag{1}$$

where E is the instantaneous elastic modulus and E_0 its initial value. In practical cases, the value of E is either taken as that of the unloading modulus observed upon the start of unloading, E_u, or as that corresponding to the average value of the unloading and the reloading modulus, E_a. In the latter case only the stress or strain range where no inflection point occurs in the stress versus strain curve upon unloading should be covered to avoid attributing any influence to crack closure. This way of quantifying damage has received considerable attention in creep and fatigue studies of metals [1] and is based on the original idea of Kachanov [2]. However, whereas it is possible to attribute an intuitive meaning to the damage parameter D in Eq 1 as the loss of load-bearing cross-sectional area of the test piece, it does not give any indication with respect to the damage mechanism(s) causing a decrease in the instantaneous elastic modulus. The purpose of this contribution is to indicate how a more elaborate investigation of the unloading-reloading stress-strain curve can give qualitative as well as semi-quantitative information on the damage mechanisms governing the mechanical behavior of continuous-fiber ceramic composites (CFCCs).

MATERIAL AND TESTING PROCEDURE

The mechanical response under uniaxial loading of two bidirectionally reinforced CFCCs has been studied at room and elevated temperatures. The thermal expansion mismatch between fibers and matrix is of opposite sign in the two composites, resulting in vastly different mechanical behavior. Both composites have a silicon carbide matrix obtained by chemical vapor infiltration and are reinforced by fiber bundles in a 2D weave. The main constituent properties are listed in Table 1.

TABLE 1--Characteristics of the composite constituents.

	SiC Matrix	Al$_2$O$_3$ Fiber	C Fiber
Type	isothermal CVI	Sumitomo	Besfight
Elastic modulus, GPa	420 (RT-1200°C)	160 (RT), 140 (1100°C)	238 (RT)
Tensile strength at RT, GPa	...	1.9	3.4
Rupture strain at RT, %	0.05	0.6	1.3
Longitudinal CTE, 10^{-6} K^{-1}	4.5	8.8	-0.5
Weave type	...	plain	8H satin
Volume fraction	0.4	0.4	0.44

Uniaxial tests under load control are performed in a machine equipped with an induction heater and a graphite susceptor. Flat rectangular cross-sectional specimens of 10 by 3 mm^2 with a total length of 200 mm are tested under a vacuum better than 10^{-3} Pa to avoid oxidative attack of the interphases after the formation of matrix cracks. In all tests, one of the fiber orientations coincides with the loading direction. Strain is recorded by a contacting extensometer with a 10 mm gage length. Isothermal tests featuring unloading-reloading cycles have been performed over the temperature range extending from RT to 1200°C. A loading rate of 2 MPa/s has been used in the tension tests and for all unloading-reloading sequences. The strain and stress data are recorded digitally and stored for further evaluation. Further information on the experimental setup can be found in Ref. 3.

INTERPRETATION OF UNLOADING-RELOADING CURVES FOR CFCCs

In a fiber-reinforced composite unloading followed by reloading usually gives rise to a hysteresis loop, indicating that some type of energy-dissipating mechanism is operating. The discussion here focuses on the material response observed during unloading-reloading under stress-controlled conditions.

A number of important parameters can be derived from the hysteresis loop (Fig. 1). First, the area of the loop, W, represents the amount of dissipated energy during the unloading-reloading cycle. Secondly, the unloading tangent modulus at maximum stress, E_u, corresponds to the instantaneous stiffness of the test piece, which is a measure of the current damage state (Eq 1). Linear unloading is followed by an unloading part with negative curvature (A), indicating that strain accumulates nonelastically in the unloading direction even before the applied stress is zero. Upon continued unloading, an inflection point may subsequently appear (B), which is a manifestation of an increase in the stiffness and, in the case of isotropic materials, has either been attributed to crack closure by meeting of the crack flanks or by the presence of debris in the crack wake. Whereas for these materials, the occurrence of the crack closure effect exclusively relies on the development and presence of a macro-crack, which by its size affects the load-bearing area of the test piece, in CFCCs, the relief of compressive axial residual stresses in the matrix upon interfacial debonding can also trigger the occurrence of an inflection point in the unloading curve [4]. Further unloading beyond the inflection point is characterized by an increasing tangent modulus (range C), which, depending on whether cracks are fully closed at the minimum stress level, may reach the value E_0 of the material in its initial condition.

Reloading (D) from the minimum stress starts with either a linear region with tangent modulus E_0 or immediately nonlinear. In the latter case, it is not possible to attribute any physical meaning to the value of the reloading tangent modulus at minimum stress, since it depends on the amount of crack closure attained in the preceding unloading cycle. Similarly as for the nonlinear unloading range A, strain again lags behind stress in this range, indicating that a "frictional" phenomenon occurs.

For CFCCs, the resulting width and area of the loop have been associated with frictional sliding along the fiber-matrix interfaces. The nonlinear reloading curve may terminate in a straight line portion when the interfacial slip length extends over the complete distance between matrix cracks. In that case, the tangent modulus at maximum stress corresponds for all practical purposes to the fiber stiffness.

When no additional damage has been generated during the unloading-reloading cycle, the hysteresis loop is completely closed and the reloading curve goes through the previous stress and strain maximum. If this is not the case, that is, the reloading line reaches the previously attained maximum strain at a stress level below the previous maximum, additional damage in the form either of matrix cracking or of fiber failure has occurred.

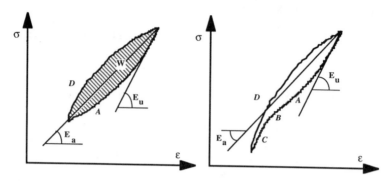

FIG. 1--Schematic of hysteresis loops without and with an inflection point upon unloading.

In addition to the above-mentioned features, which are observable within an individual hysteresis loop, there is also an important parameter that can be retrieved from hysteresis loops obtained from subsequent unloading-reloading cycles performed during the mechanical test. In the absence of additional damage generated during individual consecutive loops, the average linear regression lines to the unloading-reloading curves over the stress range in which crack closure does not occur have a common intersection point. The stress level corresponding to that intersection point is related to the average axial residual stress in the fibers [4].

The evolution of the aforementioned parameters with loading history can be used as an indicator of damage evolution. The elastic modulus E_a over the stress range in which matrix cracks are open (see Fig. 1) has been widely used for this purpose, as has been the minimum strain observed in consecutive hysteresis loops. However, as indicated in Ref. 4, care should be taken when attributing a physical meaning to this minimum (also called irreversible) strain, since its evolution may be different depending on whether crack closure occurs, that is, when an inflection point is present upon unloading or not.

RESULTS OF TENSION TESTS

Typical stress-strain curves with unloading-reloading cycles obtained at room temperature are shown in Fig. 2. Above a given applied stress, the unloading-reloading curves do not superimpose and give rise to the formation of a hysteresis loop. The width of these loops increases with stress as a consequence of the increase in interfacial friction caused by progressive interfacial debonding. The loop width and area are much larger for Al_2O_3/SiC than for C/SiC, indicating much larger friction in the former than in the latter CFCC. Also, the unloading curve of Al_2O_3/SiC clearly shows an inflection point, whereas this is not observed for C/SiC at room temperature. This indicates that for C/SiC the matrix cracks are sufficiently wide open for the matrix blocks not to touch each other upon unloading. For Al_2O_3/SiC on the other hand, the gradual development of an inflection point is a manifestation of the relief of compressive axial residual stresses in the matrix upon progressive debonding along the fiber-matrix interface, caused by the maximum stress increasing from loop to loop. This is also confirmed by the position of the common intersection point, P, in the first quadrant of the stress-strain plane, indicating that the fibers are under residual tension, and the matrix hence under residual compression. A close investigation shows that the inflection point moves in the direction of lower stresses with each unloading-reloading cycle, as expected when its occurrence is due to a relief of residual stresses. The common intersection point for the C/SiC composite lies in the third quadrant, indicating that the fibers are under residual compressive stress and the matrix under residual tension.

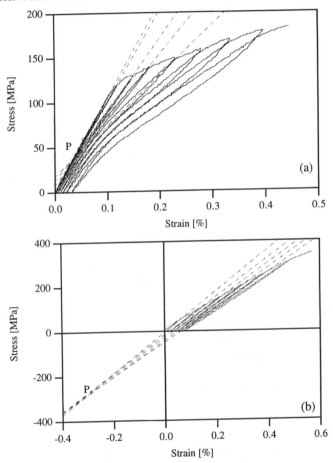

FIG. 2--Tension stress-strain curves with unloading-reloading cycles (full) and modulus extension lines (dashed) at room temperature for (a) Al_2O_3/SiC and (b) C/SiC.

The hysteresis loops clearly change with temperature as shown in Figure 3. Whereas for the Al_2O_3/SiC, the occurrence of an inflection point is suppressed at high temperatures, the opposite is true for C/SiC and an inflection point starts to appear upon unloading from a certain temperature upwards. This is completely in line with the evolution of the position of the common intersection point which moves towards the first quadrant for C/SiC, whereas it gets more compressive for Al_2O_3/SiC. Also, from the area within the loops, the interfacial friction at high temperature is found to be larger for Al_2O_3/SiC, as expected from the radial residual compression across the interface induced by the thermo-elastic mismatch. For the C/SiC composite, the width of the loops is hardly affected by temperature.

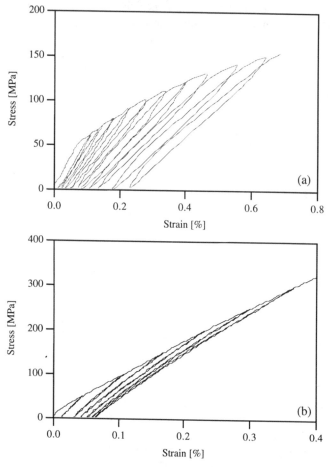

FIG. 3--Tension stress-strain curves with unloading-reloading cycles at 1100°C for (a) Al_2O_3/SiC and (b) C/SiC.

To enable comparison between the two CFCCs, the average modulus E_a is normalized with respect to the axial fiber stiffness E_fV_f (V_f is the volume fraction of fibers in the direction of loading). The evolution of the normalized average slope of the hysteresis loops with the previously attained maximum stress over the stress range in which the matrix cracks are open, is shown in Fig. 4. Figure 4 a shows that complete off-loading to the fibers is not reached for any of the composites in the tension tests, and that overall composite failure intervenes before that stage is attained. For Al_2O_3/SiC, a stepwise decrease in modulus occurs which is caused by the advent of matrix microcracking during loading. The fact that the dropoff occurs earlier at higher temperatures is in agreement with the change in sign from compressive to tensile of the residual axial stresses in the matrix. When the stresses are related to the "true" stresses,

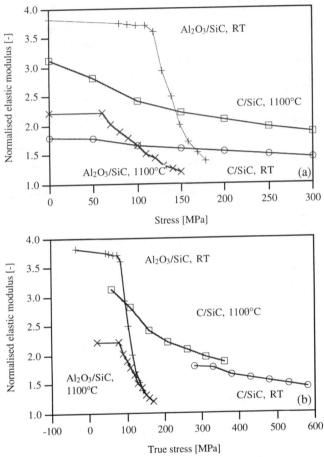

FIG. 4--Evolution of normalized elastic modulus with nominal applied stress (a) and with true stress (b), considering the presence of axial residual stresses.

taking into account the aforementioned common intersection point and hence the axial residual stresses, the sudden decrease in modulus occurs for the same stress level (Fig. 4 b). The fact that the modulus decreases more slowly with true stress at high temperature is a consequence of the residual radial compressive stresses that oppose interfacial debonding. For C/SiC, a stepwise drop in modulus is absent which is explained by the fact that the matrix is already saturated with cracks after cooling down from the processing temperature, and hence, additional matrix cracking is unlikely. Moreover, a quasisimilar modulus evolution is observed at both temperatures, which agrees with the fact that the width of the hysteresis loops does not seem to depend on temperature for this CFCC (compare Figs. 2 b and 3 b).

RESULTS OF CREEP TESTS

Figure 5 shows the evolution of the normalized loop width observed in a creep test on the Al_2O_3/SiC composite. As for the tension tests, the unloading-reloading hysteresis loops have been recorded at an applied stress rate of 2 MPa/s. After the initial increase in width, which is similar to that observed in the tension tests and manifests the increased friction caused by progressive interfacial debonding, the loop width stabilizes. This is contrary to the expectation of decreasing width caused by reduced friction because of Poisson contraction of the fibers under the applied axial creep load and suggests that an additional mechanism is playing a part. From the evolution of the average elastic modulus with strain, again normalized with respect to E_fV_f (Fig. 6), it appears that progressive interfacial debonding is occurring during creep. Because of this progressive debonding, the sliding length increases and this compensates the decrease in friction caused by radial fiber contraction. We conclude that accelerated or tertiary creep of the composite is caused by

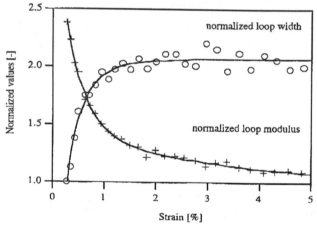

FIG. 5--Evolution of normalized modulus and normalized loop width in a creep test on the Al_2O_3/SiC composite (T = 1100°C, σ = 100 MPa).

stationary creep of the fibers over a steadily increasing debonded fiber length [5]. This finding has been used in the establishment of a creep model for a CFCC and can explain the occurrence of the anomalously high stress exponents of the minimum creep rate, as shown in Fig. 6 [6].

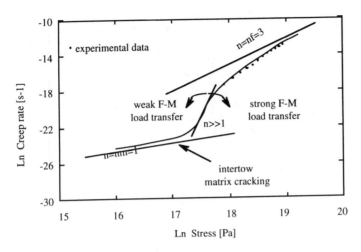

FIG. 6--Model prediction of minimum creep rate for the Al_2O_3/SiC composite at 1100°C.

The creep behavior of the C/SiC composite is qualitatively similar to that of Al_2O_3/SiC. After a transition period, a steady-state condition is observed for both the hysteresis loop width and the elastic modulus.

RESULTS OF FATIGUE TESTS

For the Al_2O_3/SiC composite, fatigue loading at room temperature at 1 Hz and an R-ratio of 0.1 results in hysteresis loops which in the beginning of the test show an inflection point. With increasing number of cycles, the width of the loops increases, the average modulus decreases, and the stress corresponding to the inflection point gradually decreases (Fig. 7). All these observations point into the direction of progressive interfacial debonding occurring during fatigue. This relieves the residual stress state and hence causes the inflection point to disappear. However, the maximum loop width at the same maximum stress is less than that observed in the tension tests and decreases to zero with increasing cycle number. This suggests that cyclically induced frictional wear is occurring along the sliding interface. The total vanishing of the loop width implies that the fibers are free to slide in the matrix along the debonded length (the interface is indeed under residual tension at room temperature). Also the elastic modulus stabilizes, but at a level higher than $E_f V_f$, indicating that the interface is not debonded over its full length. In line with this observation, the irreversible strain accumulation also saturates. It is hence possible to distinguish two phases in the fatigue test: at low cycle numbers damage accumulates fast, as evidenced by the drop in modulus and the increase in width. This stage is followed by a stabilization period characterized by constant modulus, irreversible strain, and width. In this phase, the hysteresis loop does not move in the stress-strain plane ("*shakedown*"), and the composite is expected to have an infinite fatigue life.

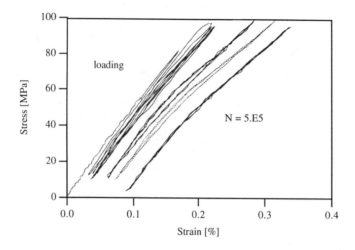

FIG. 7--Evolution of hysteresis loops in a room temperature fatigue test on the Al₂O₃/SiC composite.

For C/SiC, a similar picture is obtained. The hysteresis loops do not show however an increase in opening, suggesting that the frictional condition existing at the interface in tension tests at room temperature is not modified by cycling. The modulus of the linear loops gradually decreases to reach the value corresponding to $E_f V_f$, indicating that full interfacial debonding is induced by the fatigue loading. Together with the modulus the irreversible strain also saturates, resulting in shakedown (Fig. 8).

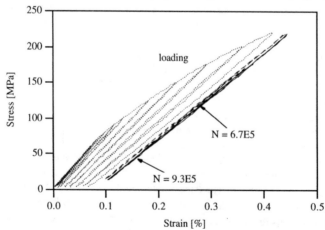

FIG. 8--Evolution of hysteresis loops in a room temperature fatigue test on the C/SiC composite.

RESULTS OF CREEP-FATIGUE INTERACTION TESTS

Figure 9 a shows the hysteresis loops obtained during cycling of an Al_2O_3/SiC specimen at 1100°C and a frequency of 0.1 Hz (R=0.1). The modulus decreases fast with number of cycles and saturates at a level very close to E_fV_f, indicating that complete interfacial debonding has occurred. As for the creep test at the same temperature and maximum stress (Fig. 6), the loop width progressively increases up to saturation, indicating that the increase in friction due to a larger debond length is compensated by another mechanism, most probably cyclically induced frictional wear, as indicated by the fact that the fatigue loops are much narrower than observed in the high temperature creep and tension tests. Whereas at room temperature a complete wearout is achieved, this is

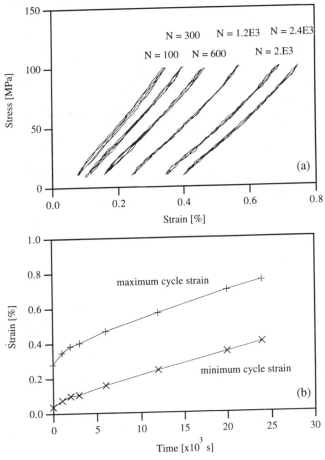

FIG. 9--Evolution of hysteresis loops (a) and cyclic strain (b) in a creep-fatigue interaction test on the Al_2O_3/SiC composite (maximum stress 100 MPa, R = 0.1, T = 1100°C).

not the case at high temperature because of the residual radial clamping stress. Contrary to the modulus and loop width which both stabilize, the irreversible strain continuously increases with the number of cycles. This indicates that instead of the shakedown observed at room temperature, ratchetting occurs at high temperature. This ratchetting is caused by steady-state creep of the fibers over the complete debonded length and hence should occur at a constant rate, as confirmed by Figure 9 b. Composite failure under high temperature fatigue loading is hence expected to occur by fiber creep failure. Consequently, fatigue tests at high temperature with the same maximum stress but different frequencies show the same strain accumulation and lifetime on a time basis, whereas they scale with cycle period on the basis of cycle number [7].

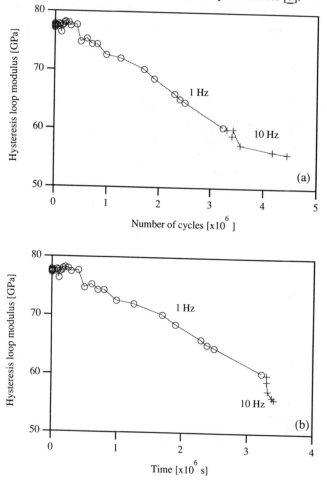

FIG. 10--Evolution of hysteresis loop modulus with number of cycles (a) and time (b) in a fatigue test on the C/SiC composite (maximum stress 300 MPa, R = 0.1, T = 1200°C).

The behavior of C/SiC under fatigue loading at high temperature is somewhat different. Under conditions in which an inflection point is not present in the unloading cycle, the overall loop modulus decreases again to $E_f V_f$ when failure does not intervene previously. However, at different frequencies the modulus decreases smoothly as a function of the number of cycles (Fig. 10 a), whereas a jump is observed when it is plotted as a function of accumulated cycle time (Fig. 10 b). This suggests that the modulus decrease is caused by cyclically induced interfacial debonding. We hence expect that the ratchetting strain rate will not only be purely a function of elapsed time (as is the case for Al_2O_3/SiC), but will also show a dependence on the number of cycles. This is indeed observed from Fig. 11, in which the maximum cycle strain is plotted versus cycle number for tests performed at the same maximum stress but different frequencies. For all tests, the ratchetting strain rate tends to the same value, indicating its cycle-dependent nature. Although it can be expected that the absolute value of the ratchetting strain should increase with increasing frequency resulting in a higher cyclic damage accumulation rate at the start of the test, this dependence is masked by the different residual stress states in different specimens before the test [4].

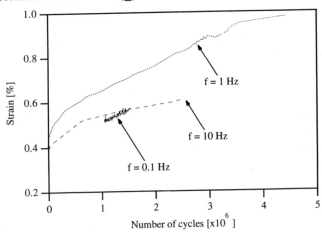

FIG. 11--Accumulation of maximum cyclic strain versus number of cycles in fatigue tests on the C/SiC composite (maximum stress 300 MPa, R = 0.1, T = 1200°C).

REVERSED STRESS HIGH TEMPERATURE FATIGUE

The above description of the high temperature fatigue behavior is limited to tension-tension fatigue, where the matrix cracks are open during the fatigue cycle and the creeping bridging fibers are not constrained. Under these conditions, an inflection point does not occur in the unloading part of the hysteresis loop. The occurrence of an inflection point in the unloading part is promoted by a decrease in the minimum stress of the cycle, as is the case in tension-compression fatigue testing. Figure 12 shows the strain accumulation observed in high temperature fatigue tests on the C/SiC composite.

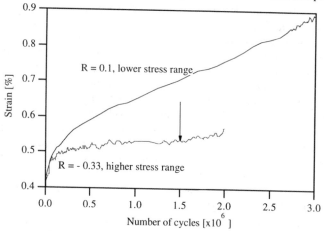

FIG. 12--Comparison of cyclic strain accumulation in fatigue tests on C/SiC (maximum stress 300 MPa, T = 1200°C) without inflection point (R > 0), and with inflection point upon unloading (R < 0).

The tests are performed at different minimum stress, but under otherwise identical experimental conditions. In the tests with the lowest minimum stress (largest stress range, negative R-ratio), the cyclic strain at maximum stress reaches saturation early in life and accumulates much slower than in the test at the same maximum stress but higher minimum stress (lower stress range, positive R-ratio), where it increases continuously. For the latter test, an inflection point is not observed in the hysteresis loop, indicating that the matrix cracks are open during the whole fatigue cycle. For the test with the negative R-ratio, on the other hand, an inflection point appears upon unloading. This causes a decrease in strain range compared to that in the absence of an inflection point, and the cyclically induced damage is hence expected to be smaller. The strain range is however still larger than for the R>0 test. Nevertheless, the strain accumulation is less.

This observation can be explained as follows: when upon unloading crack closure occurs the cracks are open and the fibers exposed to the full applied stress for a smaller portion of the fatigue cycle. The smaller time spent with open cracks is expected to result in a decrease of the damage per cycle. In the case considered here, the damage rate is not only reduced, but seems to be nearly suppressed altogether. Two explanations can be put forward. The first is that creep damage occurring during the part of the cycle with open cracks is completely recovered during the part with closed matrix cracks, implying that reverse (i.e. compressive) creep of the fibers occurs in the latter part of the cycle. In order to result in the observed near-zero cyclic strain accumulation (see Fig. 12), this reverse creep should be of the same magnitude as the tensile creep of the fibers, which is very unlikely since the load in the part of the cycle where matrix cracks are closed is shared between the matrix and the fibers. Moreover, compressive fiber creep recovery cannot explain the absence of forward cyclic strain in a non-symmetrical tension-compression fatigue test, as considered here (R = - 0.33 ≠ - 1).

The second explanation relies on the offloading of stress from the fibers to the matrix induced by their creep strength mismatch. During the early part of the test this results in the build-up of a compressive residual fiber stress [8]. Not only do the fibers thus experience the applied stress for a smaller time during the cycle, but in addition, the stress level during this part is lower. In view of the power-law dependence of creep rate on stress, the bridging fibers creep at a considerably lower rate, giving rise to a much lower composite strain rate.

In the case of cycle-dependent fatigue behavior (as it prevails at room temperature), the smaller period of the cycle during which cracks are open is not expected to affect the behavior as dramatically as in the case of time-dependent behavior. Indeed, cycle-dependence implies that it is the magnitude of the strain range which controls the behavior, and the cyclic damage per cycle is expected to scale linearly with the strain range corresponding to open cracks. This argument has been used to explain the higher fatigue lives observed for higher stress ratios at room temperature [9].

As indicated by the arrow in Fig. 12, a strain rate increase is observed in the R<0 test for N>1.5E6 cycles. Interestingly, this coincides with the disappearance of the inflection point upon unloading. Indeed, progressive interfacial debonding (possibly triggered from a new flaw population on the surface of the fibers induced during cycling) gives rise to a relief of the residual axial stresses, and the inflection point vanishes. For C/SiC tested at a temperature above the manufacturing temperature the matrix is under a small residual axial tension, contrary to the expectation from the expansion mismatch between fiber and matrix [4]. Debonding hence causes the matrix blocks to shrink, and the matrix microcracks open up. Upon unloading to the minimum applied stress, this increased opening causes the inflection point to be lost. Consequently, the strain range corresponding to the applied stress range increases, which in turn results in an increase of the maximum strain in the cycle. The stationary strain rate in this stage is however still much smaller than that observed under tension-tension. This is a consequence of the fact that the net stress experienced by the bridging fibers is much smaller than that observed in tension-tension fatigue because of the development of compressive residual fiber stresses in the preceding load history.

It hence appears that the initial presence of an inflection point upon unloading can result in a considerable reduction of the strain accumulation at the maximum cyclic stress in the case that damage occurring during the fatigue test contains a time-dependent component. Because fatigue failure is ultimately governed by the attainment of the failure strain of the bridging fibers, a positive creep-fatigue interaction, which gives rise to an extension of the time to failure under cyclic loading occurs. The extent to which the number of cycles to failure increases depends on the relative magnitude of the time- and cycle- dependent damage components. At high frequencies, the effect is expected to be smaller than at low frequencies.

This interaction exhibits two stages: the first is of transient nature and ends with the disappearance of the inflection point as a consequence of the decay in residual stress relief caused by progressive cyclic interfacial debonding; the second consists of a permanent reduction in the fiber creep rate caused by the development of creep-mismatch induced compressive residual stresses in the fibers. This has been found in the high temperature fatigue of both composites studied here, which contain fibers which are less creep resistant than the matrix. In the opposite case, that is, when the creep resistance of the fibers is higher than that of the matrix, the second interaction is expected to give rise to a negative effect. The stress experienced by the fibers in that case increases because of the offloading from the less creep resistant matrix. This causes an acceleration in the fiber creep rate and results in a life reduction. This conjecture has yet to be confirmed experimentally.

CONCLUSIONS

The characteristic features, namely average slope, presence of an inflection point upon unloading, irreversible strain, and width of the unloading-reloading loops, observed during mechanical testing of two types of CFCCs are studied. Their evolution with applied stress or strain, time or with number of cycles provides valuable clues for the determination of the deformation and damage mechanisms prevailing under a given set of loading conditions.

It is shown that notwithstanding the vastly different fiber properties and reinforcement architecture of the two studied CFCCs their response to mechanical loading is quite similar, provided that due account is taken of the presence of axial residual stresses. The latter can be determined experimentally from the unloading-reloading loops performed during tension tests. Uniaxial creep of both composites is controlled by creep of the bridging fibers. At room temperature their fatigue behavior is purely cycle-dependent whereas at high temperature time-dependent creep of the bridging fibers dominates the response. Over the experimentally covered frequency range the tension-tension fatigue behavior at high temperature of the Al_2O_3/SiC composite is purely time-dependent. The C/SiC composite on the other hand shows both cycle- and time-dependent behavior. Tension-compression fatigue loading at high temperatures is dramatically affected by the presence or absence of an inflection point upon unloading.

ACKNOWLEDGEMENTS

Part of this work has been performed within the Specific Research and Development Programme of the European Commission. The authors would like to thank Société Européenne de Propulsion for providing the composite materials.

REFERENCES

[1]   Lemaitre, J. and Chaboche, J. L., Mécanique des Matériaux Solides, Dunod, Paris, 1985.

[2]   Kachanov, L. M., Introduction to Continuum Damage Mechanics, Martinus Nijhoff, Dordrecht, 1986.

[3]   Steen, M., Adami, J. N., and Bressers, J., "A uniaxial test facility for the study of CMCs under tensile and creep loading," Proceedings of the Sixth European Conference on Composite Materials, Woodhead Publishing Limited, Abington Cambridge, 1993, pp 403-408.

[4]   Steen, M., "Residual stress state and damage mechanisms in ceramic matrix composites inferred from uniaxial tests incorporating unloading and reloading sequences", Fourth Euro Ceramics, S. Meriani and V. Sergo, Eds., Vol. 3, pp 63-70.

[5]   Lamouroux, F., Steen, M., and Vallés, J. L., "Uniaxial tensile and creep behaviour of an alumina fibre reinforced ceramic matrix composite: 1 - experimental study", Journal of the European Ceramic Society, 14, 1994, pp 529-537.

[6]   Lamouroux, F., Vallés, J. L., and Steen, M., "Uniaxial tensile and creep behaviour of an alumina fibre reinforced ceramic matrix composite: 2 - modelling of tertiary creep", Journal of the European Ceramic Society, 14, 1994, pp 538-548.

[7]   Steen, M., Lamouroux, F., and Vallés, J. L., "Mechanical behaviour of an alumina fibre reinforced silicon carbide matrix composite at high temperature", Ceramic Transactions, Vol. 57, 1995, pp 449-454.

[8]   Holmes, J. W., and Wu, X., "Elevated Temperature Creep Behavior of Continuous Fiber-Reinforced Ceramics", High Temperature Behavior of Ceramic Composites, S. V. Nair and K. Jakus, eds., Butterworth-Heinemann, Newton, MA, 1995, pp. 193-259.

[9]   Holmes, J. W., and Sørensen, B. F., "Fatigue Behavior of Continuous Fiber-Reinforced Ceramic Matrix Composites", High Temperature Behavior of Ceramic Composites, S. V. Nair and K. Jakus, eds., Butterworth-Heinemann, Newton, MA, 1995, pp. 261-326.

High-Temperature Test Results/Methods

Larry P. Zawada[1] and Shin S. Lee[1]

THE EFFECT OF HOLD TIMES ON THE FATIGUE BEHAVIOR OF AN OXIDE/OXIDE CERAMIC MATRIX COMPOSITE

REFERENCE: Zawada, L. P. and Lee, S. S., **"The Effect of Hold Times on the Fatigue Behavior of an Oxide/Oxide Ceramic Matrix Composite,"** Thermal and Mechanical Test Methods and Behavior of Continuous-Fiber Ceramic Composites, ASTM STP 1309, Michael G. Jenkins, Stephen T. Gonczy, Edgar Lara-Curzio, Noel E. Ashbaugh, and Larry P. Zawada, Eds., American Society for Testing and Materials, 1997.

ABSTRACT: Ceramic matrix composites (CMCs) consisting of an oxide matrix, no fiber-matrix interphase, and an oxide fiber are attractive for high-temperature structural applications because of their inherent resistance to oxidation. Such a system has recently been evaluated using tension, tensile fatigue, and tensile creep rupture. The CMC system consists of an aluminosilicate matrix reinforced with Nextel 610 fibers. The Nextel 610 fibers were in the form of an 8HSW. Results from the mechanical behavior studies showed this CMC to perform extremely well in fatigue at both room temperature and 1000°C. However, the system experienced significant creep strain under sustained loading because of creep deformation that occurs in the oxide fiber. To study the interaction between fatigue and creep, fatigue tests with hold times were conducted at a temperature of 1000°C. For all tests, the maximum fatigue stress was 75 MPa and the load ratio was 0.01. Hold times of 1, 10, and 100 s were applied at maximum load to develop the creep deformation fully. Hold times of 10 seconds were also applied at both maximum and minimum load to study creep recovery. The effect of frequency was also characterized using frequencies of 1, 0.5, and 0.1 Hz. In all tests, the measured strain accumulation was found to be linear with time with no evidence of tertiary creep behavior. The CMC exhibited increased rates of strain accumulation with decrease in frequency and increase in hold times.

KEYWORDS: ceramic matrix composite, creep rupture, fatigue, frequency, hold times, Nextel 610, oxide/oxide, strain rate, tension

[1]Materials research engineer and associate research engineer, respectively, Materials Behavior Branch, Metals and Ceramics Division, Materials Directorate, Wright Laboratory, Wright-Patterson AFB, OH 45433-7817.

It is generally accepted that advanced high-temperature material systems with long–term thermal and mechanical stability are the key factor in the evolution of current aerospace propulsion systems. In fact, the success of developing new high performance propulsion systems with increased thrust to weight relies mainly on the development of high-temperature materials with good long-term high-temperature performance and durability. Only slight advances can be made using innovative design approaches [1-3]. Incorporating new classes of materials into prototype designs requires a thorough understanding of the influence of mechanical-environmental coupled effects on material behavior and failure mechanisms of each advanced material system at the projected operating temperatures.

Among the available high-temperature material systems currently being developed, fiber reinforced ceramic matrix composites (CMCs) have attracted great attention for aerospace applications. They offer low densities and high operating temperatures. Unlike the traditional monolithic ceramics, CMCs exhibit remarkable damage tolerance and a fracture toughness several times that measured for monolithic ceramics. The toughening mechanism in CMCs is the deflection of matrix cracks at the weak fiber-matrix interphase. This deflection absorbs the high fracture energy associated with a crack propagating in a ceramic matrix and prevents the matrix crack from continuing through the fiber. Detailed descriptions of this process have been presented and analyzed by several authors [4-6].

In the early CMC systems that were first developed, the weak interphase between fiber and matrix contained carbon. The carbon layer was either formed *in-situ* during processing or was applied directly to the fiber. However, the carbon layer can easily be oxidized in high-temperature oxygen-rich environments, with a threshold for oxidation being approximately 375°C. The literature is full of examples of such behavior. As early at 1987 it was shown by Prewo [7] that CMCs containing a carbon interphase readily oxidize at intermediate [8] and high temperatures. More recently, Heredia et al. [9] studied two different CMCs with carbon interphases and found them to degrade in the temperature range of 500 to 800°C. Once the carbon is removed, the oxygen reacts with the fiber to cause a silica layer to form, and there may be other reactions with the matrix. Thus, the carbon layer is removed and replaced by a layer of silicon dioxide (SiO_2) on the surface of the fiber. Such reactions turn the weak interface into a strong interface [10-15], and a significant decrease in fracture toughness and tensile strength results.

As an alternative, researchers have tried applying a coating other than carbon to the fiber before the matrix is added. The most common fiber coating is one containing boron nitride (BN). [16,17]. However, the BN fiber coating must be deposited at relatively low temperatures to both minimize damage to the fiber and control deposition rates. Deposition at lower temperatures results in a nonstoichiometric or turbostratic form of BN that has been shown to be sensitive to moisture and oxidation [18-20]. Recent investigations have shown a typical BN interphase to react during processing and oxidize at temperatures from 650 to 850°C. [9,11,12,21]. Multiple fiber coatings have also been investigated [21-24]. These have included multiple layers of the same material as well as layers of different composition, but they also experience rapid oxidation of the interphase during cyclic loading whenever the applied stress is above the matrix cracking stress[23]. A review and discussion of current fiber coating approaches involving single, double, and multiple coatings has been presented by Naslain [25]. Exterior composite coatings, surface glaze coating, and flash oxidation of the surface are also used to extend the life of CMCs, but they do not solve the oxidation problem [26,27].

Over the last decade a large fraction of total resources being spent on research activities associated with CMCs has been directed at evaluating and improving the stability of the fiber/matrix interphase. The loss in damage tolerance is especially rapid whenever the applied stresses are above the matrix cracking stress. Such damage enhanced oxidization behavior is typically the determining factor for the high-temperature long-term behavior and performance of CMCs.

Within the last several years, there has been an innovative research activity to develop a new CMC that demonstrates excellent fracture toughness without relying on an interphase to provide toughness. The concept centers on developing a fiber–dominated composite similar to polymer matrix composites. The matrix is required to be sufficiently dense to provide adequate compressive and shear properties while still providing a weak path for crack propagation. In addition, an oxide fiber and oxide matrix were selected because of demonstrated thermal stability at temperatures up to 1000°C. With a stable matrix and fiber, and no interphase to oxidize, this CMC avoids the rapid thermal degradation reviewed above. This relatively new CMC uses NEXTEL 610 alpha alumina oxide fibers in an aluminosilicate matrix and has been developed by General Electric Aircraft Engines.

Extensive mechanical behavior characterization has been carried out on this CMC by the manufacturer and author's as part of an Advance Research Projects Agency (ARPA) Ceramic Insertion Program (CIP) [28-31]. Results from those investigations have shown this oxide/oxide system to exhibit an exceptionally high fatigue limit at 1000°C. However, it does experience substantial strain accumulation under sustained loading conditions at 1000°C. From these earlier tension creep rupture tests, the creep or stress exponent (n) was determined for this CMC using the temperature-independent Norton-Bailey equation:

$$\dot{\varepsilon} = A_0\sigma^n \qquad (1)$$

where $\dot{\varepsilon}$ is the minimum creep rate, A_0 is a pre-exponential constant, and σ is the tensile stress. A stress exponent value of 3.06 was determined from tension creep rupture tests conducted at 1000°C. Significant creep is to be expected at 1000°C with an oxide fiber and relatively porous matrix. Creep rates are very important, as many of the aerospace applications selected for

CMCs are currently designed with creep performance as one of the most important factors. However, to date, there is very little information in the literature concerning the interaction between creep and fatigue in CMCs. This investigation was undertaken to provide an initial assessment as to how different loading cycles affect rates of strain accumulation.

EXPERIMENTAL PROCEDURE

Composite Material Investigated

The oxide/oxide CMC system studied in this investigation was manufactured by General Electric. The oxide fibers used in the composite were NEXTEL™ 610 alpha alumina fibers from the 3M Company [32]. The fibers are sol-gel derived, high purity, polycrystalline Al_2O_3 with a grain size of <0.5 µm, and were supplied in the form of an eight–harness satin weave (8HSW) cloth. Individual sections of cloth were taken as is and prepregged using a mixture of fine single crystal alumina powder and a silica forming polymer. No coating was applied to the fibers before prepregging. Twelve individual sections of prepregged cloth were stacked on top of each other in a 0/90 orientation using a hand layup procedure. The laminate was warm molded in an autoclave to produce a dense green-state ceramic tile. Molding was followed by pressureless sintering in air at approximately 1000°C. Sintering removes the organic binders and converts the polymer to a porous silica matrix. The resulting matrix contains approximately 87 w/o alumina and 13 w/o silica. Test coupons were then machined out of the tiles using diamond tooling.

Micrographs of transverse cross sections showing the typical fiber distribution and porosity are given in Figs. 1a and b. Image analysis produced a fiber volume fraction of 29 to 33%. Note that the matrix is extensively microcracked from the pyrolysis processing. The cracks are very evenly distributed at approximately 200 µm. A common result of this type of processing is the presence of very fine residual porosity. Based on measurements, the porosity of the material evaluated here was predominantly open at 17 to 23%. Approximately half of this measured porosity was associated with large pores and matrix cracks, while the rest of the porosity was associated with very small pores. Measurements of pore surface area were made using the Brunauer-Emmett-Teller (BET) method. This method of surface area measurement uses absorption isotherms and produced surface area measurements of approximately 25 to 35 m^2/gram. This is a larger value than submicron ceramic power (15 m^2/gm) and substantially larger than coarse 2 µm micron ceramic power (2 m^2/gm). These surface area values for Nextel 610/AS verify the existence of extensive fine porosity in the matrix. Surface measurements were also conducted on a Nicalon/MAS-5 crossply CMC composite from Corning Glass for comparison, and produced a surface area of 0.16 m^2/gm. It is believed that this very fine porosity helps provide good composite behavior for this CMC by aiding the

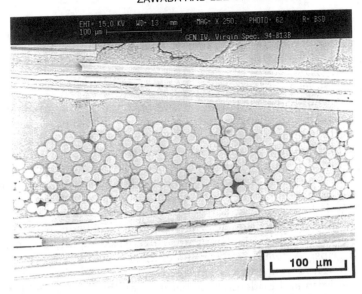

Figure 1a. Scanning Electron Microscopy micrograph of a transverse cross section of 8HSW NEXTEL610/AS.

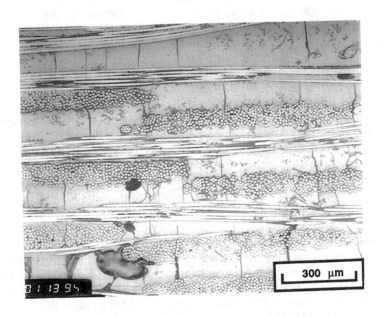

Figure 1b. Optical micrograph of a transverse cross section of 8HSW NEXTEL610/AS.

propagation of low energy cracks in the matrix. At the present time, the matrix cannot be manufactured separately, thus prohibiting direct characterization of the matrix properties.

Mechanical Testing: Test Apparatus

All of the mechanical behavior tests were conducted on a unique horizontal servohydraulic fatigue machine using rigid hydraulic clamping grips and quartz lamp heating. Test control, data acquisition, and interactive data analysis functions for the CMC test station are provided by the Mate Program [33] installed on a IBM-compatible personal computer (PC) that is linked to the test frame via an analog-to-digital (A/D) board. Temperature was measured by bonding five "S" type thermocouples to each specimen using an alumina-based ceramic adhesive. Temperature was controlled to within ±1% within the extensometer gage length, and outside this temperature-controlled zone the temperature decreased rapidly out to the water cooled grips. A detailed description of the test equipment is given elsewhere [34]. The specimen design selected was a reduced gage section "dogbone" specimen and is identical to that used by the High Speed Civil Transport (HSCT) Enabling Propulsion Materials (EPM) program, and was first suggested by Worthem [35]. For elevated temperature testing, test specimens were ramped to temperature in 15 min and then held at the test temperature for approximately 20 min to allow the specimens to equilibrate.

For most of the data that follow, zero to two repeat tests were conducted. The authors clearly acknowledge that this is an extremely limited data set, and no statistical basis can be formed from the test results. However, extreme care has been used in generating the data. Selective repeat tests have shown the data to be very repeatable and usually within the X2 or greater scatter normally associated with strain rates from creep rupture testing. It is in this light that the following data and observations are presented.

Mechanical Testing: Tension Testing

Both room temperature and elevated temperatures tension tests were conducted under stroke control with a constant loading rate of 0.05 mm/s. This loading rate produces a failure in several seconds and minimizes time-dependent behavior during the elevated temperature tests. This is especially important for CMCs that contain residual glassy phases or oxide fibers. The temperatures investigated were room temperature and 1000°C, and three tests were conducted at each temperature.

Mechanical Testing: Creep Rupture

One creep rupture test was conducted under load control at 1000°C. Once at temperature, creep strain was recorded from the instant the specimen reached the test stress level. The applied stress level was 75 MPa and was selected according to the 1000°C tension test to be 10 MPa below the proportional limit. In addition, the maximum applied stress was roughly equal to the maximum design stress for several possible high-temperature aerospace applications. The runout condition for the creep rupture test was defined as 100 h for this investigation and roughly duplicates the time at maximum temperature for many of the anticipated applications. Creep rupture simulates the long duration that occurs during most mission profiles. Measurement of creep rates is important for design purposes, and steadystate creep rates were required for evaluating the interaction of creep and fatigue.

Mechanical Testing: Fatigue

The fatigue test was conducted under load control with a load ratio of 0.05. The maximum applied stress level was 75 MPa, and the wave form was triangular. The run out condition was 100 h (360 000 s). Test frequencies investigated were 1, 0.5, and 0.1 Hz. A repeat test, using all three frequencies and only one specimen, was used to avoid the slight variation in fiber volume normally associated with CMCs. Changes in test frequency result in substantial changes in the rate at which the load is applied. Lower test frequencies should allow for more time dependent deformation, whereas the faster frequencies will not.

Mechanical Testing: Fatigue with Hold Times

Several different loading profiles were used to evaluate the interaction between static loading and fatigue loading. For all of the creep/fatigue interaction experiments the loading rate was 0.5 Hz, and the duration of testing was 360 000 seconds for reasons stated above. A schematic representation of each loading profile is shown in Fig. 2. Figure 2a represents standard fatigue loading and standard creep rupture loading. These two tests were conducted to generate the baseline creep rate information. The first type of creep/fatigue loading investigated involved superimposing a hold time at maximum load onto the standard fatigue cycle. Hold times were selected to be 1, 10 and 100 s, as shown in Fig. 2b. These hold times were selected to simulate realistic conditions for turbine engine exhaust components [3]. The

FIG. 2 - A schematic representation of each loading profile used in this investigation:

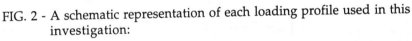
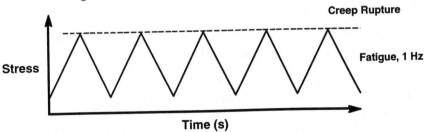

FIG. 2a - Represents standard fatigue loading for a triangular waveform and standard creep rupture loading, both using the same maximum stress.

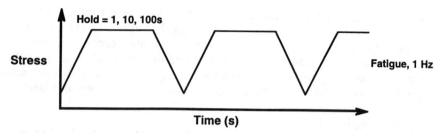

FIG. 2b - Represents fatigue testing with a hold time applied at maximum load.

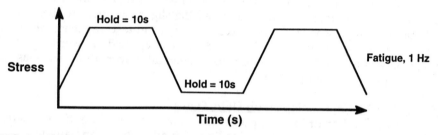

FIG. 2c - Represents a 10 second hold superimposed on a standard fatigue cycle at maximum and minimum load.

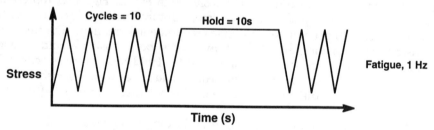

FIG. 2d - Represents block loading with a block of five fatigue cycles followed by a 10 second hold at maximum load.

second combination investigated is shown in Fig 2c and involved a 10-s hold time superimposed onto the standard fatigue cycle at both maximum and minimum load. The intent of this type of loading is to study the phenomenon of creep recovery. In addition, a third type of wave form, shown in Fig. 2d, investigated the effect of block loading with a block of fatigue cycles followed by static loading at maximum load. Such loading simulates typical loading profiles experienced by aerospace components and should identify if there is a transient response, or history effect, when switching between blocks of cyclic loading and blocks of static loading.

RESULTS AND DISCUSSION

The measured rate of strain accumulation was linear with time for each loading waveform. There was essentially no primary strain region and a complete absence of any tertiary creep. The absence of tertiary creep was also noted in all earlier creep rupture testing of this CMC [29,31]. Steadystate creep behavior made it possible to use the strain data over nearly the entire 100 h to calculate a strain rate for each waveform. A complete listing of test condition, specimen number, and strain rate is given in Table 1.

Table 1 - Test conditions and measured strain rates.

Test Conditions (For all tests: $\sigma = 75$ MPa, $T = 1000°C$)	Specimen Number	Strain Rate At Max Stress (m/m/s)	Strain Rate At Min Stress (m/m/s)
Creep Rupture			
75 MPa; 1000°C	94-B04	2.71E-08	————
	95-076	1.14E-08	————
Fatigue			
$f=1$; R=0.05	95-077	1.62E-09	3.71E-10
	95-084A	1.49E-09	1.49E-09
$f=0.5$; R=0.05	95-084	2.46E-09	2.47E-09
	95-084C	3.27E-09	3.59E-09
$f=0.1$; R=0.05	95-080	1.40E-09	1.28E-09
	95-084B	3.32E-09	3.59E-09
	95-085	2.47E-09	2.37E-09
Fatigue with Hold Time			
Hold Time @ Max Stress			
1s Hold @ Max, R=0.05; $f=0.5$	95-086	4.64E-09	4.54E-09
10s Hold @ Max; R=0.05; $f=0.5$	95-072	1.37E-08	1.35E-08
100s Hold @ Max; R=0.05; $f=0.5$	95-073	1.13E-08	1.12E-08
Hold Time @ Max and Min Stress			
10s Hold; R=0.05; $f=0.5$	95-079	7.58E-10	6.04E-10
	95-083	5.57E-09	5.53E-09
	95-086A	1.57E-09	1.63E-09
	95-092	8.81E-10	8.61E-10
Hold Time @ Max Stress Every 6th Cycle			
10s Hold; R=0.05; $f=0.5$	95-081	2.34E-09	————
	95-082	5.20E-09	5.19E-09

Monotonic Tension

Room temperature tensile stress-strain behavior is shown in Fig. 3a as a plot of stress versus strain for one of the three tension tests and lists values averaged from the three tests. The average room temperature tensile strength and strain to failure were approximately 205 MPa and 0.33%, respectively. The elastic modulus was 70 GPa, and the stress-strain curve was nearly linear to failure. However, one can detect a slight deviation from linearity at approximately 100 MPa. This slight deviation from linearity was identified as the proportional limit. The stress versus strain response was nearly identical for the three tension tests [28].

The overall high-temperature tensile response was similar to the room temperature tensile behavior. Tensile stress-strain behavior for the 1000°C tension test is shown in Fig. 3b. A total of three tests were conducted at the elevated temperature. The averaged tensile strength at 1000°C was 173 MPa, while the modulus was 77 MPa, and the proportional limit was 83 MPa. The tensile stress strain response was nearly identical for the three tests [28]. With the reduction in UTS, there was a corresponding decrease in strain to failure to approximately 0.28%. Comparing the room temperature behavior to the 1000°C behavior, several observations can be made. For both temperatures, the stress versus strain response remains basically linear to failure. However, UTS drops by 15.6%. The elastic modulus increased by 7 GPa and the proportional limit decreased by 17 MPa. With only slight changes in measured properties, this CMC system exhibits attractive short-term mechanical performance at both room temperature and 1000°C.

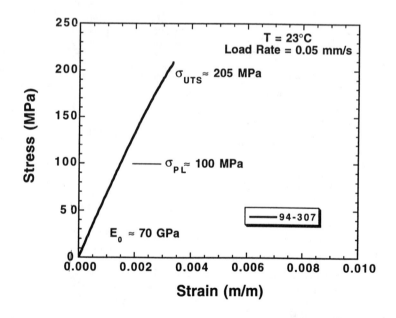

FIG. 3a - Tensile stress versus strain behavior of NEXTEL610/AS tested at 23°C.

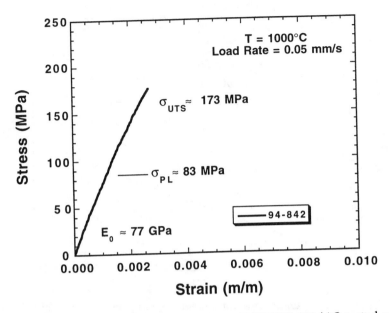

FIG. 3b - Tensile stress versus strain behavior of NEXTEL610/AS tested at 1000°C.

Creep Rupture

Creep rupture testing was conducted at a stress level of 75 MPa and 1000°C. A plot of creep strain versus time is shown as Fig. 4. From the figure, it is observed that this CMC exhibits little primary creep and extremely linear steadystate creep behavior. There was no evidence of tertiary creep. A linear fit to the data produced a strain rate of 1.14×10^{-8} mm/mm/s. Approximately 0.43% creep strain was recorded during the 100-h experiment. Creep strains for this oxide/oxide CMC are almost three times larger than creep strains measured for Nicalon fiber containing CMCs. Creep strains for 8HSW Nicalon fiber containing CMCs are normally less than 0.15% for similar test conditions [7,29,36]. Earlier work identified that the primary creep mechanism in the matrix was the formation of very small matrix cracks. These cracks typically propagated between fibers that were relatively close together [31].

Fatigue Testing

Fatigue tests were conducted at 1000°C using a maximum applied stress of 75 MPa and frequencies of 1.0, 0.5, and 0.1 Hz. In addition, a second

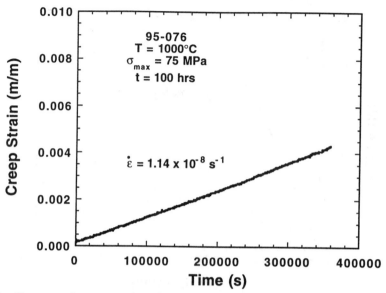

FIG. 4 - Creep strain versus time for a creep rupture test of NEXTEL610/AS
tested at 75 MPa and 1000°C.

test was conducted using one specimen for all three frequencies to eliminate specimen-to-specimen variation in fiber volume fractions. The three frequency tests conducted on the one specimen were run for times of 100 000 s or longer to produce a good fit to the strain data. A frequency of 0.5 Hz served as the baseline frequency for subsequent fatigue with hold time tests. Strain measurements from the 0.5 Hz test are given in Fig. 5 as strain versus time and includes the strain measured at both maximum load and minimum load. It appears that the specimen exhibited identical rates of strain accumulation at maximum stress as well as minimum stress. Two tests produced an average strain rate during fatigue of 2.87×10^{-9} mm/mm/s. This rate is almost an order of magnitude slower than the rate measured from the creep rupture test. There appears to be no strain hardening or softening during fatigue testing. The difference between maximum and minimum strain remained constant throughout the fatigue tests for all three frequencies investigated. Each of the test frequencies produced extremely linear strain accumulation rates, with higher rates for slower test frequencies. An important finding from the fatigue tests is that the rate of strain accumulation is approximately an order of magnitude slower than the creep rate measured from the creep rupture tests and may be a key indicator as to why this CMC performs well in fatigue but not as well for static loading.

For the three frequencies tested there was a small but systematic increase in strain accumulation with decreasing frequency. A plot of strain rate versus frequency is given in Fig. 6 for all of the data. There is a fair amount of scatter

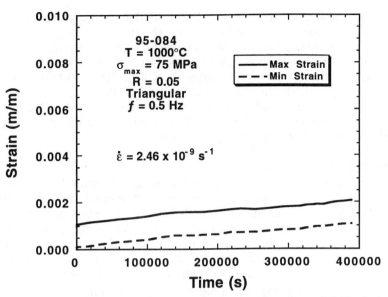

FIG. 5 - Maximum and minimum strain versus time for a 0.5-Hz fatigue test of NEXTEL610/AS tested at 75 MPa and 1000°C.

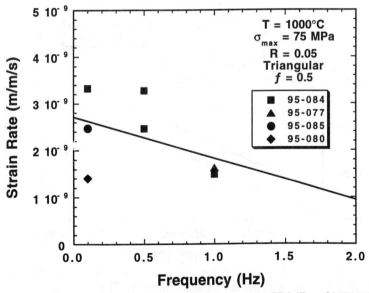

FIG. 6 - Strain Rate versus time for a fatigue test at 75 MPa of NEXTEL610/AS tested at 1000°C and frequencies of 0.1, 0.5, and 1 Hz.

in the data, but a linear regression to the entire data set suggests a decrease in strain rate with increase in test frequency. The trend is stronger when one only studies the data generated from one test coupon, Specimen 95-084. Such behavior clearly shows the influence of loading rate on strain accumulation. It is suggested that slower loading rates allow time dependent damage mechanisms to activate, resulting in faster rates of strain accumulation. No attempt was made to model the observed dependence on test frequency, but the behavior suggests it could be predicted by integrating the fraction of strain at each increment of stress over an entire cycle.

Fatigue With Hold Times
        Fatigue tests with the hold time applied at maximum load were conducted with hold times of 1, 10, and 100 s. Once again the rates of strain accumulation were linear for the three hold times investigated. In addition, the strain range also remained constant throughout testing, with no strain hardening or softening with continued cycling. A plot of both maximum strain and minimum strain versus test time is shown in Fig. 7 for the 10-s hold, while Fig. 8 presents maximum strain versus time for all three hold times investigated. For the 100-s hold time, the strain rate was 1.13×10^{-8} mm/mm/s. This strain rate is nearly identical to the rate measured from the

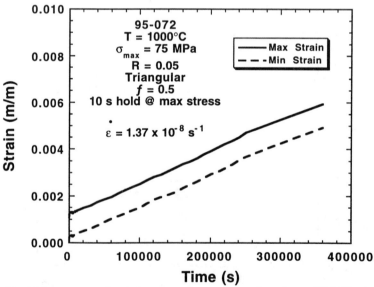

FIG. 7 - Maximum and minimum strain versus time for a 75 MPa fatigue test with a 10-s hold applied at the maximum. The material is NEXTEL610/AS and the test temperature was 1000°C.

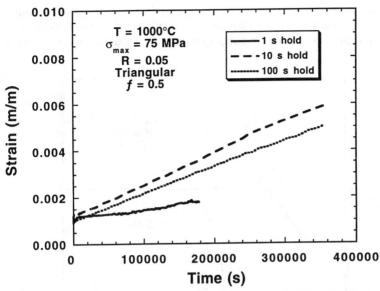

FIG. 8 - Maximum strain versus time for fatigue tests with a 1, 10, and 100-s
hold applied at the maximum stress of 75 MPa. The material is
NEXTEL610/AS and the test temperature was 1000°C.

creep rupture test and implies that there is little contribution to the creep rate
from fatigue loading. When the hold time was only 10 s, the measured rate
of strain accumulation was 1.37×10^{-8} mm/mm/s. This rate is 20% higher
than that measured during the 100-s hold test and suggests there is an
interaction between fatigue and short hold times. However, many more tests
would need to be conducted to verify such an interaction, especially in light of
the scatter associated with measuring strain rates from such tests. For the 1-s
hold time, the strain rate was distinctly lower. It is suspected that short hold
times do not allow sufficient time for time-dependent deformation to be fully
activated.

The following discussion will first focus on the experiments in which
the hold time was applied at maximum load. A plot of strain rate versus
hold time is shown as Fig. 9a. In generating the plot, a hold time of 0.1 s was
assigned to the 0.5-Hz fatigue tests, and the creep rupture data was plotted as a
hold time of 360,000 s. From Fig. 9a it is clear that the strain rate is a
minimum for the fatigue test and increases with increasing hold time up to a
hold time of 10 s. From a hold time of 10 s out to simple static loading the
strain rate remains approximately constant. As stated above, the hold time of
10 s produced a slight acceleration in strain rate. However, the change is only
approximately 20% and well within the standard scatter for creep data.
Several repeats would be necessary to determine if the effect is real. Still, the
data supports that even relatively short hold times will accelerate the rate of

strain accumulation. One important finding is that superimposing hold times on fatigue tests did not produce any interactive damage mechanisms resulting in strain accumulation rates greater than those measured during static loading.

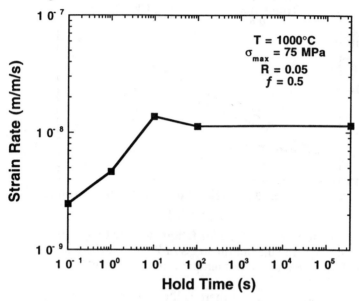

FIG. 9a - Measured strain rate versus hold time at maximum load for NEXTEL610/AS tested at 1000°C and a maximum stress of 75 MPa.

As discussed above, the strain rate increased from a minimum for the conventional fatigue test to a maximum for the fatigue with a 10-s hold at the peak stress.. This increase in strain rate with increasing hold time is quite easily predicted using a two-term linear summation technique. The percentage of the loading cycle associated with fatigue loading is multiplied by the rate of strain accumulation measured during fatigue loading. Next the percentage of the loading cycle associated with static loading is multiplied by the rate of strain accumulation measured during static loading. These two products are then added together to produce the final strain rate. The basic equation is as follows:

$$\dot{\varepsilon} = \dot{\varepsilon}_F(t_F/t_C) + \dot{\varepsilon}_H(t_H/t_C) \tag{2}$$

where $\dot{\varepsilon}$ is the total strain rate, $\dot{\varepsilon}_F$ is the strain rate from fatigue, $\dot{\varepsilon}_H$ is the strain rate from static loading, t_C is the total cycle time, and t_F and t_H are the time for fatigue loading and time during hold for one complete cycle. The fatigue test produced an average strain rate of 2.87×10^{-9} mm/mm/s while static loading produced a strain rate of 1.14×10^{-8} mm/mm/s . For a 1-s hold time test, a complete loading cycle would have a total cycle time of 3 s, a time during fatigue loading of 2, and a time during hold of 1 s. Linear summation predicts a strain rate of 5.71×10^{-9} mm/mm/s for the 1-s hold and agrees well with the measured value was 4.64×10^{-9} mm/mm/s. A plot of strain rate versus hold time for measured strain rates and predicted strain rates is given in Fig. 9b. Linear summation does a nice job of reproducing the trend in the measured data. From the predicted data, one can observe that the strain rate remains relatively constant for hold times of 10 s or greater.

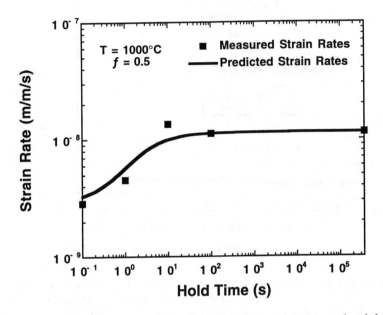

FIG. 9b - Predicted strain rate versus hold time at maximum load for
NEXTEL610/AS tested at 1000°C and a maximum stress of 75 MPa.

The phenomenon of creep recovery has been reported by several researchers [36-39]. A fatigue test with a 10-s hold at both maximum stress and minimum stress was used to study this effect. The intent was to determine if the hold at minimum load results in a retardation of the time dependent damage process. A plot of maximum and minimum strain versus time is given in Fig. 10. The measured strain rate of 8.81×10^{-10} mm/mm/s is substantially lower than the measured rate of 1.37×10^{-8} mm/mm/s for the specimen fatigue tested with a hold of 10 s at only the maximum load. Assuming no contribution from a hold at minimum load, linear summation predicts a strain rate of 5.44×10^{-9} mm/mm/s. Such a low value for the measured strain rate implies that there is substantial recovery in creep deformation resulting from the additional hold at minimum load. Wu and

Holmes [36] have shown that a 0/90 Nicalon/CAS composite creep tested at a stress of 60 MPa and then unloaded demonstrated viscous strain recovery of approximately 49%. The crossply composite developed 0.5% creep strain, and recovered creep strain of approximately 0.25% after the load was reduced. Such a large value of recovery has severe implications concerning life

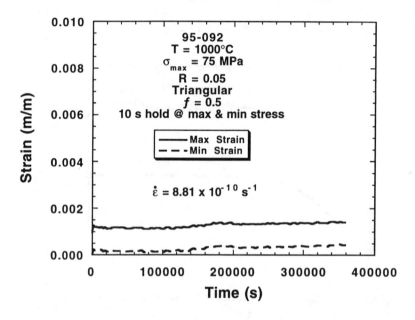

FIG. 10 - Maximum and minimum strain for a fatigue test with a 10-s hold applied at both maximum and minimum load. The material is NEXTEL610/AS, the test temperature was 1000°C and the maximum stress was 75 MPa.

prediction. It appears that a creep recovery mechanism operates in oxide/oxide CMCs as well, even for the short hold times at minimum load. It is apparent that a much more thorough investigation is needed to address the mechanism for this behavior in oxide/oxide CMCs.

Block loading using blocks of fatigue cycles followed by a hold time produced revealing information. The strain results from this test are presented in Fig. 11 as a plot of maximum and minimum strain versus time. A fit to the maximum strain produced a strain rate of 5.2×10^{-9} mm/mm/s. Using the linear summation approach stated above produces a predicted rate of 6.75×10^{-9} mm/mm/s. This prediction is close to the measured rate and implies there is not a strong history effect for the block loading investigated.

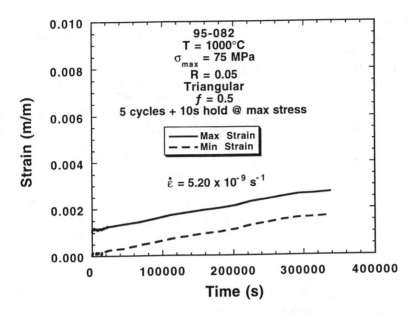

FIG. 11 - Maximum and minimum strain for a fatigue test with blocks of five fatigue cycles followed by a 10-s hold applied at maximum load. The material is NEXTEL610/AS, the test temperature was 1000°C and the maximum stress was 75 MPa.

GENERAL DISCUSSION

In this section, we discuss the pertinent literature concerning the creep and fatigue behavior of constituent ceramic materials as well as the limited data on CMCs. Discussion will address the current understanding of deformation mechanisms associated with static loads, loading rates, frequencies, hold times, and how these may influence or relate to the observed creep rates of the Nextel 610/AS composite.

General Discussion on Creep Behavior

The observed strain accumulation for this CMC is very different from the behavior of other CMCs in the literature. A very detailed review of the literature concerning the creep behavior of continuous fiber-reinforced CMCs has been conducted by Holmes and Wu [40]. In this review, there was very little information on the behavior of oxide/oxide CMCs, but there was significant information on the creep performance of CMCs containing silicon carbide fibers of Nicalon and SCS-6. In addition, there is significant information in the literature concerning the uniaxial creep behavior of oxide fibers and bonded polycrystalline alumina. A detailed review of creep behavior in ceramic materials was conducted by Cannon and Langdon [41,42] with over 30 pages of tabulated creep data supported with more than 365 references. The following discussion will review several of these investigations and correlate their findings with the behavior observed in the present investigation.

Creep Behavior of Alumina

Flexural methods have been widely and extensively used to study the creep deformation of alumina at elevated temperatures because of the simplicity of the test equipment and loading configuration. Therefore, there exists a substantial body of literature on this subject [43-51]. Murphy et al. [43] conducted flexural creep rupture tests on vitreous-bonded alumina in air at 1150°C. In a plot of percent creep strain versus time to failure, two relevant observations were made. The first was that under all conditions steadystate creep was observed from the onset of the test until failure within experimental uncertainty. This behavior is identical to the behavior observed for Nextel 610/AS. Secondly, higher stress levels systematically produced higher strain rates and reduced the strain to failure. They found that the creep-nucleated cracks were intergranular in nature and stated that the lack of a noticeable tertiary creep region suggested that the spontaneous linkage of creep-nucleated cracks occurred abruptly just before failure. Cracks continued to nucleate throughout the creep process until a critical crack density was reached, causing spontaneous linkage and failure.

As stated above, flexural creep testing has been extensively used to evaluate ceramics. However, there is only limited data for creep rupture involving uniaxial tensile loading of aluminum oxide [45,50,52]. Dey and Socie [52] recently investigated the creep behavior of a commercial grade of glass-bonded, 94% aluminum oxide. Testing was performed using uniaxial tensile static loading, as well as cyclic loading, at temperatures of 1000 and 1100°C. The fatigue testing used a square waveform with a load ratio of $R = 0.1$ and a test frequency of 2 Hz. This investigation is particularly relevant to the present investigation because of the similar loading profiles, test temperature, and the fact that their material was a polycrystalline alumina ceramic containing a continuous grain boundary viscous phase at elevated temperature. It was observed that for the same maximum stress level, the steadystate creep strain rate under static loading was more than an order of magnitude greater than that during fatigue loading. This finding is identical to what was observed for the Nextel 610/AS composite. The authors could not explain the enhanced creep resistance of the material during cyclic loading. Microstructural observations identified that failures for stress levels above a critical transition stress were all the result of the growth of a single dominant crack with no evidence of creep damage. However, at stress levels below the critical transition stress, the specimens failed because of the nucleation, growth, and linkage of multiple microcracks. The creep damage zone of the fracture surface was characterized as intergranular, while the fast fracture zone was predominantly transgranular. Such behavior clearly identifies the sensitivity of this class of materials to time-dependent deformation that results during low applied stress levels or slow loading rates or both.

A detailed investigation into the creep response of two slightly different hot-pressed aluminas (HPA) was conducted by Robertson et al. [50] using both uniaxial and flexural loading configurations. In this investigation, the creep behavior of the ARCO HPA at 1250°C under tensile loading was found to be linear from start to failure, with no evidence of any transitional creep behavior. Increasing the applied stress level greatly decreased the strain to failure and significantly increased the minimum creep rate. Both of these observations mirror the tensile creep behavior of N610/AS.

In a companion paper to the work performed by Robertson, Wilkinson et al. [45] examined the mechanisms responsible for creep damage accumulation for the two aluminas studied by Robertson. Wilkinson identified three damage regimes, all controlled by crack propagation. At high applied stress levels, a single crack controlled failure and grew in a linear elastic stress field. Crack propagation was sufficiently rapid to avoid the creep relaxation process that occurs at lower stresses. For experiments at intermediate stresses, crack tip stresses relax, and many microcracks are observed to nucleate, grow, and link under strain control. At the lowest stress levels, extensive cavitation with little microcrack development was observed. Damage accumulation was dominated by isolated cavities growing by a combination of surface diffusion and grain-boundary sliding. The formation of cavities effectively blunts microcracks and slows down the rate of crack growth, which further increases the tendency to cavity blunting. Therefore, there is a rapid decrease in crack propagation rate, along with an increase in creep life, for slight decreases in stress. One result of studying two very similar aluminas was clear identification that creep behavior is very dependent on composition and processing. Wilkinson [45] suggested that differences in impurity and dopant levels lead to significant differences in diffusion coefficients and thus creep rates.

Creep Behavior of Oxide Fibers

Creep rupture testing of oxide fibers intended for CMCs is a critical characterization procedure because of historically poor creep performance. Polycrystalline oxides are subject to diffusive creep at high temperature, and this problem is magnified by the extremely fine grain size of this class of oxide fibers. Tressler and DiCarlo have discussed the role of creep in ceramic and oxide fiber reinforcements in detail [53]. Creep rupture experiments by Pysher et al. [54,55] on two different polycrystalline oxide fibers revealed creep strain versus time behavior extremely similar to that observed for the polycrystalline aluminas discussed above. Experiments on PRD-166 at 1200°C showed a pronounced decrease in strain to failure and sharp increase in strain rate with increasing stress. The mechanism controlling steadystate creep of these alumina-based fibers was suggested to be interface-reaction-controlled diffusional creep.

The NEXTEL 610 fibers used to manufacture the composite have been extensively characterized by the manufacturer [32]. In addition, Wilson et al. [56] performed a detailed investigation of the creep performance of the fiber. Creep data were collected over a temperature range of 900 to 1200°C and a load range of 20 to 550 MPa for singe filaments of NEXTEL 610 . The stress exponent n for NEXTEL 610 in air at 1000°C was found to be 2.8, and the activation energy was approximately 660kJ/mol. At the maximum test temperature, fibers reached strains of 30%. Ends of the NEXTEL 610 fibers that failed during creep testing were examined to determine the mechanism of failure. Wilson found that failure during creep rupture testing occurred via the coalescence of cavities into large cracks. Cavities nucleated on grain boundaries and coalesced to form large cracks that extended across several grains. It was presumed that fiber failure occurred when these cracks linked up to form a critical flaw. Cavitation has been shown to contribute to increased stress exponents.

The creep rupture behavior of the fiber is nearly identical to the behavior measured for the Nextel 610/AS composite. Wilson found the stress exponent for the fiber to be 2.8, while the value for the composite measured in an earlier investigation was approximately 3.06 [29,31]. Such a close match in stress exponent for the fiber and this composite suggests that the fiber plays an important role in the creep deformation process. Zuiker [57] modeled the 1000°C creep behavior of this CMC using a micromechanics-based model that incorporates creeping fibers embedded in a creeping matrix, and identified the role of the fiber and matrix in the creep deformation process. Results from that modeling effort identified that the correlation is sensitive to the matrix elastic properties, and that the matrix has a slightly higher stress exponent than the matrix. As reviewed earlier, it is common for this type of matrix to have the same stress exponent as measured for the CMC for a temperature of 1000°C. Fracture studies of fiber ends from the earlier creep rupture investigation revealed an intergranular fracture morphology, consistent with interface reaction rate-controlled creep and cavitation formation. It was postulated by Wilson that the creep rate of NEXTEL 610 was controlled by an interface reaction mechanism and that the diffusion rate did not control the creep rate. This conclusion is similar to the one reached by Cannon et al. [51] for plastic deformation in fine-grained alumina.

Creep Behavior of CMCs

The tensile creep behavior of unidirectional and cross-ply Nicalon/CAS-II cor posites has been studied in detail by Wu and Holmes [36]. Creep experiments were conducted in high purity argon to negate the rapid environmental degradation reviewed earlier. They found that for stresses up to 200 MPa, all specimens exhibited a well-defined primary creep region, a decelerating creep rate, and runout at 100 h. Steadystate creep was not observed. Increasing the creep stress to 250 MPa caused rapid failure and a substantially lower total strain to failure. An important finding of their work was that at a temperature of 1200°C, both the unidirectional and cross-ply composites had a creep stress exponent of approximately 1.3 at 100 h. This stress exponent is similar to that found for the creep of Nicalon fibers and indicated that the creep rate was primarily controlled by creep of the Nicalon fibers. Wu and Holmes rationalized that, based on fiber volume fractions, the results showed that transverse fibers can contribute significantly to overall creep resistance. Therefore, the effect of transverse fibers cannot be neglected in analytical models of creep deformation. Many other researchers have studied the creep behavior of Nicalon containing CMCs [7,28,29,37,58-64], and several have reported decreasing creep rates during tension and flexure creep testing [28,29,37,59,60,63,64]. Two factors are thought to contribute to the decelerating creep rate: (1) grain growth in the fibers for tests at extremely high temperatures and (2) realignment of off-axis fibers with the creep loading direction. Weber et al. [63] documented abnormal grain growth at the surface of Nicalon fibers during flexural creep rupture testing at 1200°C. Nicalon is a polycrystalline fiber with a grain size of several nanometers, and the surface grains were observed to grow to approximately 10 to 15 nm. For a diffusional creep mechanism, an increase in the average grain size would decrease the creep rate of the fibers. For lower temperatures, where Nicalon fibers do not demonstrate grain growth, the primary mechanism attributed to decreasing strain rate is continual loading of elastic fibers in the creep loading direction. As creep strain increases, more and more fibers are elastically loaded, effectively decreasing the rate of strain accumulation. For the Nextel 610 fibers, there is no observed grain growth for 100 h at 1000°C [31]. Both the fiber and matrix exhibit linear creep strain with time. Therefore, one would not expect to observe transient behavior for the oxide/oxide CMC. In addition, it is suggested that realignment of off-axis fibers with the creep loading direction does not influence creep behavior, as the creep rates are linear with time.

Tyranno is also a polycrystalline SiC fiber, and composites made with this fiber also demonstrate decreasing strain rate with increase time during creep rupture testing [60,65]. Figure 12 shows uniaxial creep strain versus time for a Tyranno/BMAS CMC tested at 1000°C and four stress levels. For each stress level, there is a well-defined primary creep region, and the strain rate clearly decreases with increasing time. Such behavior is very similar to the behavior of Nicalon fiber containing CMCs reported above.

Composites made with large SiC fibers of SCS-6 also exhibit transient creep behavior. Holmes [39,66] investigated the tensile creep behavior of unidirectional SCS-6/HPSN composites in air at temperatures of 1200 to 1350°C. He reported that for stresses of 75 MPa and higher, a decreasing strain rate persisted for approximately 50 to 75 h, followed by a region of nearly constant creep rate. Hilmas et al. [67] studied a similar CMC (SCS-6/RBSN) and observed similar behavior to that observed by Holmes. In both studies, periodic fiber rupture was identified as the primary microstructural damage mode for the tensile creep of the composites.

Adami [68] studied the tensile creep behavior of an Al_2O_3/CVD-SiC composite with a two-dimensional (2-D) cross-ply fiber architecture. For all temperature and stress levels examined in this study, primary, secondary , and tertiary creep regimes were observed. An important finding from this study was that the steadystate creep rate exhibited two distinct regimes depending upon the creep stress, giving rise to two creep stress exponents. A high stress exponent of 9.5 at low stresses was attributed to matrix creep and

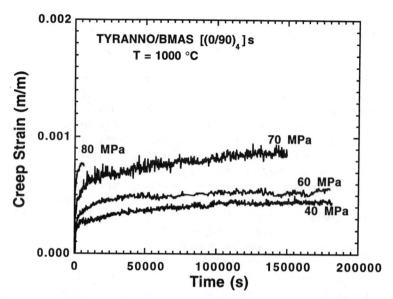

FIG. 12 - Creep strain versus time for TYRANNO/BMAS [(0/90)4]s tested at
1000°C and several stress levels.

stress redistribution. A lower stress exponent of 4.5 for high stresses was
similar to the oxide fiber and suggested that the creep rate of the composite
was controlled by creep of the bridging fibers. It is believed that with a
substantially cracked matrix in the present investigation, the creep response is
similar to that observed by Adami in which the creep response is primarily
governed by the fibers.

General Discussion on Fatigue Behavior

Over the last four years there has been an ever increasing amount of
data presented in the open literature concerning high-temperature fatigue
behavior of CMCs. A detailed review of the fatigue behavior of CMCs has
been conducted by Holmes and Soroson [69]. However, very little of this data
contains information concerning the effect of hold times during fatigue.
Strain versus time data was not generally reported, and such values are not
easily or accurately obtained from studying the hysteresis loops presented in
the literature. However, from the limited data several observations can be
made that relate to the behavior observed in the present investigation.

Wang et. al. [70] conducted tension-tension and compression-
compression fatigue on C/SiC at room temperature. Fatigue data was
presented in the form of hysteresis loops on a plot of load versus strain. This
study was particularly interesting because a decreasing rate of strain
accumulation was observed for both tension-tension fatigue and
compression-compression fatigue. For both types of loading, decreased
frequency increased the rate of strain accumulation. This frequency

dependence is similar to that observed in the present system and may have to do with time dependency of stress redistribution as presented by Holmes [39,40,69].

Butkus et al. [71] conducted 1100°C fatigue tests on Nicalon/CAS-II. Testing included isothermal fatigue and isothermal fatigue with a 60-s hold. In all fatigue tests, the maximum stress was held constant at 100 MPa, used triangular loading with 60-s ramps, and applied the hold at maximum load. A stress of 100 MPa was selected to be substantially below the matrix cracking stress of 250 MPa. During isothermal fatigue, the maximum and minimum strain demonstrated identical transient behavior. For the first 100 cycles, the strain accumulation was rapid, after which the rate of strain accumulation slowed and transitioned to a steadystate rate. For the isothermal fatigue with a 60-s hold time, similar behavior was observed. However, the test with the hold time was observed to produce a more rapid increase in accumulated strain than did the material subjected to the triangular waveform. After approximately 200 cycles, the rates of strain accumulation were nearly identical between the hold and no hold experiments based on cycles.

The data presented by Butkus et al. consisted of plots for strain versus cycles. The data from the isothermal fatigue tests were digitized by the authors and plotted as strain versus time. A comparison of maximum strain versus time for the two tests is shown in Fig. 13. The measured strain versus time behavior between the hold and no hold tests is nearly identical. In fact, a linear fit was performed on the data from 20 000 to 120 000 s, and the values were 8.5 and 8.7 x 10^{-9} mm/mm/s for no hold and 60-s hold, respectively. These rates are nearly identical. Not only did both tests develop strain at the same rate and amount, but both exhibited nearly linear rates of strain accumulation with time after an initial 20 000 s transition period. This result (hold and no hold tests producing the same strain) is significantly different from what was observed for the Nextel 610/AS CMC. It is postulated that the difference lies in the 60-s ramp rate used in the investigation by Butkus. Such a slow loading rate has been shown by several researchers to produce significant time dependent behavior for Nicalon/CAS-II and other CMCs, even during room temperature tension testing [72-74]. A similar conclusion concerning test frequency can be made about the Nextel 610/AS. As shown in Fig. 5, decreasing the frequency increases the rate of strain accumulation.

Discussion on Test Technique and Procedure

The influence of waveform appears to be very important for not only the Nextel 610/AS system studied in this investigation, but also for the system studied by Butkus [71]. The slower the loading rate the more time for time-dependent mechanisms to operate. In the present investigation, hold times of only 10 s dominated the rate of strain accumulation. From 10 s to infinite hold time, the rate of strain accumulation was approximately constant. Butkus found no influence of hold times when the cycle frequency was 0.0083 Hz. In the present investigation, there was clearly a frequency effect. However, no attempt was made to reduce the test frequency to

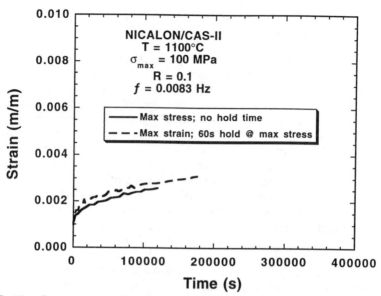

FIG. 13 - Comparison of maximum strain versus time for isothermal fatigue tests with and without a 60-s hold at maximum load for NICALON/CAS-II tested at 1100°C.

anywhere near the frequency used by Butkus. Creep behavior of CMCs is strongly dependent on the initial damage state of the composite. This initial damage condition is strongly influenced by processing, prior loading history, and the rate at which the creep load is initially applied. Ramping to the creep rupture load quickly has been shown to produce significantly lower creep rupture lives [39]. Such an observation most certainly applies to test frequency as well.

Creep behavior of this CMC appeared to be sensitive to slight changes in temperature. A change of a few degrees in the building was observed to affect slightly the measured strain data. The effect was not noticed during creep rupture testing, but was slightly noticeable during the fatigue tests. Figure 5 shows typical variation of strain during a fatigue test. As can be seen from the figure, the transitions occur over hours, not minutes or seconds. Similar observations have been made by Holmes [75]. An investigation by Lin et al. [76] discusses several techniques for minimizing scatter and increasing reliability of elevated temperature tensile creep displacement measurements. They were able to reduce the scatter in the laser measurements from ±5 to ±0.5 μm. Such findings clearly identify the need for very tight control of the environment around the furnace to generate precise creep data necessary for accurate prediction of creep/fatigue interactions.

CONCLUSIONS

1. Strain rates were highest for the sustained loading conditions and are suggested to result from time-dependent creep deformation.

2. The composite exhibited linear strain accumulation with time during creep rupture, fatigue, and fatigue with hold time testing. There was essentially no primary creep, and tertiary behavior was not observed. Both the fiber and matrix exhibit linear creep strain with time. In addition, fatigue tests exhibited the strain rates at maximum and minimum load, with no evidence of strain softening or strain hardening.

3. Fatigue tests with different frequencies revealed that slower frequencies produced faster rates of strain accumulation as a function of time. It is postulated that for the low stress value of 75 MPa, the controlling creep deformation was a combination of interface-controlled diffusion creep in the fiber coupled with fine cracks in the matrix.

4. Fatigue tests with hold times applied at maximum load demonstrated rates of strain accumulation equal to the creep strain rate when the hold times were 10 s or greater. Rates of steadystate strain accumulation during fatigue with hold times applied at maximum load are accurately predicted using a two-term linear summation approach.

5. Fatigue tests with a hold time of 10 s applied at both maximum and minimum load demonstrated severely retarded strain accumulation. Additional work is required to determine the exact mechanism.

6. Block loading with sets of five fatigue cycles followed by a 10-s hold at maximum load showed no apparent history effect for the conditions investigated in this study.

7. The creep behavior of CMCs is strongly dependent on the initial damage state of the composite, which is influenced by processing and prior loading history, the rate at which a creep load is initially applied, and the rate of cycling. Such behavior appears to be very important for oxide/oxide CMCs that have a fiber and matrix that both creep at 1000°C.

Acknowledgments

The authors express their sincere thanks to Miss Jennifer Finch for her dedicated and persistent efforts in data reduction and preparation of this manuscript, and to Mr. Ken Goecke for his valuable assistance in conducting the varied and time-consuming test matrix.

REFERENCES

[1] Integrated High Performance Turbine Engine Technology (IHPTET).1995 Brochure, Chris Lykins and Kathleen Watson, Eds., WL/POT Bldg. 18, 1950 Fifth St., WPAFB, OHIO, 45433-7251.

[2] Dix, D. M. and Petty, J. S., "Aircraft Engine Technology Gets a Second Wind," Aerospace America, July 1990, pp. 36-39.

[3] Hill, R. J., "The Challenge of IHPTET," in Eleventh International Symposium on Air Breathing Engines, Frederick S. Billig, Ed., American Institute of Aeronautics and Astronautics, 19 September, 1993.

[4] Evans, A. G., "The Mechanical Properties of Reinforced Ceramics, Metal and Intermetallic Matrix Composites," Material Science and Engineering, A143-A163, 1991.

[5] Evans, A. G. and Zok, F. W., "The Physics of Brittle Matrix Composites," Solid State Physics, Vol. 47, 1994, pp. 177,

[6] Marshall, D. B. and Evans, A. G., "Failure Mechanisms in Ceramic-Fiber/Ceramic-Matrix Composites," Journal of the American Ceramic Society, Vol. 68, No. 5, 1985, pp. 225-231.

[7] Prewo, K. M., "Fatigue and Stress Rupture of Silicon Carbine Fibre-Reinforced Glass-Ceramics," Journal of Materials Science, Vol 22, No. 8, 1987, pp. 2695-2701.

[8] Prewo, K. M., Johnson, B., and Starrett, S., "Silicon Carbide Fiber-Reinforced Glass-Ceramics Tensile Behavior at Elevated Temperature," Journal of Materials Science, Vol. 24, 1989, pp. 1373-1379.

[9] Heredia, F. E., McNulty, J. C., Zok, F. W., and Evans, A. G., "Oxidation Embrittlement Probe for Ceramic-Matrix Composites," Journal of the American Ceramic Society, Vol. 78, No. 8, 1995, pp. 2097-2100.

[10] Huger, M., Souchard, S., and Gault, C., "Oxidation of Nicalon SiC Fibres," Journal of Materials Science Letters, Vol. 12, 1993, pp. 414-416.

[11] Brennan, J. J., "Glass and Glass-Ceramic Matrix Composites," Fiber Reinforced Ceramic Composites, K. S. Mazdiyasni, Ed., Noyes, Park Ridge, NJ, 1990, Chap. 8.

[12] Prewo, K. M., Layden, G. K., Minford, E. J., and Brennan, J. J., "Advanced Characterization of SiC Fiber Reinforced Glass-Ceramic Matrix Composite," ONR Report R85-916629-1 under ONR Contract N00014-81-C-0571, June 1985.

[13] Brennan, J. J., "Interfacial Chemistry and Bonding in Fiber Reinforced Glass and Glass-Ceramic Matrix Composites," in Ceramic Microstructures '86, MRS 21, J. A. Pask and A. G. Evans, Eds., Plenium Press, 1987, pp. 387-400.

[14] Bischoff, E., Ruhle, M., Sbaizero, O., and Evans, A. G., Microstructural Studies of the Interfacial Zone of a SiC-Fiber-Reinforced Lithium Aluminum Silicate Glass-Ceramic," Journal of the American Ceramic Society, Vol. 72, No. 5, 1989, pp. 741-745.

[15] Brennan, J. J., "Interfacial Characterization of Glass and Glass-Ceramic Matrix/Nicalon Fiber Composites," in Materials Science Research, Vol. 20, Plenum Press, New York, 1986, pp. 549-560.

[16] Rice, R. W., "BN Coating of Ceramic Fibers for Ceramic Fiber Composites," US Patent 4,642,271, 10 Feb., 1987.

[17] Naslain, R., Dugne, O., and Guette, A., "Boron Nitride Interphase in Ceramic-Matrix Composites," Journal of the American Ceramic Society, No. 10, 1991, pp. 2482-2488.

[18] Matsuda, T., "Stability to Moisture for Chemically Vapour-Deposited Boron Nitride," Journal of Material Science, Vol. 24, 1989, pp. 2353-2358.

[19] Cofer, C. G. and Economy, J., "Oxidative and Hydrolytic Stability of Boron Nitride – A New Approach to Improving the Oxidation Resistance of Carbonaceous Structures," Carbon, Vol. 33, 1995, pp. 389-395.

[20] Parthasarathy, T. A. and Folsom, C. A., "Effects of Salt Water and Temperature on the Strength of Uncoated and BN-Coated Nicalon Fibers," presented at the 20th Annual Conference of Composites, Materials and Structures, 8-11 Jan., 1996.

[21] Brennan, J. J., "Interfacial Studies of Coated Fiber Reinforced Glass-Ceramic Matrix Composites," Annual Report R91-918185-2 on AFOSR Contract F49620-88-C-0062, 30 Sept., 1991.

[22] Sun, E. Y., Nutt, S. R., and Brennan, J. J., "Interfacial Microstructure and Chemistry of SiC/BN Dual-Coated Nicalon-Fiber-Reinforced Glass-Ceramic Matrix Composites," Journal of the American Ceramic Society, Vol. 77, No. 5, 1994, pp. 1329-1339.

[23] Brennan, J. J., Nutt, S. R., and Sun, E. Y., "Interfacial Microstructure and Stability of BN Coated Nicalon Fiber/Glass-Ceramic Matrix Composites," in High-Temperature Ceramic-Matrix Composites II: Manufacturing and Materials Development, A. G. Evans and R. Naslain, Eds., Ceramic Transactions, Vol. 58, 1995, pp. 53-64.

[24] Fareed, A. S., Sonuparlak, B., Lee, C. T., Fortini, A. J., and Schiroky, G. H., "Mechanical Properties of 2-D Nicalon Fiber-Reinforced Lanxide Aluminum Oxide and Aluminum Nitride Matrix Composites," Ceramic Engineering and Science Proceedings, Vol. 11, Nos. 7-8, 1990, pp. 782-794.

[25] Naslain, R., "The Concept of Layered Interphases in SiC/SiC ," in High-Temperature Ceramic-Matrix Composites II: Manufacturing and Materials Development, A. G. Evans and R. Naslain, Eds., Ceramic Transactions, Vol. 58, 1995, pp. 23-39.

[26] Zawada, L. P. and Wetherhold, R. C., "The Effects of Thermal Fatigue on a SiC Fibre/Aluminosilicate Glass Composite," Journal of Material Science, Vol. 26, 1991, pp. 648-654.

[27] Strife, J. R. and Sheehan, J. E., "Ceramic Coatings for Carbon-Carbon Composites, Ceramic Bulletin, Vol. 67, No. 2, 1988, pp. 369-373.

[28]   Zawada, L. P., and Lee, S. S., "Mechanical Behavior of CMCs for Flaps and Seals," in Proceedings from 1994 Advanced Research Projects Agency (ARPA) Advanced Ceramics Technology Insertion Program (ACTIP) Review, W. S. Coblenz, Ed., Washington, DC, Aug., 1994.

[29]   Zawada, L. P. and Lee, S. S., "Mechanical Behavior of CMCs for Flaps and Seals," in Proceedings from 1994 Advanced Research Projects Agency (ARPA) Advanced Ceramics Technology Insertion Program (ACTIP) Review, W. S. Coblenz, Ed., Washington, DC, Aug., 1995.

[30]   Zawada, L. P. and Lee, S. S., "Evaluation of Four CMCs for Aerospace Turbine Engine Divergent Flaps and Seals," Ceramic Engineering & Science Proceedings, Vol. 16, No. 4, 1995, pp. 337-339.

[31]   Lee, S. S., Zawada, L. P., Hay, R., Staehler, J., and Carper, D., "Mechanical Behavior of an Oxide/Oxide CMC," submitted to Journal of the American Ceramic Society, Sept., 1996.

[32]   3M Company Product Data Sheet, 3M Ceramic Fiber Products, 3M Center - Building 207-1W-11, St. Paul, MN 55144-1000.

[33]   Hartman, G. A. and Ashbaugh, N. E., "A Fracture Mechanics Test Automation System for a Basic Research Laboratory," in The Applications of Automation Technology to Fatigue and Fracture Testing, ASTM STP 1092, A. A. Braun, N. E. Ashbaugh, and F. M. Smith, Eds., American Society for Testing and Materials, West Conshohocken, PA., 1990, pp. 95-110.

[34]   Butkus, L. M., "Thermomechanical Fatigue Behavior of a Silicon Carbide Fiber-Reinforced Calcium Aluminosilicat Glass-Ceramic Matrix Composite," Air Force Materials Directorate Technical Report, WL-TR-92-4071, Aug. 1992.

[35]   Worthem, D. W., "Flat Tensile Specimen Design for Advanced Composites," NASA C.R. 185261, 1990.

[36]   Wu, X, and Holmes J. W., "Tensile Creep and Creep-Strain Recovery Behavior of Silicon Carbide Fiber/Calcium Aluminosilicate Matrix Ceramic Composites," Journal of the American Ceramic Society, Vol. 76, No. 10, 1993, pp. 2695-7800.

[37]   Sun, E. Y., Nutt, S. R., and Brennan, J. J., "Flexural Creep of Coated SiC-Fiber-Reinforced Glass-Ceramic Composites," Journal of the American Ceramic Society, Vol. 78, No. 5, 1995, pp. 1233-1239.

[38]   Chermant, J. L. and Holmes, J., "Elevated Temperature Creep and Cyclic Creep Behavior of Fiber-Reinforced Ceramics," in High-Temperature Ceramic-Matrix Composites I: Design, Durability, and Performance, A. G. Evans and R. Naslain, Eds., Ceramic Transactions, Vol. 57, American Ceramic Society, Westerville, OH, 1995, pp. 95-106.

[39]   Holmes, J. W., Park, Y. H., and Jones, J. W., "Tensile Creep and Creep Recovery Behavior of a SiC-Fiber-Si_3N_4-Matrix Composite," Journal of the American Ceramic Society, Vol. 76, No. 5, 1993, pp. 1281-1293.

[40]   Holmes, J. W. and Wu, X., "Elevated Temperature Creep Behavior of Continuous Fiber-Reinforced Ceramics," in High Temperature Mechanical Behavior of

Ceramic Composites, S. V. Nair and K. Jakus, Eds., Butterworth-Heinemann, 1995, Chap. 5, pp. 193-260.

[41]   Cannon, W. R. and Langdon, T. G., "Review Creep of Ceramics: Part 1 Mechanical Characteristics," Journal of Materials Science, Vol. 18, 1983, pp. 1-50.

[42]   Cannon, W. R. and Langdon, T. G., "Review Creep of Ceramics: Part 2 An Examination of Flow Mechanisms," Journal of Materials Science, Vol. 23, 1988, pp. 1-20.

[43]   Murphy, D., Jakus, K., Ritter, J. E., and Hill, B. C., "High-Temperature Behavior of Indent and Creep-Nucleated Cracks in Vitreous-Bonded Alumina," Journal of the American Ceramic Society, Vol. 78, No. 7, 1995, pp. 1914-1920.

[44]   Wiederhorn, S. M., Hockey, B. J., Krause, R. F., Jr., and Jakus, K., "Creep and Fracture of a Vitreous-Bonded Aluminum Oxide," Journal of Materials Science, Vol. 21, 1986, pp. 810-824.

[45]   Wilkinson, D. S., Caceres, C. H., and Robertson, A. G., "Damage and Fracture Mechanisms During High-Temperature Creep in Hot-Pressed Alumina," Journal of the American Ceramic Society, Vol. 74, No. 5, 1991, pp. 922-933.

[46]   Dalgleish, B. J., Johnson, S. M., and Evans, A. G., "High-Temperature Failure of Polycrystalline Alumina: I, Crack Nucleation," Journal of the American Ceramic Society, Vol. 67, No. 11, 1984, pp. 741-750.

[47]   Blumenthal, W., and Evans, A. G., "High-Temperature Failure of Polycrystalline Alumina: II, Creep Crack Growth and Blunting," Journal of the American Ceramic Society, Vol. 67, No. 11, 1984, pp. 751-759.

[48]   Johnson, S. M., Delgleish, B. J., and Evans, A. G., "High-Temperature Failure of Polycrystalline Alumina: III, Failure Times," Journal of the American Ceramic Society, Vol. 67, No. 11, 1984, pp. 759-763.

[49]   Jakus, K., Wiederhorn, S. M., and Hockey, B. J., "Nucleation and Growth of Cracks in Vitreous-Bonded Aluminum Oxide at Elevated Temperatures," Journal of the American Ceramic Society, Vol., No. 10, 1986, pp. 725-731.

[50]   Robertson, G. A., Wilkinson, D. S., and Caceres, C. H., "Creep and Creep Fracture in Hot-Pressed Alumina," Journal of the American Ceramic Society, Vol. 74, No. 5, 1991, pp. 915-921.

[51]   Cannon, R. M., Rhodes, W. H., and Heuer, A. H., "Plastic Deformation of Fine-Grained Alumina (Al2O3): I, Interface-Controlled Diffusional Creep," Journal of the American Ceramic Society, Vol. 63, Nos. 1-2, 1980, pp. 46-53.

[52]   Dey, N. and Socie, D. F., "Tensile Creep Behavior of Alumina Under Static and Cyclic Loading," Ceramic Engineering & Science Proceedings, Vol. 15, No 5, 1994, pp. 634-641

[53]   Tressler, R. E. and DiCarlo, J. A., "Creep and Rupture of Advanced Ceramic Fiber Reinforcements," in High-Temperature Ceramic-Matrix Composites I: Design, Durability, and Performance, A. G. Evans and R. Naslain, Eds., Ceramic Transactions, Vol. 57, American Ceramic Society, Westerville, OH, 1995, pp. 141-155.

[54] Pysher, D. J. and Tressler, R. E., "Creep Rupture Studies of Two Alumina-Based Ceramic Fibres," Journal of Materials Science, Vol. 27, 1992, pp. 423-428.

[55] Pysher, D. J. and Tressler, R. E., "Tensile Creep Rupture Behavior of Alumina-Based Polycrystalline Oxide Fibres," Ceramic Engineering & Science Proceedings, Vol. 13, Nos. 7-8, 1992, pp. 218-226.

[56] Wilson, D. M., Lueneburg, D. C., and Lieder, S. L., "High Temperature Properties of Nextel 610 and Alumina-Based Nanocomposite Fibers," Ceramic Engineering & Science Proceedings, Vol. 14, Nos. 7-8, 1993, pp. 609-621.

[57] Zuiker, J. R., "A Model for the Creep Response of Oxide/Oxide Ceramic Matrix Composites," in this volume.

[58] Abe, F., Vicens, J., and Chermant, J. L., "Creep Behavior and Microstructural Characterization of a Ceramic Matrix Composite," Journal of Material Science Letters, Vol. 8, 1989, pp. 1026-1028.

[59] Doreau, F., Gilbert, F., Vincens, J., and Chermant, J. L., "On the Creep Behavior of SiCf - YMAS Composites," in High-Temperature Ceramic-Matrix Composites I: Design, Durability, and Performance, A. G. Evans and R. Naslain, Eds., Ceramic Transactions, Vol. 57, American Ceramic Society, Westerville, OH, 1995, pp. 363-368.

[60] Sutherland, S. and Lewis, M. H., "Creep Deformation of Ceramic Matrix Composites," in High-Temperature Ceramic-Matrix Composites I: Design, Durability, and Performance, A. G. Evans and R. Naslain, Eds., Ceramic Transactions, Vol. 57, American Ceramic Society, Westerville, OH, 1995, pp. 357-362.

[61] Maupas, H. and Chermant, J. L., "Creep Behavior of a 0-90° SiCf-MLAS Composite, in High-Temperature Ceramic-Matrix Composites I: Design, Durability, and Performance, A. G. Evans and R. Naslain, Eds., Ceramic Transactions, Vol. 57, American Ceramic Society, Westerville, OH, 1995 pp. 369-374.

[62] Verrilli, M. J., Calomino, A. M., and Brewer, D. N., "Creep-Rupture Behavior of a SiC/SiC Composite," in this volume.

[63] Weber, C. H., Lofvander, J. P. A., and Evans, A. G., "Creep Anisotropy of a Continuous-Fiber-Reinforced Silicon Carbide/Calcium Aluminosilicate Composite," Journal of the American Ceramic Society, Vol. 77, No. 7, 1994, pp. 1745-1752.

[64] Khobaib, M. and Zawada, L. P., "Tensile and Creep Behavior of a Silicon Carbide Fiber-Reinforced Aluminosilicate Composite," Ceramic Engineering and Science Proceedings, Vol. 12, Nos. 7-8, 1991, pp. 1537-1555.

[65] Zawada, L. P., "Fatigue in Fiber Containing Glass Ceramics," The Technical Cooperation Program Final Report on Study Assignment PTP-2-S3, Report PTP2/94/02, 1995.

[66] Holmes, J. W., "Tensile Creep Behavior of a Hot-Pressed SiC Fiber-Reinforced Si_3N_4 Composite," Journal of Materials Science, Vol. 26, 1991, pp. 1808-1814.

[67] Hilmas, G. E., Holmes, J. W., Bhatt, R. T., and DiCarlo, J. D., "Tensile Creep Behavior and Damage Accumulation in a SiC-Fiber/RBSN-Matrix Composite," in Advances in Ceramic Matrix Composites, N. Bansal, Ed., Ceramic Transactions, Vol. 38, American Ceramic Society, Westerville, OH, 1993, pp. 291-304.

[68] Adami, J. N., "Comportement en Fluage Uniaxial sous Vide d'un Composite a Matrice Ceramique Bidirectional Al2O3-SiC," These de Docteur es Sciences Techniques, L'Ecole Polytechnique Federale de Zurich, Switzerland, 1992.

[69] Holmes, J. W. and Sorensen, B. F., "Fatigue Behavior of Continuous Fiber-Reinforced Ceramic Matrix Composites," in High Temperature Mechanical Behavior of Ceramic Composites, S. V. Nair and K. Jakus, Eds., Butterworth-Heinemann, 1995, Chapter 6, pp. 261-326.

[70] Wang, Z. G., Liard, C., Hashin, Z., Rosen, W., and Yn, C. F., "The Mechanical Behavior of a Cross-Weave Ceramic Matrix Composite, Part II, Repeated Loading," Journal of Material Science, 1991, pp. 5335-5341.

[71] Butkus, L. M., Holmes, J. W., and Nicholas, T., "Thermomechanical Fatigue Behavior of Silicon Carbide Fiber-Reinforced Calcium Aluminosilicate Composite," Journal of the American Ceramic Society, Vol. 76, No. 11, 1993, pp. 2817-2825.

[72] Shuler, S. F. and Holmes, J. W., "Influence of Loading Rate on the Monotonic Tensile Behavior of Fiber Reinforced Ceramics," Research Memorandum 102, Sept. 1990, available through Ceramic Composites Research Laboratory, Dept. of Mechanical Engineering and Applied Mechanics, 2250 GGBL, The University of Michigan, Ann Arbor, MI 48109-2125.

[73] Sorensen, B. F. and Holmes, J. W., "Effect of Loading Rate on the Monotonic Tensile Behavior and Matrix Cracking of a Fiber-Reinforced Ceramic," Journal of the American Ceramic Society, in press.

[74] Martin, A., Puente, I., Sanchez, J. M., Elizalde, M. R., Martinez, J. M., et al., "Failure Mechanisms in CAS/SiC Composite as a Function of the Strain Rate," in High-Temperature Ceramic-Matrix Composites I: Design, Durability, and Performance, A. G. Evans and R. Naslain, Eds., Ceramic Transactions, Vol. 57, American Ceramic Society, Westerville, OH, 1995, pp. 323-328.

[75] Holmes, J. W., "A Technique for Tensile Fatigue and Creep Testing of Fiber-Reinforced Ceramics," Journal of Composite Materials, Vol. 2, No. 6, 1992, pp. 916-933.

[76] Lin, H., Becher, P. F., and Ferber, M. K., "Improvement of Tensile Creep Displacement Measurements," Journal of the American Ceramic Society, Vol. 77, No. 10, 1994, pp. 2767-2770.

Daniel R. Mumm,[1] Winfred L. Morris,[2] Mahyar S. Dadkhah,[2] and Brian N. Cox[2]

SUBCRITICAL CRACK GROWTH IN CERAMIC COMPOSITES AT HIGH TEMPERATURE MEASURED USING DIGITAL IMAGE CORRELATION

REFERENCE: Mumm, D. R., Morris, W. L., Dadkhah, M. S., and Cox, B. N., "Subcritical Crack Growth in Ceramic Composites at High Temperature Measured Using Digital Image Correlation," Thermal and Mechanical Test Methods and Behavior of Continuous-Fiber Ceramic Composites, ASTM STP 1309, Michael G. Jenkins, Stephen T. Gonczy, Edgar Lara-Curzio, Noel E. Ashbaugh, and Larry P. Zawada, Eds., American Society for Testing and Materials, 1997.

ABSTRACT: An *in situ* experimental technique is described that allows high resolution, high sensitivity determination of displacements and full-field strains during high temperature mechanical testing. The technique is used to investigate elevated temperature crack growth in SiC/Nicalon composites. At 1150°C, the reinforcing fibers have a higher creep susceptibility than the matrix. Fiber creep leads to relaxation of crack bridging tractions, resulting in subcritical crack growth. Differential image analysis is used to measure the crack opening displacement profile $u(x)$ of an advancing, bridged crack. With appropriate modeling, such data can be used to determine the traction law, from which the mechanics of cracking and failure may be determined.

KEYWORDS: crack growth, bridging, differential image correlation, creep, composites

---

Fiber reinforcement has been demonstrated to be an effective means of toughening intrinsically brittle materials, such as ceramics and intermetallics. A principal source of the improved toughness is crack bridging by fibers left intact in the wake of an advancing crack [1,2]. If crack bridging is the primary toughening mechanism, the force/displacement behavior of the bridging fibers determines the crack shielding. The mechanics of cracking and failure can be determined fully provided the magnitude and distribution of the crack bridging tractions are known [3]. When the bridging zone is large relative to the size and spacing of the bridging elements, the discrete tractions may be approximated as a continuous closure pressure acting on the crack faces. Numerous models have been devel-

---

[1] Member of Technical Staff, Structural Ceramics Department, Rockwell Science Center, 1049 Camino Dos Rios, Thousand Oaks, CA 91360.

[2] Members of Technical Staff and Manager, respectively, Design & Reliability Department, Rockwell Science Center, 1049 Camino Dos Rios, Thousand Oaks, CA 91360.

oped expressing the crack bridging tractions as a function, $p(u)$, of the crack opening displacement, $u(x)$, at a position, x, in the crack wake. Cox and Marshall [3] have developed a method for deducing the function $p(u)$ from experimental measurements of the crack opening profile $u(x)$ of a single crack. For an assessment of both the functional form and quantitative validity of bridged crack models for brittle-matrix composites, precise crack opening profile measurements are needed. However, few such measurements have been reported.

Analysis of bridging tractions from crack opening profiles requires an accuracy in displacement measurements of ~1% of the opening at the notch root or the crack mouth [3]. For a composite such as Al_2O_3/SiC_w, loaded to the critical applied stress intensity, the maximum opening of a crack of length 100 μm may be on the order of 1 μm. The required measurement accuracy is then ~10 nm. This is beyond the limits of conventional techniques for strain and displacement measurement, but within the capabilities of stereoscopy [4,5] or related automated displacement mapping techniques [6,7] based upon differential image analysis. The present article addresses the need for critical measurements of crack opening profiles during mechanical testing of ceramic composites by describing an experimental technique that allows quantitative measurement of crack opening displacement profiles for bridged cracks in brittle-matrix composites.

At high temperatures, crack-bridging tractions may be affected by one or more of the following: (1) creep of the composite constituents, (2) viscous deformation of interphase layers, grain boundary phases or matrices with glassy phases, (3) relief of residual stresses resulting from thermal expansion mismatch, and (4) environmental attack, for example, oxidation of the fiber-matrix interface. Although modelling must account for the temperature and time dependence of the crack opening profile, understanding the mechanics of crack growth and failure remains a question of determining the crack bridging tractions from measurements of $u(x)$.

The purpose of this work is to develop a high temperature test system that is capable of providing optical images of suitable quality for differential image correlation and thence to provide $u(x)$ data of sufficient resolution for use with bridged-crack models accounting for temperature-dependent and time-dependent crack growth in CMCs. The test system described in this work is used to investigate an important damage mechanism for high temperature ceramic composites, where crack growth occurs owing to a systematic degradation of bridging tractions with creep relaxation of crack bridging fibers.

In this work, crack growth studies are performed with SiC/Nicalon$_f$ composites. Analysis of images acquired at 1150°C show that multiple cracking occurs upon monotonic loading. However, with constant applied load, stable growth of a single dominant crack is observed, with propagation to failure. Degradation of the bridging tractions is characterized by measuring crack opening displacement profiles as a function of time. Although the materials studied are woven composites, the measured bridging zones are large relative to the size and spacing of the crack bridging elements. Therefore, the crack bridging tractions can be considered as a continuous closure pressure, and the measured profiles provide data for bridging parameter evaluation using models such as those cited above.

Cracking and damage can be significantly affected by oxidation occurring at the fiber/matrix interface. Studies of these effects are beyond the scope of this paper, and all testing reported here is done in an argon atmosphere to avoid interfacial degradation.

STRAIN MEASUREMENTS VIA DIFFERENTIAL IMAGE CORRELATION

<u>Image Acquisition and Analysis</u>

Strain measurement using differential image analysis requires high quality images of the specimen surface contrast during various stages of a test procedure. Sensitive measurements of surface strains are made through comparison of a pair of optical micrographs, one taken before a change in the material takes place (the reference) and the other taken after. For example, a pair of micrographs may be taken before and after specimen loading, or the micrographs may be from different times of a constant load creep experiment. Strains or crack openings are measured by determining the relative changes in position of surface contrast features. The relative displacements may be measured by comparing pairs of micrographs using a stereoviewer, in which in-plane displacements are perceived as changes in height [4,5]. Stereoimaging takes advantage of the exceptional sensitivity of the human visual system to small changes in apparent depth [4,5]. A crack appears as a sharp ledge viewed from above. Quantitative displacement measurements are made by comparison of the perceived surface profile with a calibrated travelling spot [8]. Since the observed features are essentially unchanged from one image to the next, other than in precise position, the accuracy of measurement exceeds the point-to-point resolution of the microscope used to record the images [6]. Relative displacements of ±5 μm can be determined on high quality optical micrographs. This corresponds to a displacement sensitivity of ~100 nm on micrographs of only 50× magnification, that is, over a field of view of ~2 mm on the sample.

Manual methods of differential image analysis (stereoscopy) suffer from being tedious; considerable time can be spent analyzing displacements or strains from a single pair of micrographs. Furthermore, only the displacements parallel to the axis of the stereoviewer are measured. To obtain the orthogonal component of the relative displacement required for accurate determination of shear strains, both micrographs must be rotated exactly 90°, and the displacements must be measured from precisely the same reference position. Such limitations can be alleviated by automating the differential image analysis through digital image processing techniques [6,7] making use of cross-correlation procedures. In addition to improving the speed at which measurements may be obtained, automated image correlation is a powerful technique for determination of shear strains, as both components of the in-plane displacement are measured simultaneously. In this work, manual stereoscopic image analysis is used, as displacements are sought only in one direction, and only a small number of measurements are made per pair of micrographs.

<u>Specimen Preparation</u>

The strain measurement technique relies on imaging contrast that occurs on the surface of the specimen. A specimen surface with a dense, random distribution of highly contrasting features is ideal. In many cases, sufficient contrast exists naturally on the specimen surface. Material inhomogeneity or the microstructure can provide useful contrast. A highly polished sample is not always optimal. For instance, with the composites discussed in the following part of this paper, a highly polished surface shows large, matrix-rich regions with no contrast. Strain measurements cannot be obtained from such regions. In other materials, the scale of the microstructure or other natural features providing contrast is too fine (or, possibly too coarse) to provide useful contrast at the desired magnification. In such cases, intentional contamination, surface decoration, or even fine scratching of the specimen surface can be introduced. For accurate strain measurement during high temperature testing, the features providing contrast must be thermally stable. The specimen surface must be flat (relative to the depth of field of the viewing instrument at the given magnification) so that the area over which measurements are to be made is in focus, and stays in focus with deformation of the specimen.

EXPERIMENTAL APPARATUS

The apparatus developed for quantitative investigation of high temperature crack growth has four independent systems to allow: (1) acquisition of high resolution images; (2) precise control of loading, deformation, and fracture; (3) accurate temperature control; and (4) atmosphere control. The system is built around a standard benchtop-sized servo-hydraulic test frame with associated electronics (servo-controller and signal conditioners). Images are acquired using an optical microscope attached to a high-stiffness, three-axis positioning system. To control vibrations transmitted from the surroundings, the loading system and optical microscope are rigidly fixed to a common plate and attached to a large mass sitting on pneumatic isolators. A means of securing the camera assembly was devised so that inserting and removing polaroid film does not disturb positioning or focal conditions, while still allowing fine adjustments of the microscope for initial focussing.

The specimen is heated with a compact, custom-built furnace with a flat Kanthal heating element designed to allow viewing of the specimen while minimizing thermal gradients. The furnace includes a quartz window which is partially mirrored to reflect much of the radiant energy. Sample temperature is determined with attached thermocouples. The loading system includes water-cooled grips. The optical microscope incorporates a custom coaxial light source with a fiber-optic cable and high intensity xenon lamp. The resulting intense illumination overpowers the thermal radiation of the sample, providing high quality images with consistent contrast, regardless of temperature. The current system includes an enclosure so that testing may be done in air or with a slight overpressure of inert gas, although there are no technical barriers to more elaborate atmosphere control. The ability to control the test environment can be a significant advantage over *in situ* techniques making use of a scanning electron microscope, in which all testing is done in vacuum, because high temperature failure mechanisms involving environmental degradation may be directly investigated.

In examining potential sources of error, the magnification uniformity for this system has been analyzed over the available magnification range of 6.3 to 32×. Analysis of control micrographs, in which the only change made is the position of the imaging system, shows that with positioning errors as large as 100 μm (relative to the sample surface), errors in the measured strains are well below the measurement resolution.

HIGH TEMPERATURE CRACK GROWTH IN SiC/NICALON$_f$ COMPOSITES

At high temperature, brittle matrix composites are subject to a variety of cracking and damage modes, some depending on the relative creep susceptibilities of the fiber and matrix [9,10]. In many ceramic composites, fine-grained fibers exhibit creep behavior while the matrix remains elastic at service temperatures. Such materials are susceptible to crack growth at high temperature owing to an interactive process involving fiber creep and matrix cracking. Creep relaxation of bridging fibers leads to crack propagation as the shielding effect is reduced and stress transfer to the matrix occurs. With crack propagation, new fibers are brought into the bridging zone and fiber stresses increase, advancing creep relaxation effects [11]. Materials exhibiting this behavior include SiC/ Nicalon$_f$ composites such as those used in this work.

Experimental work reported by Henager and Jones [12] showed that under constant load conditions, steady-state cracking is observed with SiC/Nicalon$_f$ composites at 1100°C. The reported crack growth rates were calculated on the basis of compliance change, assuming all changes were entirely due to crack growth. However, compliance changes continuously with relaxation of bridging tractions even in the absence of crack propagation. The *in situ* technique described above is used to investigate time-dependent crack growth in SiC/Nicalon$_f$ composites at 1150°C. The technique allows direct measurement of crack length and crack opening displacement profiles, so that changes may be directly correlated with test parameters: the load, temperature, and time.

Materials and Specimen Preparation

Nicalon reinforced CVI β–SiC composites (E.I. Dupont de Nemours & Co., Inc., Wilmington, DE), with reinforcement in the form of plain weave 0/90° cloth layers, were tested. The reinforcements have a carbon-rich coating, providing a weak interface in the composite. The as-supplied eight-ply composites were approximately 3.5 mm thick. Compact-tension (CT) specimens were machined from a 200- by 200-mm plate in accordance with ASTM Test Method for Measurement of Fatigue Crack Growth Rates (E 647), with specimen dimensions of $W = 31.75$ mm and $B = 3.00$ mm. The specimens were notched to a depth of 13.40 mm ($a_o/W = 0.42$), with a half chevron notch present 2.24 mm farther into the material. A Knoop indent (5 kg applied load) was placed at the tip of the chevron notched region to facilitate further the initiation of a sharp crack. The sample surfaces were ground flat to a 25-μm finish. Additional specimen polishing was not done, as it reduces the density of contrast features useful for image correlation.

A pertinent review of the available creep data for CVD SiC and Nicalon fibers is given by El-Azab and Ghoniem [13]. Using data reported by Gulden and Driscoll [14], who measured the creep characteristics of CVD SiC, and the results of DiCarlo and Morscher [15], who measured creep strains for Nicalon fibers over the temperature range 1000°C to 1500°C, the relative creep rates of the composite constituents are compared. At a temperature of 1150°C, the creep rate of Nicalon fibers is more than five orders of magnitude greater than that of CVD SiC. Therefore, in this work, creep effects are considered only for the bridging fibers.

Test Procedures

Specimens were precracked at room temperature by fatigue loading at 5 Hz, at a stress intensity range of $\Delta K = 10.6$ MPa·m$^{1/2}$ and an R ratio of 0.1. Sharp cracks initiated at the tip of the Knoop indent, growing approximately half the distance to the end of the chevron notch. The samples were unloaded before heating to the test temperature of

1150°C. Precracking and testing were done in a flowing argon atmosphere to minimize environmental effects (interfacial oxidation). Examination of the fracture surfaces after failure (Fig. 1) shows substantial fiber pullout and no evidence of fiber/matrix interface degradation (i.e. SiO_2 formation).

FIG. 1 — Fracture surface of SiC/Nicalon$_f$ composite showing substantial fiber pullout and no evidence of interfacial oxidation following subcritical crack growth to failure at 1150°C.

Observations and measurements made during testing of a single specimen are as follows. The specimen was held at an applied stress intensity of 0.1 MPa·m$^{1/2}$ while heating to 1150°C. After stabilizing at the desired test temperature, reference micrographs were obtained before the load was increased monotonically. Loading was interrupted at 350 and 700 N for image acquisition. The load was held at 700 N to acquire images over ~200 min. The specimen was then loaded to 800 N and held for over 110 h, until failure occurred with creep crack growth. All optical images were obtained at 30× magnification.

RESULTS AND DISCUSSION

The ability to map displacements with high precision allowed detection of damage that would not have been observable by direct imaging. An example is shown in Fig. 2. With monotonic loading to 350 N (less than half the maximum precracking load, K_{app} ~5.0 MPa·m$^{1/2}$), partial opening of the fatigue precrack was observed (see Fig. 1a). Continued loading, above the precracking load, to 800 N (K_{app} ~13.3 MPa·m$^{1/2}$) caused subcritical growth of the initial crack. Secondary cracks developed to the sides of the main crack, indicating the distributed nature of the damage occurring with monotonic loading (Fig. 2b). While holding at constant load, the main crack continued to open and extend, presumably because of creep relaxation of crack bridging fibers (Fig. 2c,d). It is important to note that (at this magnification), the secondary cracks, and significant portions of the main crack, could not be observed in individual micrographs as the resolution is insufficient. Even on high magnification images of highly polished specimens, cracks such as those indicated here are difficult to detect because they are often within the interfacial coating on fibers aligned with the crack growth direction. Such cracks were detected and measured only through differential image analysis, in which a crack appears as a discontinuity in the differential displacement of contrast features.

The orientations of surface ply fiber tows are indicated in Fig. 2a (0° tows are parallel to the loading axis). A pore resulting from incomplete infiltration during CVD

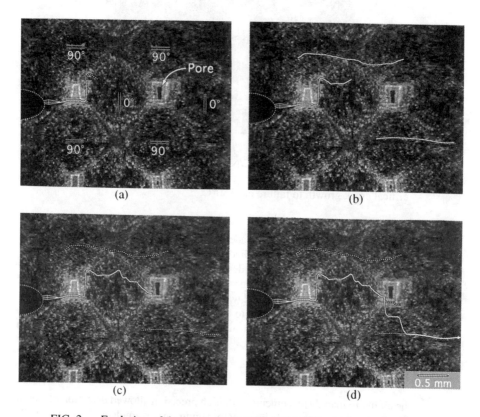

FIG. 2 — Evolution of damage with loading at 1150°C: (a) partial opening of the fatigue precrack at 350 N, (b) crack extension and secondary cracking observed immediately upon loading to 800 N, and after holding at constant load for (c) 706 min and (d) 4232 min. Width of field = 3.61 mm.

processing is also noted. The precrack initiated within a matrix-rich region between tows and deflected at the edge of a 0° tow. Secondary cracking during monotonic loading (Fig. 2b) occurred parallel to the fibers within 90° tows. The main crack extended perpendicular to the 0° fibers, eventually linking up with one of the secondary cracks. The crack paths appear to correlate with geometrical features of the fiber architecture visible in the surface ply. However, far-field deformations indicate that cracks illustrated in Fig. 2 are present as through-thickness features, rather than as surface cracks. Furthermore, although the overall 0°/90° orientation of fiber tows is maintained, the individual plies are randomly offset relative to one another, so that 0° tows in one ply may be aligned with 0° tows, 90° tows, matrix-rich regions, or pores in other plies. A developing crack encounters microstructural features other than those noted on the specimen surface. Therefore, the *overall* crack growth is not correlated with any particular microstructural feature noted in the outermost ply of the composite.

Crack opening displacements measured at various points along the main and secondary cracks immediately following monotonic loading to 800 N are shown in Fig. 3. The measured crack profiles are qualitatively consistent with expectations for bridged edge and center cracks. More importantly, the crack opening displacement at the notch root is more than double that measured anywhere along either of the side cracks. Stress in the bridging fibers is proportional to the local crack opening displacement, and the rate of creep will, therefore, be greater for bridging fibers at the notch root. Growth of the crack emanating from the notch root occurs while attendant changes in the secondary cracks are not observed.

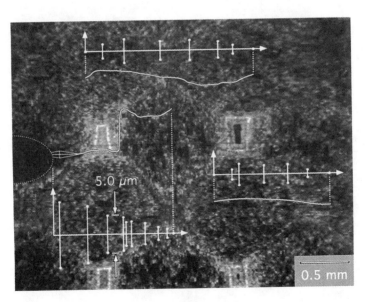

FIG. 3 — Crack opening displacements measured immediately after loading to 800 N at 1150°C. Width of field = 3.61 mm.

To investigate the effects of fiber creep independently of crack growth, the initial loading of the specimen was interrupted at a level (700 N) just below that used for precracking. At this load, bridging fibers were likely to be stressed above the creep threshold, so that creep relaxation would occur while holding at constant load. Moreover, slight degradation of the bridging tractions could occur without attaining a critical condition for crack advance. Crack opening displacement profiles were determined from micrographs taken immediately after the loading interruption and after holding at constant load for 184 min. The results are plotted in Fig. 4. Changes in the crack opening of < 0.5 μm were resolved. Although the crack tip position remained unchanged over this time period, the crack opening increased with time, the largest changes occurring nearest the notch in which the bridging tractions were highest and the fibers were most susceptible to creep.

Similar measurements were made while holding at 800-N load. Changes in the crack opening displacement profile and the crack length were characterized over a period of ~110 h, at which point matrix crack propagation occurred unstably across the remainder of the specimen. The results are summarized in Fig. 5. The profile measurements show a continuously increasing crack opening displacement, again owing to stress relaxation in the bridging fibers. Crack growth occurred intermittently, presumably because of local variations in the crack resistance with material heterogeneity (matrix-rich regions and local variations in the fiber volume fraction). Measurements such as those plotted in

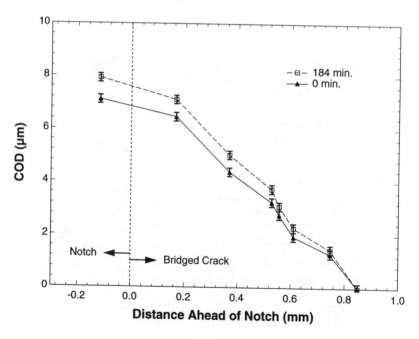

FIG. 4 — Evolution of the crack opening displacement profile with creep relaxation of bridging fibers, under constant load conditions at 700 N.

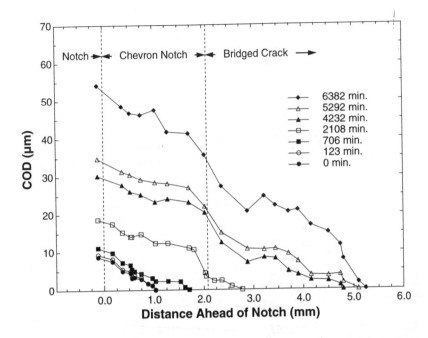

FIG. 5 — Evolution of the crack opening displacement profile with creep relaxation of bridging fibers, under constant load conditions at 800 N. Relaxation of bridging stresses leads to subcritical crack propagation.

Fig. 5, obtained as a function of temperature and time, provide $u(x)$ data for direct comparison to theoretical predictions of crack growth at high temperature.

CONCLUSIONS

An *in situ* technique permitting high resolution, high sensitivity strain measurements during elevated temperature mechanical testing of brittle-matrix composites is discussed. The technique has general utility for investigation of damage and failure mechanisms for high temperature, high performance structural materials. The technique is applied to study crack growth in a ceramic composite at 1150°C, in which the reinforcing fibers are subject to creep. Crack opening displacements are determined as a function of position behind the crack tip, providing data for a direct evaluation of the mechanics of crack bridging at high temperature. At constant applied load, crack growth can be correlated with degradation of the crack-bridging tractions, measured as an increased crack opening displacement along the length of the bridged crack. Such data can be used with appropriate models to determine the traction law during various stages of crack growth. The measurements and observations presented demonstrate the utility of this technique for investigation of high temperature crack growth and failure mechanisms for CMCs.

ACKNOWLEDGMENTS

This work was funded mainly by the U.S. Department of Energy, Contract DE-FG03-89ER45400. Funding by the U.S. Department of Energy does not constitute endorsement of the views expressed herein.

REFERENCES

[1] Aveston, J., Cooper, G. A., and Kelly, A., "Single and Multiple Fracture," in *The Properties of Fiber Composites: National Physical Laboratory Conference Proceedings*, IPC Science and Technology Press, Teddington, U.K., 1971, pp. 15-26.

[2] Marshall, D. B., and Evans, A. G., "Failure Mechanisms in Ceramic-Fibre/Ceramic-Matrix Composites," *Journal of the American Ceramic Society*, Vol. 68, No. 5, 1985, pp. 225-231.

[3] Cox, B. N., and Marshall, D. B., "The Determination of Crack Bridging Forces," *International Journal of Fracture*, Vol. 49, 1991, pp. 159-176.

[4] Davidson, D. L., "The Observation and Measurement of Displacements and Strain by Stereoimaging," *Proceedings: Scanning Electron Microscopy 1979*, Washington, D.C., April 1979, SEM, Inc., AMF O'Hare, IL, 1979, Vol. 2, pp. 79-86.

[5] Williams, D. R., Davidson, D. L., and Lankford, J., "Fatigue-Crack-Tip Plastic Strains by the Stereoimaging Technique," *Experimental Mechanics*, Vol. 20, 1980, pp. 134-139.

[6] James, M. R., Morris, W. L., and Cox, B. N., "A High Accuracy Automated Strain-field Mapper," *Experimental Mechanics*, Vol. 30, No. 1, 1990, pp. 60-67.

[7] Franke, E. A., Wenzel, D. J., and Davidson, D. L., "Measurement of Microdisplacements by Machine Vision Photogrammetry (DISMAP)," *Review of Scientific Instruments*, Vol. 62 No. 5, 1991, pp. 1270-1279.

[8] Cox, B. N., Morris, W. L., and James, M. R., "High Sensitivity, High Spatial Resolution Strain Measurements in Composites and Alloys," in *Proceedings of the Nondestructive Testing and Evaluation of Advanced Materials and Processes Conference*, Colorado Springs, CO, 1986.

[9] Evans, A. G., and Zok, F. W., "The Physics and Mechanics of Fibre-Reinforced Brittle Matrix Composites," *Journal of Materials Science*, Vol. 29, 1994, pp. 3857-3896.

[10] McMeeking, R. M., "Models for the Creep of Ceramic Matrix Composites," in *Elevated Temperature Mechanical Behavior of Ceramic Matrix Composites*, S. V. Nair and K. Jakus, Eds., Butterworth-Heinemann, Stoneham, MA, 1994.

[11] Begley, M. R., Cox, B. N., and McMeeking, R. M., "Time Dependent Crack Growth in Ceramic Matrix Composites with Creeping Fibers," *Acta Metallurgica et Materialia*, Vol. 43, No. 11, 1995, pp. 3927-3936.

[12] Henager, C. H., and Jones, R. H., "High-Temperature Plasticity Effects in Bridged Cracks and Subcritical Crack Growth in Ceramic Composites," *Materials Science and Engineering*, Vol. A166, 1993, pp. 211-220.

[13] El-Azab, A., and Ghoniem, N. M., "Investigation of Incubation Time for Sub-Critical Crack Propagation in SiC-SiC Composites," *Journal of Nuclear Materials*, Vol. 219, 1995, pp. 101-109.

[14] Gulden, T. D., and Driscoll, C. F., "Creep of Chemically Vapor-Deposited B-SiC with an Analysis of Creep in Bending," *Gulf General Atomic Report GA-10366*, 1971.

[15] DiCarlo, J. A., and Morscher, G. N., "Creep and Stress Relaxation Modeling of Polycrystalline Ceramic Fibers," in *Failure Mechanisms in High Temperature Composite Materials*, G. K. Haritos, G. Newaz and S. Mall, Eds., ASME AD-Vol. 22, AMD-Vol. 122, 1991, p. 15.

Özer Ünal[1]

TENSILE AND FATIGUE BEHAVIOR OF A SILICON CARBIDE/SILICON CARBIDE COMPOSITE AT 1300°C

REFERENCE: Ünal, Ö., "Tensile and Fatigue Behavior of a Silicon Carbide/Silicon Carbide Composite at 1300°C," Thermal and Mechanical Test Methods and Behavior of Continuous-Fiber Ceramic Composites, ASTM STP 1309, Michael G. Jenkins, Stephen T. Gonczy, Edgar Lara-Curzio, Noel E. Ashbaugh, and Larry P. Zawada, Eds., American Society for Testing and Materials, 1997.

ABSTRACT: Monotonic and fatigue properties of a silicon carbide/silicon carbide composite were studied at 1300°C in tension. All tests were conducted in nitrogen (N_2) to eliminate oxidation. Because of the composite architecture and the differences between matrix and fiber properties, the composite failure under both monotonic and cyclic loads took place in stages. In a monotonic test, the composite failure occurred by the creep of bridging fibers, and thus, fibers displayed nonbrittle fracture features. In fatigue tests, although creep was also occurring under cyclic loads, the fracture surface analysis showed that final fracture took place in a brittle manner.

KEYWORDS: silicon carbide, creep, fatigue, high temperature, tensile

INTRODUCTION

Silicon carbide (SiC) based ceramics are receiving much attention for their potential in high-temperature applications. Although they have very good physical and chemical properties, their use in monolithic form is limited because of their brittle nature. To solve this problem, the fibers are commonly incorporated into the SiC matrix. The continuous SiC fiber-reinforced SiC composites synthesized by chemical vapor infiltration (CVI) are particularly attractive since this combination leads to a composite with very high fracture toughness [1].

As high-temperature structural materials, the SiC/SiC composites are expected to be used under both static and cyclic loads. Therefore, the investigation of their response under these conditions is an important area of study for their proper use. As compared to room temperature tests, however, high-temperature studies on composites are much more difficult since there are numerous experimental variables that need to be considered. Furthermore, since composites typically have at least two constituents with different properties, the response of each constituent becomes important while selecting a proper test

---

[1] Associate Ceramist, 207 Metals Development, Ames Laboratory, Metallurgy and Ceramics Program, Ames, IA 50011.

condition. In this particular SiC/SiC composite, for instance, the oxidation of the carbon layer at fiber/matrix takes place readily below 1000°C [2]. The loss of the interfacial carbon layer is a very serious problem in this material since the mechanical properties deteriorate as a result [3,4]. Without some overlay coating, it is almost impossible to study the long-term response of this composite at elevated temperatures. Even then, as the matrix cracks develop, the oxidation of carbon occurs easily. Thus, the purpose of this investigation was to eliminate the oxidation using an inert atmosphere and to study tensile and fatigue behavior of a SiC/SiC composite at 1300°C.

EXPERIMENTAL PROCEDURE

Test Specimen

A commercial SiC/SiC composite obtained from Du Pont Lanxide Composites, Inc. (Newark, DE) contained Nicalon fibers (Nippon Carbon Co., Tokyo, Japan). The important advantage of using small diameter (5-15 μm) Nicalon fibers is that they can be woven to manufacture complex parts. The ceramic grade Nicalon fibers, also known as the Si-C-O fibers due to its oxygen content, had an amorphous microstructure with free carbon. The composites had two-dimensional plain-weave fiber mats stacked up in 0°/90° orientations. The mats were first coated with 0.5 μm pyrolitic carbon and then the CVI method was used to form the SiC matrix. The composite with 3.3mm thickness had about 40% fiber volume and about 10% porosity. The uniaxial tension tests were carried out with dog-bone shaped specimens having a 150mm overall length and a 28mm gauge length (Fig. 1). The width of the test specimens was about 12 and 10mm at the end and gauge sections, respectively. To protect hydraulic wedge-grips from abrasion during clamping, copper plates were glued onto the specimen ends.

30 mm

Fig. 1. SiC/SiC composite tensile specimen used in this study.

Mechanical Testing

Mechanical tests were conducted in a servohydraulic unit equipped with water-cooled hydraulic grips, a short furnace with graphite heating elements capable of reaching 2000°C, and a high-temperature contact extensometer with a 25mm gauge length. As shown by the sketch in

Fig. 2, the extensometer was positioned outside of the hot-zone, and the strain was measured by means of the SiC contact rods. The loading apparatus shown in the sketch was contained entirely in an environmental chamber to carry out tests in controlled atmospheres. Since the ceramic-based materials are brittle and generally exhibit very small deformation, the alignment and the stability of the whole unit at all temperatures have been found to be extremely critical for the acquisition of accurate and reproducible data. Before tests the load-train was carefully aligned to minimize the bending moments and thus to prevent premature failure. This was accomplished by means of a dummy specimen containing twelve strain gauges. At the end, a bending strain of less than 3% was obtained at 5 kN. This value decreased further at higher loads. The hydraulic grip pressure used for gripping test specimens was 500 psi (3447 kPa).

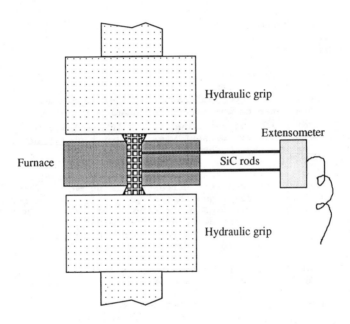

Fig. 2. Schematic drawing of the high temperature mechanical testing unit used.

To improve thermal stability of the contact extensometer, a constant temperature circulator with the capability of maintaining cooling water temperature at ±0.1°C was used. Moreover, to help mechanical stability of the contact rods on the specimen surface, particularly under cyclic fatigue loads, a spring capable of exerting 600g force on a specimen through the extensometer rods (300 g for each rod) was installed. As a result, no slippage of the extensometer rods was observed, and thermal stability of the unit was very good. Furthermore, the examination of failure locations in the fractured specimens showed that the failure did not originate from the contact areas, indicating that the force level applied by the spring was not detrimental for the current specimen geometry.

All tests were conducted in a nitrogen atmosphere and under a small (1.7 kPa) positive pressure. The specimens were heated to the test temperature of 1300°C in load control using a small load. Before tests, the specimens were allowed to equilibrate with the furnace for at least one hour. The monotonic tension tests were conducted in strain control with a cross-head speed of 0.1 μm/s, corresponding to a strain rate ($\dot{\varepsilon}$) of 4 x 10^{-6} s^{-1}. The cyclic tension tests were conducted in load control using a sinusoidal wave-form with a frequency of 0.5 Hz and a stress ratio (R = $\sigma_{min}/\sigma_{max}$) of 0.1. Microstructural analyses of the test specimens were carried out by optical microscopy, scanning electron microscopy (SEM), and transmission electron microscopy (TEM).

RESULTS AND DISCUSSION

Monotonic Tension Test

Recently, ASTM Committee C-28 on Advanced Ceramics published a test standard for monotonic tensile testing of continuous fiber-reinforced composites at room temperature [5]. It is recommended that to avoid environmental effects while testing in ambient air, the tests be conducted at strain rates on the order of 5 x 10^{-4} and 5 x 10^{-5} s^{-1}. No such ASTM standard, however, presently exists for high temperature testing. In this study, as in the case of the tests conducted at room temperature, a slow strain rate (4 x 10^{-6} s^{-1}) was used for the monotonic tensile test. At such a slow loading rate, the composite is expected to redistribute transient stresses arising mainly from the differences in elastic, creep, and thermal properties of constituents and to accumulate creep strain. Since the total strain of 1300°C is the sum of creep and inelastic damage strains (the elastic component is negligible), it is possible to determine the net creep strain from the comparison of results obtained at room temperature and 1300°C.

The uniaxial tensile stress-strain curve obtained at 1300°C is shown in Fig. 3. As marked in the figure, the curve appears to have four distinct regions. It should be mentioned that the features seen in Fig. 3 appear to be typical at elevated temperatures since the curve obtained at 1200°C was similar. First is the elastic region (Region 1), where both the fiber and matrix were strained elastically. The area of Region 1, which represents the amount of elastic energy stored in the specimen, clearly indicates that elastic deformation at 1300°C was very limited. Region 1 ends at the point of deviation from linearity as a result of the macrocrack formation in the matrix. In composite literature, this point is referred to as the proportional limit, σ_{pl}, and its exact location in the curve depends on the sensitivity of displacement and load transducers used. It was shown by the surface replication [6,7], acoustic emission [7,8], and frictional heating measurement [6] methods that the proportional limit seen in stress/strain curve is not the point at which the first matrix crack occurs (microcracking threshold). This threshold stress could not be determined for the present composite since the techniques mentioned above to detect this point were not employed.

Beyond σ_{pl} (Region 2), the composite became increasingly compliant with stress. In contrast to room temperature tests in which the increase in compliance is entirely due to crack formation, the increase at 1300°C is due to both the crack formation and creep since Region 2 in Fig. 3 covers a larger strain range under similar stress levels than at room temperature [9]. At about 160 MPa, the decrease in tangential modulus of the composite ceased and is designated as the matrix crack saturation limit, σ_{mcsl}. At this point, matrix cracks are assumed to have fully formed and further deformation was due to the bridging fibers only, as can be seen clearly from the constancy of the stress/strain slope in Region 3. Up to this point, the stress/strain curve in Fig. 3 is in agreement with the prediction by Aveston, et al. [10], in which they foresaw the formation of such distinct regions in the curve of unidirectional composites exhibiting multiple matrix fracture.

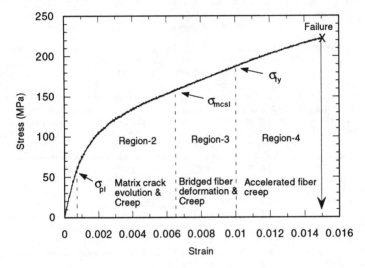

Fig. 3. Monotonic stress/strain curve of the SiC/SiC composite obtained at 1300°C. Note that the specimen exhibited distinct deformation regions.

At the end of Region 3, the composite became compliant again with increasing stress. The start of this new region (Region 4) is designated as the fiber yielding point, σ_{fy}, because of the dominance of creep under increasing stresses. The fiber failure and pullout are also expected to account for some of the increase in compliance in Region 4; however, the relatively large size of Region 4, extending from 1 to 1.5% strain, suggests that the primary event was the creep of the bridging fibers. The comparison of test results obtained at room temperature and 1300°C showed that the net strain accumulated due to creep was about 1%. In the absence of creep, Region 4 probably would not have appeared in Fig. 3 or would have been small since brittle fiber fracture leads to catastrophic composite failure. This is believed to be the reason why the curves obtained at room temperature tests did not have Region 4 [9].

Based on the stress/strain behavior of the composite in Fig. 3,

the discussion above implicitly indicated that the fibers displayed
distinct deformation stages because the deformation behavior of the
composite was dominated by the fibers. However, because Fig. 3 was
obtained under increasing load, there may not be a one-to-one
correlation between the Region 2, 3, and 4 in Fig. 3 and the primary,
secondary and tertiary regions of the creep curves obtained from the
individual fibers under constant loads. Nonetheless, the stress
relaxation starting with σ_{fy} in Region 4 under constant strain-rate
clearly suggests occurrence of an accelerated creep event similar to
that seen in the tertiary region of the creep curves. Bodet, et al.
[11] conducted creep testing of Nicalon fibers between 1200 and 1400°C.
They reported the presence of only primary creep in argon and both the
primary and steady-state creep in an argon/carbon monoxide (Ar/CO)
environment. In some instances, however, they observed accelerated
creep (tertiary) as a result of necking in an Ar/CO environment. As will
be shown later, we have also observed evidence (necking) for the
presence of tertiary creep in the composite in Fig. 3.

The stress/strain curve in Fig. 3 in general is similar to the one
observed in the SiC/CAS composites, although the tests with the SiC/CAS
composites were conducted at room temperature [12]. Figure 3, however,
exhibits some important differences with respect to that obtained from
the same composite at room temperature [9]. While both 1300°C and room-
temperature curves showed almost identical elastic regions (Region 1),
inelastic regions and their boundaries were different. For instance,
the composite failure at room temperature took place in Region 3 where
bridged fibers were deforming elastically. Moreover, the failure strain
at the room temperature test was only one-third of the strain seen in
Fig. 3, yet the overall fracture stress of the composite was almost the
same. The fracture stress results (both at 1200 and 1300°C) suggest
that the Nicalon fibers, which are the primary constituent carrying the
load, did not deteriorate at 1300°C in a N_2 environment. TEM
observations showed that the interfacial carbon was intact and no
microstructural change took place in the fibers. Thus, in nonoxidizing
environments, the short-term strength up to 1300°C appears to be
independent of temperature. In an oxidizing atmosphere, however, the
fibers were shown to have lost about 45% of their room temperature
strength at 1300°C [13].

Fractography showed that the fracture surfaces obtained during
monotonic tests were nonplanar and rough, as compared to those obtained
during similar tests at room temperature. The fracture surfaces
included steps that were parallel to 0° fibers, indicating the presence
of shear failure. On a microscopic level, the fracture surface also had
distinctive features. Figure 4 shows a typical SEM micrograph obtained
from the specimen in Fig. 3. The fibers had debris, both matrix
particles and interfacial carbon. Most importantly, they exhibited
features that suggest occurrence of necking at this temperature. Thus,
the fiber fracture surfaces in general were nonplanar. In spite of
evidence that creep took place, TEM studies showed that no
microstructural changes occurred in the fibers during the slow strain-
rate test in Fig. 3. Since SiC fibers are amorphous, it was suggested
in the fiber creep studies [11] that the viscous flow of this phase is
responsible for the long-term creep of the Nicalon fibers.

Since the fibers have higher strain to failure, the matrix
cracks formed early, and the fibers ended up carrying most of the load.
During microscopic evaluations by SEM and TEM, it was seen that the

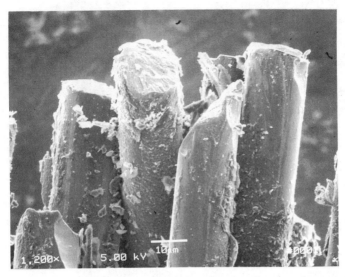

Fig. 4. SEM micrograph of the fracture surface of the monotonically
loaded specimen in Fig. 3. The fibers generally had carbon/matrix debris
on them. The distinctive rough fracture surfaces in fibers indicate the
occurrence of nonbrittle fracture.

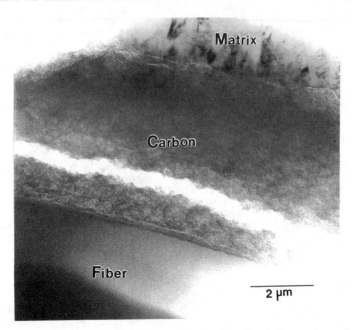

Fig. 5. TEM micrograph from the monotonically loaded specimen in Fig. 3.
The crack formation within the carbon layer at the fiber/matrix
interface was commonly observed in this specimen.

fiber/matrix interface often had cracks. These cracks were observed at both the fiber/carbon interface and within the carbon layer. A TEM micrograph showing the crack in the latter case is seen in Fig. 5. The cracks in the specimen tested at room temperature were at the fiber/carbon interface cracks. Thus, it appears that the crack formation within the interfacial carbon is exclusive at elevated temperatures. The cracks similar to those in Fig. 5 sometimes deviated from interface and entered into the matrix. These observations explain why the fibers generally had carbon and matrix debris on them. Note that the interfacial cracks mentioned above could not be introduced during the specimen preparation since as-received (untested) specimens prepared in the same way did not exhibit similar fiber/matrix detachment unless the specimen was oxidized; thus, the carbon layer was lost.

Fatigue Testing

It was shown experimentally on previous occasions that there is a very good correlation between the increase in crack density and the decrease in stiffness of the composites [14,15]. Thus, in this study, the crack evolution under cyclic loads was monitored by the in-situ stiffness measurements.

The maximum stress (σ_{max}) values for the fatigue tests were selected based on the monotonic stress/strain curve in Fig. 3. As a result, σ_{max} values of 108, 145, and 188 MPa, which correspond to about 50, 65, and 85% of the failure stress (FS) observed in the monotonic test were used. In all three cases, the fatigue tests were started from the zero load and continued until the end of test without any interruption. The data acquisition was made in a logarithmic interval. Moreover, to be able to catch the events taking place in the specimen prior to a possible specimen failure, a buffer was used to record the last several cycles. At the end of the tests, only the specimen fatigued with σ_{max} = 50% FS survived the intended number of cycles of 72 000 (40 hrs). The specimens fatigued with σ_{max} = 65 and 85% FS failed in 7100 and 890 cycles, respectively. The specimens during these tests exhibited similar behavior. As an example, the stress/strain data obtained during the fatigue test with σ_{max} = 65% FS is shown in Fig. 6. The individual loading/unloading cyclic curves were recorded throughout the test, but for clarity, only the selected curves are included in the figure. Notice that since the test was conducted under constant $\Delta\sigma$, the loading/unloading curves moved to right along the strain axis with increasing fatigue cycles. This is a clear indication that the test specimen accumulated irreversible (residual) strain under cyclic loads at 1300°C. Moreover, the specimen exhibited a hysteresis loop, but its area decreased with fatigue. These two observations at 1300°C are in contrast to those made on the similar composites at room temperature [2,16], where the specimens showed almost no residual strain and hysteresis loops in spite of the presence of matrix cracks.

Figure 7a shows all the strain data recorded during the fatigue test in Fig. 6. The variations of total, residual, and elastic strains as a function of fatigue cycle are clearly seen. The total strain (ε_t) was measured at maximum stress, while the residual strain (ε_r) was obtained at zero stress (specimen unloaded). The elastic strain (ε_e) was determined from the relationship in equation (1),

$$\varepsilon_e = \varepsilon_t - \varepsilon_r. \qquad (1)$$

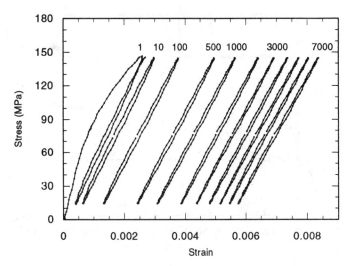

Fig. 6. Loading/unloading curves obtained from the specimen fatigued with σ_{max} = 65% FS (145 MPa). Notice that the specimen crept under the cyclic load.

Note in Fig. 7a that because of the decrease in stiffness at the beginning of tests in Fig. 6, the elastic strain increased a small amount but remained relatively constant afterwards. The residual strain, on the other hand, increased rapidly at the beginning to about 1000 cycles and then slowed down with the increasing fatigue cycles (creep curve). As a result, the total strain ($\varepsilon_e + \varepsilon_r$) reflected the change of residual strain accumulated during the test. The total strain values obtained during the tests with σ_{max} = 108, 145, and 188 MPa were 0.32, 0.85, and 0.86% respectively. The deformation curve in Fig. 7a is redrawn in Fig. 7b in terms of strain-rate. Initially, the strain-rate was high, between 10^{-4} and 10^{-5} s^{-1}, but dropped quickly as the test proceeded. The decrease in strain rate was continuous, and a steady-state regime was not reached. This means the region up to 6000 cycles was still the primary creep area. Beyond 6000 cycles, the strain rate showed fluctuations, which are believed to be the indications of fiber failure since the specimen failure occurred afterwards. Just before composite fracture, the strain rate exhibited a sudden increase, as expected. From the observations in Fig. 7b it seems that the strain rate plot is sensitive for the event in the specimen, particularly those taking place before the fracture.

To compare the initial level of damage introduced into the specimens under different loads, the first two loading/unloading cycles of three tests are compared in Fig. 8. The origins of the tests were displaced for clarity. The proportional limits in Fig. 8 appear to be the same as the one observed in the monotonic test (Fig. 3). The comparison of slopes of the first and second loading cycles in each test clearly suggests that a significant amount of overall damage was introduced during the initial loading. Moreover, the matrix damage introduced into the specimens increased with the increasing applied load. An important observation made in this study is that for given

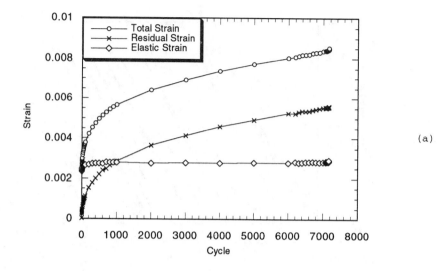

(a)

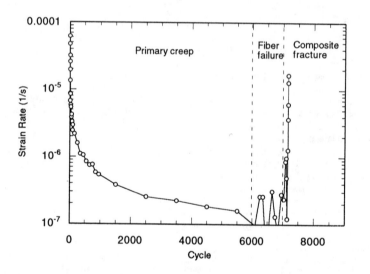

(b)

Fig. 7. Change of (a) the total strain, residual strain, and elastic strain and (b) the strain rate, as a function of fatigue cycle during the test in Fig. 6.

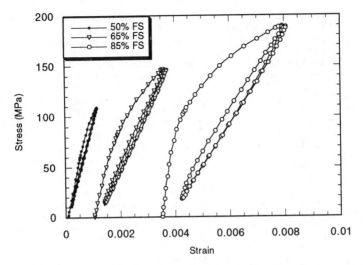

Fig. 8. Comparison of the first two loading/unloading curves obtained in three different specimens where the maximum fatigue stress, σ_{max}, was 50% (108 MPa), 65% (145 MPa), and 85% (188 MPa) FS.

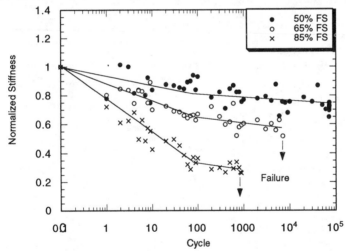

Fig. 9. Variation of normalized stiffness as a function of fatigue cycle in all three fatigue tests.

stress values the fatigue tests were seen to lead to much smaller strain levels in the test specimens than the monotonic tests, that is, less damage is introduced during the fatigue test. This observation, which can be seen clearly from the comparison in Figs. 3 and 8, suggests the presence of a strain-rate effect in the SiC/SiC composite since the fatigue tests were typically conducted in strain rates about three orders of magnitude higher than the monotonic tests.

Figure 9 shows the normalized stiffness as a function of fatigue cycle in all three tests. Normalized stiffness values were obtained by dividing the instantaneous values by initial stiffness (elastic modulus). The stiffness measurements were made automatically during the tests from the loading portions of the loading/unloading curves. The scatter in stiffness values is believed to be due to the varying degrees of wedging and bridging in each cycle in this relatively porous composite, and as expected, it decreased with increasing applied stress. The stiffness curves in Fig. 9 show that the damage accumulation occurred in two distinct steps. Up to 100 cycles, the stiffness decreased rapidly in all three cases, but the rate with which this occurred was strongly dependent on the applied stress, increasing with increasing stress. The high-rate region up to 100 cycles is believed to correspond to crack formations within the matrix of 90° bundles since the fibers in these bundles are loaded in radial direction and thus are not effective carrying the load. Because the matrix has a very low strain-to-failure, the lateral cracks took place readily and appeared to be reaching a saturation. Furthermore, the strong dependency of stiffness loss on applied stress suggests that the higher loads lead to higher crack density, that is, reduced crack spacing.

After 100 cycles, however, the decrease in stiffness shown in Fig. 9 leveled off and its rate appeared to be weakly dependent on the applied stress. In this region, the cracks are postulated to be forming within both the 90° and 0° bundles. Notice also that the overall stiffness loss at failure does not appear to have any significance for the occurrence of specimen failure, that is, there is not a specific stiffness loss value at which the failure is expected to take place. For instance, Fig. 9 shows that the specimen fatigued with σ_{max} = 65% FS failed after it had about 60% of the initial stiffness at 7100 cycles, while the specimen with σ_{max} = 85% FS failed after it had about 30% of the initial stiffness at 890 cycles. The test with σ_{max} = 50% FS survived the 72,000 cycles. It is clear that both the normalized stiffness and the fatigue life decreased with increasing applied stress level. This implies that both the matrix cracking and the fiber damage increased with the fatigue stress since the matrix is primarily responsible for the stiffness loss, and the fiber damage is the one that determines the fatigue life, at least in inert atmospheres.

The optical micrograph in Fig. 10 shows the typical crack pattern developed in the composite subjected to fatigue with σ_{max} = 85% FS. The 90° bundles in this figure are perpendicular to the micrograph; thus, the load was applied along the longitudinal fibers in Fig. 10. As a result, the lateral matrix cracks occurred primarily within the 90° laminates. Except for the crossing points at the 0° fiber bundles, the cracks were relatively continuous across the specimen thickness. At crossing points, the matrix cracks were deflected and, thus, the 0° fibers were generally intact. The average crack spacing in this specimen was about 300 μm, corresponding to a crack density of $3.3mm^{-1}$.

In general, the fracture surfaces of the fatigued specimens were smoother than those obtained under monotonic loading. Moreover, at a microscopic level, the brittle fracture features were observed. The SEM image in Fig. 11 is from the specimen fatigued with σ_{max} = 85% FS. The features seen in this micrograph are typical for the fatigued specimens: the fiber surfaces in general are smooth and the fracture surfaces of the fibers are relatively flat, indicating the dominance of brittle fracture rather than creep failure. Both of these observations are in

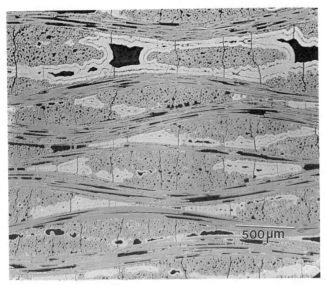

Fig. 10 Lateral crack pattern obtained in the specimen fatigued with σ_{max} = 85% (188 MPa) FS. The cracks developed mostly within the 90° fiber bundles and had about 300 µm spacing.

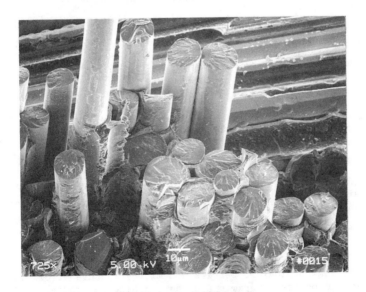

Fig. 11 SEM micrograph of the fracture surface of the fatigued specimen with σ_{max} = 85% (188 MPa) FS. The fiber surface became smooth as a result of the repetitive loading. The commonly seen flat fiber fracture surface suggests the dominance of brittle fracture.

contrast to those made on the fracture surface of the monotonically fractured specimen, where rougher specimen and the fiber fracture surfaces were seen. Since both the monotonic and fatigue tests were conducted at the same temperature and creep took place in both cases, the differences in the observations are believed to be due to the differences in the rate of loading in these two tests. Since the fatigue tests were conducted at a faster rate and the brittle fracture seemed to be the fracture mode, these observations in the SiC/SiC composite at 1300°C are similar to those in metals. In metallic materials, it is well established that a high strain rate promotes brittle fracture because the dislocations are relatively immobile in these tests.

CONCLUSIONS

1. The monotonic stress/strain curve of the SiC/SiC at 1300°C exhibits distinct regions. Matrix cracks first develop within the 90° bundles, and as the crack density saturates, the load is carried primarily by the bridging fibers. Eventual composite failure occurs by the rupture of fibers. While the composite fracture stress at 1300°C is similar to that at room temperature, the fracture strain increases by about 200%, clearly illustrating the effect of creep at this temperature.

2. The creep is also prominent under cyclic loads, although its magnitude was dependent on applied stresses. The overall crack density increases and the fatigue life decreases with the applied cyclic stress. Up to 100 cycles stiffness loss strongly depends on the applied stress; beyond that, however, the dependence is weak.

3. The fracture surfaces of the monotonically loaded and fatigued specimens are different. Although creep takes place in all specimens, because of the difference in strain rates the final fracture under monotonic load occurs by the creep of fibers while that under cyclic load takes place by brittle fracture of the fibers.

ACKNOWLEDGMENT

The author would like to thank F. C. Laabs for his help in SEM. Funding for this work was provided by DOE-OBES under contract No. W-7405-ENG-82.

REFERENCES

[1] Lamicq, J., Bernhart, G. A., Dauchier, M. M., and Mace, J. G., "SiC/SiC Composite Ceramics," American Ceramics Society Bulletin, Vol. 65, 1986, p. 336.

[2] Filipuzzi, L. and Naslain, R., "Oxidation Mechanisms and Kinetics of 1-D-SiC/C/SiC Composite Materials: II, Modeling," Journal of the American Ceramics Society, Vol. 77, 1994, p. 467.

[3] Ünal, Ö., "Mechanical Properties and Microstructure of Oxidized SiC/SiC Composites," Ceramic Engineering Science Proceedings, (in press).

[4] Lowden, R. A. and James, R. D., "Effects of Oxidizing and Combustion Environments on the Interface and the Mechanical

Properties of Nicalon/SiC Composites," in _Proceedings of the Annual Conference of Fossil Energy Materials V_, Vol. 1, N. C. Cole and R. R. Judkins, Eds., NTIS, Springfield, VA, 1991, p. 33.

[5] ASTM Standard C1275-95: Standard Test Method for Monotonic Tensile Strength Testing of Continuous Fiber-Reinforced Advanced Ceramics with Solid Rectangular Cross-Section Specimens at Ambient Temperatures, American Society for Testing Materials, Philadelphia, 1995.

[6] Holmes, J. W. and Cho, C., "Experimental Observations of Frictional Heating in Fiber-Reinforced Ceramics," _Journal of the American Ceramics Society_, Vol. 75, 1992, p. 929.

[7] Zawada, L. P, Butkus, L. M., and Hartman, G. A., "Tensile and Fatigue Behavior of Silicon Carbide and Fiber-Reinforced Aluminosilicate Glass," _Journal of the American Ceramics Society_, Vol. 74, 1991, p. 2851.

[8] Kim, R. Y. and Pagano, N. J., "Crack Initiation in Uniaxial Brittle-Matrix Composites," _Journal of the American Ceramics Society_, Vol. 74, 1991, p. 1082.

[9] Ünal, Ö., "Low-Cycle Tensile Fatigue Behavior of a SiC/SiC Composite," _Ceramic Engineering Science Proceedings_, (in press).

[10] Aveston, J., Cooper, G. A., and Kelly, A., "Single and Multiple Fracture," in _The Properties of Fiber Composites, Conference Proceedings_, National Physical Laboratory, IPS Science and Tech. Press, 4 Nov. 1971.

[11] Bodet, R., Lamon, J., and Tressler, R. E., "Effects of Chemical Environments on the Creep Behavior of Si-C-O Fibers," in _Proceedings of the 6th European Conference on Composite Materials — High Temperature Ceramic Matrix Composites_, Woodhead Publs., England, 1993.

[12] Holmes, J. W. and Sorensen, B. F., "Fatigue Behavior of Continuous Fiber-Reinforced Ceramic Matrix Composites," _High Temperature Mechanical Behavior of Ceramic Composites_, S. V. Nair and K. Jakus, Eds., Butterworth-Heinemann, Newton, MA, 1995, p. 261.

[13] Bodet, R., Bourrat, X., Lamon, J., and Naslain, R., "Tensile Creep Behavior of a Silicon Carbide-Based Fibre with a Low Oxygen Content," _Journal of Materials Science_, Vol. 30, 1995, p. 661.

[14] Karandikar, P. G. and Chou, T. W., "Damage Development and Moduli Reduction in Nicalon/CAS Composites under Static and Cyclic Fatigue," _Journal of the American Ceramic Society_, Vol. 76, 1993, p. 1720.

[15] Shuler, S. F., Holmes, J. W., Wu, X., and Roach, D., "Influence of Loading Frequency on the Room-Temperature Fatigue of a Carbon-Fiber/SiC-Matrix Composite," _Journal of the American Ceramics Society_, Vol. 76, 1993, p. 2327.

[16] Ünal, Ö., "Cyclic Tensile Stress/Strain Behavior of SiC/SiC Composites," _Journal of Materials Science Letters_, Vol. 15, 1996, p. 789.

Hua-Tay Lin[1] and Paul F. Becher[1]

STRESS-TEMPERATURE-LIFETIME RESPONSE OF NICALON FIBER-REINFORCED SILICON CARBIDE (SiC) COMPOSITES IN AIR

REFERENCE: Lin, H.-T. and Becher, P. F., "**Stress-Temperature-Lifetime Response of Nicalon Fiber-Reinforced Silicon Carbide (SiC) Composites in Air,**" Thermal and Mechanical Test Methods and Behavior of Continuous-Fiber Ceramic Composites, ASTM STP 1309, Michael G. Jenkins, Stephen T. Gonczy, Edgar Lara-Curzio, Noel E. Ashbaugh, and Larry P. Zawada, Eds., American Society for Testing and Materials, 1997.

ABSTRACT: Time-to-failure tests were conducted in four-point flexure and in air as a function of stress levels and temperatures to study the lifetime response of various Nicalon fiber-reinforced silicon carbide (designated as Nic/SiC) composites with a graphitic interfacial coating. The results indicated that all of the Nic/SiC composites exhibit a similar stress-dependent failure at applied stress greater than a threshold value. In this case, the lifetimes of the composites increased with decrease in both stress level and test temperature. The lifetime of the composites appeared to be relatively insensitive to the thickness of graphitic interface layer and was enhanced somewhat by the addition of oxidation inhibitors. Electron microscopy and oxidation studies indicated that the life of the Nic/SiC composites was governed by the oxidation of the graphitic interfaces and the formation of glass(es) in composites as a result of the oxidation of the fiber and matrix, as well as any inhibitor phases.

KEYWORDS: Nicalon fiber, silicon carbide matrix, Nic/SiC composite, static fatigue, continuous-fiber ceramic composite

---

Reinforcement by continuous fibers can substantially improve the damage tolerance of ceramics by bringing about the fiber debonding, fiber bridging, and fiber pullout processes. Such toughening mechanisms are achieved through the introduction of an interface/fiber

---

[1]Research staff member and group leader, Metals and Ceramics Division, Oak Ridge National Laboratory, Oak Ridge, TN 37831-6068.

coating. A weakly bonded interfacial layer is often used to obtain fiber debonding from the matrix. As a result, continuous fiber-reinforced ceramic composites (CFCCs) exhibit relatively large strains to failure with high toughness values, which are in sharp contrast to the monolithic ceramics that exhibit brittle, catastrophic fracture behavior.

Continuous Nicalon fiber-reinforced silicon carbide (SiC) matrix composites fabricated by chemical vapor infiltration (CVI) process are candidates for high-temperature structural applications because of their attractive mechanical performance at room and elevated temperatures [1-7]. These structural applications include radiant burners, hot gas filters, high-pressure heat exchanger tubes, and industrial gas turbine engines. Because of its strong anisotropic microstructure and its role in protecting fibers during processing, a graphitic fiber coating has been applied to facilitate interfacial debonding and fiber pullout. However, graphite oxidizes readily at temperatures above 400°C in air [8]. The mechanical performance and long-term reliability of Nic/SiC composites is, therefore, a concern under applied stresses at elevated temperatures in an oxidizing environment.

It was previously shown that the air exposure at 950°C could cause a substantial degradation in a Nic/SiC composite with a 0.3-μm graphitic fiber coating in the absence of an outer SiC seal coating [9]. In that study, no external applied stress was used during elevated temperature air exposure. A separate study showed that in the absence of applied stress a Nic/SiC composite with an external SiC seal coat exhibited no strength degradation after a 1000-h air exposure at 1000°C [10]. However, the presence of a static flexural loading during air exposure at 950°C could promote failure of a Nic/SiC composite with a 50- to 100-nm graphite interface and an external SiC seal coat [11]. Furthermore, a static fatigue study in flexure conducted by Lin et al. [12] has shown that a Nic/SiC composite with a 0.3-μm graphitic fiber coating and without an outer seal coating exhibited stress-dependent lifetimes when the applied stresses were above a threshold value, which was similar to the proportional limit of this composite. The time to failure decreased with increasing the applied stress level and test temperature. The results also revealed that a SiC seal coat played little protective function at 950°C in air [12]. The fatigue study conducted by Lin et al. indicated that the lifetimes of the Nic/SiC composite above the threshold stress were controlled by the oxidation of the graphitic interfacial layer and fibers.

At present, only a very limited database is available to provide some insight into the effect of stress, temperature, and environment on the lifetimes of Nic/SiC composites. As a part of the research efforts in the CFCC program [13], the current task is studying the effect of applied flexural stress on the lifetime response of various Nic/SiC composites at temperatures up to 1200°C in air. The current experiments at temperatures of 600 and 950°C were designed to investigate the temperature range over which oxidation effects can alter the mechanical performance and, thus, the reliability of Nic/SiC composites with a graphitic interface. The effects of modifications in the fiber coating thickness, composite density, and the chemical composition of the matrix were also evaluated.

EXPERIMENTAL PROCEDURES

Time-to-failure studies as functions of applied stress and temperature were conducted in air on several commercially available Nic/SiC composites (designated as Composite A, B, C, and D). The general microstructures of the as-received composites are shown in Fig. 1. The A and B commercial composites were produced by infiltrating a layup of 0°/90° Nicalon plain weave cloth (Nippon Carbon Company, Tokyo, Japan) with SiC matrix by CVI; each composite used a carbon fiber coating to facilitate interfacial debonding and fiber pullout. Composite A contains ~ 43 vol. % fibers with a carbon interfacial layer 0.5- to 0.7-μm thick, exhibits ~ 25 vol. % open porosity, and was tested with an as-machined surface. In addition, Composite A exhibits a banded or agate-like structure in both the darker outer layer and the CVI SiC matrix (Fig. 1a). Matrix cracks are also frequently associated with this distinct banding in the matrix. This agate-like banding is not apparent in other Nic/SiC composites investigated in the present study (Fig. 1). The dark phase was found to be enriched with boron content (10 to 20 at. %). Composite B also contains ~ 43 vol. % fibers with a carbon interfacial layer ~ 0.05- to 0.1-μm thick, less (~ 17 vol. %) open porosity, and has an external layer of CVD SiC seal coating ~ 40-μm thick.

Composites C and D were also produced by infiltrating a layup of 0°/90° Nicalon plain weave cloth with a SiC matrix by CVI. Both Composites C and D contain a mixture of carbon plus particulate fillers, as an oxidation inhibitor, to coat the fiber bundles before the final CVI of SiC (Fig. 1c). The mixture of carbon and particulate oxidation inhibitors were introduced via proprietary impregnation and carbonization processes. Auger analysis of the oxidation inhibitors indicated boron and carbon. In addition to the introduction of a mixture of carbon and oxidation inhibitor, Composite D contains an additional coating, that is oxide phase plus particulate inhibitors, between the fiber cloths for further improvement of the performance at elevated temperatures in air (Fig. 1d). Auger analysis of the oxide phase indicated silicon, carbon, and oxygen. Both Composites C and D contain ~ 43 vol. % fibers, exhibit ~ 15 vol. % open porosity, and have an external layer of CVD SiC seal coat ~ 50-μm thick. Thus, Composites A to D all differ from the previously investigated Oak Ridge National Laboratory (ORNL) Nic/SiC composite in terms of matrix composition, interfacial coating thickness, and fiber cloth layup [12]. This Nic/SiC composite, manufactured at ORNL, consisted of a CVI SiC matrix and ~ 43 vol. % Nicalon fibers in the form of plain weave cloth with the cloth layers rotated 30° between layers. The open porosity in the ORNL composite was ~ 15%. The fiber in the Nicalon cloth had a 0.3-μm graphite coating, which was deposited before infiltration of the SiC matrix.

The dimensions of bend bars prepared from Composites A and B were 3 by 4 by > 50 mm, whereas for Composites C and D the dimensions were 2.5 by 6.6 by > 50 mm. Note that these two different specimen dimensions were also used for the ORNL composite bend bars. Resutls of the ORNL composite indicated that the lifetime was not sensitive to the specimen dimensions (specimen volume) used in the present study,

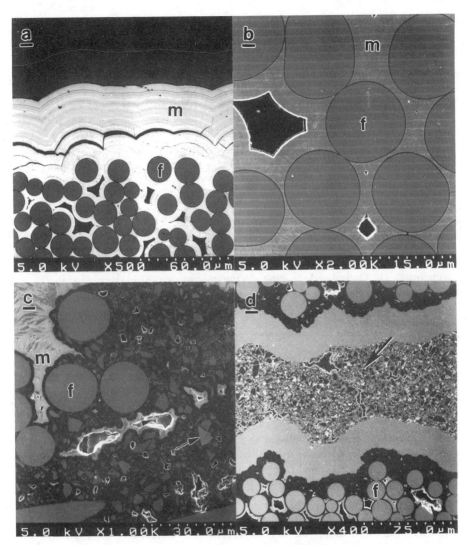

FIG. 1. General microstructures of as-received Nic/SiC composites. (a) Composite A with a 0.5-0.7 μm thick interface accompanied by a banded structure in the matrix, (b) Composite B with a 0.05-0.10 μm thick interface, (c) Composite C with a mixture of graphite and oxidation inhibitors, and (d) Composite D with an additional oxide plus oxidation inhibitors coating. The labels of "f" and "m" denote the fiber and matrix, respectively. The arrows indicate the inhibitors in (c) and additional coating in (d).

indicating minor effect of specimen volume.[2] The 0° fibers in the test bend bars were in an orientation parallel to the tensile stress direction. The static fatigue in four-point bending was conducted at temperatures of 600 and 950°C in air. The test fixtures were fabricated from sintered α-SiC with inner and outer spans of 20 and 40 mm, respectively. A pneumatic-type loading system was used to applied the load to the test bend bars through an alumina pushrod. The test bars were held in the fixture with a small load (< 15 MPa outer fiber tensile stress) and heated to the desired test temperature and allowed to equilibrate for at least 30 min before increasing applied stress to the selected level. The applied stress was held constant ($\pm$ 0.2 MPa deviation) until the test bar failed; at that point, sensors interrupted the furnace power supply circuit to allow the bend bars to cool quickly to minimize damage and oxidation of the fracture surface. The applied stress in four-point bending was calculated using the standard equation of $\sigma_a = 3PL/4wt^2$, where σ_a is the applied stress, P is the applied load, L is the outer span of the test fixture, w is the specimen width, and t is the specimen thickness. The testing procedures were carried out by following the standard methods created by the U.S. Army and the ASTM Standard C 1161 [14,15]. Similar standard procedures have been used for testing the ORNL composite. The Optical and scanning electron microscopy (SEM) were used to characterize the microstructure of the as-received composites and the high temperature fracture surfaces as a function of stress level and test temperature.

RESULTS AND DISCUSSION

High Temperature Static Fatigue Behavior

Figure 2 shows the static fatigue results for Composite A and ORNL Nic/SiC composite at temperatures of 600 and 950°C under selected stress levels in air. The results of the ORNL composite reported previously are included as a reference [12]. The results in Fig. 2 indicated that Composite A exhibited a limited structural capability at 950°C with the lowest apparent fatigue limit of ~ 60 MPa as compared to the rest of Nic/SiC composites investigated in the current and previous studies [12]. The short lifetime obtained for Composite A was possibly a result of its high open porosity. The results for the ORNL composite without seal coat showed that the mechanical performance degradation increased with increasing the open porosity after exposure to air at 950°C for 50 h.[3] This was attributed to greater oxidation effects as the open porosity affords greater access of the air to the graphitic interface coating and fibers. In addition,

[2]H. T. Lin, Oak Ridge National Laboratory, Oak Ridge, TN, unpublished results.

[3]H. T. Lin and P. F. Becher, Oak Ridge National Laboratory, Oak Ridge, TN, unpublished results.

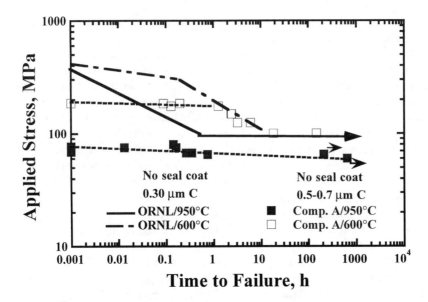

FIG. 2. Stress versus time to failure curves for Composite A and the ORNL composite tested at 600 and 950°C in air.

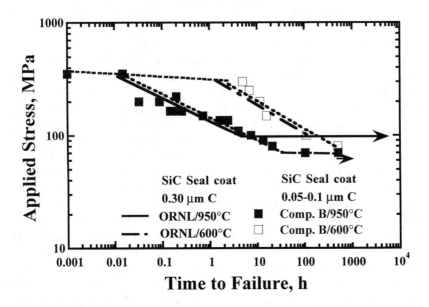

FIG. 3. Stress versus time to failure curves for Composite B and the ORNL composite tested at 600 and 950°C in air.

the presence of matrix cracks in Composite A would further enhance the ingress of oxygen and the oxidation reaction.

The performance of Composite A at 600°C improved significantly, and its performance was comparable to that of the ORNL composite at applied stresses < 200 MPa (for example, at lifetime between 1 to 10 h). Again, the low-stress carrying capability for Composite A was probably due to its high open porosity. While Composite A and the ORNL composite were tested without a SiC seal coat, this is not considered likely to be a significant factor in tests using applied stresses greater than the proportional limit at temperatures ≥ 600°C. Additional studies conducted on the ORNL composite and Composite A indicated that the seal coat provided minor or no improvement in lifetimes at temperatures of 600 and 950°C and at an applied stress above the proportional limit [12].[4]

Figure 3 summarizes the fatigue results of Composite B and the ORNL composite at temperatures of 600 and 950°C in air. In spite of the differences in interface thickness and fiber layout, the density (open porosity) and fiber content in these two composites were similar. Note that both composites were tested with an external SiC coating. The data indicated that both Composite B and the ORNL composite exhibited a similar lifetime response at both 600 and 950°C under the test conditions used. These results suggest that the lifetime response of Nic/SiC composites with a graphitic interface appears to be relatively insensitive to the interface thickness and fiber cloth layup for a similar open porosity (~ 15%). In addition, Composite B exhibited an apparent fatigue limit of ~ 70 MPa, which was lower than that obtained for the ORNL composite (~ 90 MPa). The variation in the fatigue limit between Composite B (70 MPa) and the ORNL composite (90 MPa) may arise from the difference in the fiber cloth layup.

Figures 4 and 5 show the time-to-failure results obtained for Composites C and D and the ORNL composite tested at temperatures of 600 and 950°C in air. The data showed that Composites C and D exhibited basically identical fatigue behavior under the test conditions used (Fig. 5). The results suggest that the introduction of a coating, which consists of a mixture of an oxide phase and oxidation inhibitors, between fiber cloths in Composite D does not provide any improved protective function under the applied stress level and test temperature range used. Static fatigue data (Fig. 4) also showed that Composites C and D exhibited lifetimes that were ~ 20-times longer than the ORNL composite at temperatures of 600 and 950°C in air and at an applied stress above the apparent fatigue limit. In spite of differences in matrix microstructure and fiber layup, Composites C and D exhibited a similar fatigue limit to that obtained for the ORNL composite (~ 90 MPa). The enhancement in fatigue life of both Composites C and D is presumably due to the addition of boron-containing oxidation inhibitors. The presence of oxidation inhibitors, a glass former, could react with ingress oxygen to form a boron-containing glass that could seal the cracks generated in the matrix and retard the oxidation process resulting in longer lifetimes. Nonetheless, at applied stress above the fatigue limit

[4]H. T. Lin, Oak Ridge National Laboratory, Oak Ridge, TN, unpublished results.

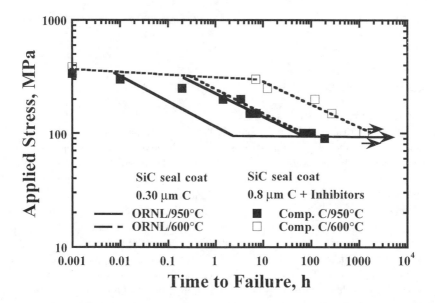

FIG. 4. Stress versus time to failure curves for Composite C and the ORNL composite tested at 600 and 950°C in air.

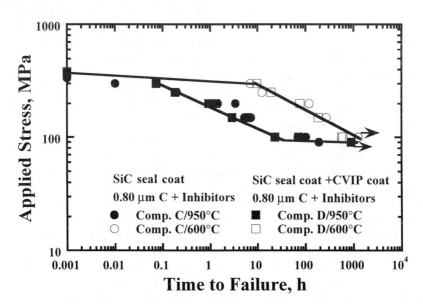

FIG. 5. Stress versus time to failure curves for Composites C and D tested at 600 and 950°C in air.

(> 90 MPa), the fatigue life of Composites C and D was still limited to < 300 h, which was only observed at 600°C.

Fatigue Damage Characterization

Previous static fatigue studies of the ORNL Nic/SiC composite with a graphitic interfacial layer indicated that the life-limiting process at elevated temperatures under stress levels above the fatigue limit was associated with the removal of the interfacial layer accompanied by the oxidation of fibers and matrix [12]. The Nic/SiC composites investigated in the present study contained graphitic interface layers with various thicknesses. It is, therefore, reasonable to anticipate that similar governing processes would occur in all the Nic/SiC composites investigated. Figure 6a shows a brittle surface feature with no fiber pullout in the tensile surface region for Composite B (with a 50- to 100-nm graphitic interfacial layer) tested at 950°C under an applied stress of 100 MPa in air. Depending upon the applied stress level and test temperature, the size of the brittle zone could vary between 50 to 80 % of the specimen cross-sectional area. Occasionally, the presence of residual interfacial graphite with limited fiber pullout could be observed in both the tensile and compressive regions for Nic/SiC composites tested at 600°C with a short fatigue life (for example, < 6 h), as shown in Fig. 6b. Similar fracture surface features as functions of stress and test temperature were also observed for Composite A and the ORNL composite [12]. At low temperatures (≤ 600°C), the oxidation of graphite was the primary process detected by thermogravimetric analysis studies [16]. However, oxidation of the Nicalon fibers was also observed by transmission electron microscopy examination in the ORNL Nic/SiC tested at 425°C in air.[5] The oxidation of the Nicalon fiber was evidenced by a formation of a skin layer of SiO_2 on the fiber surface. In this case, the strength of the Nicalon fibers will continuously decrease with time because of oxidation reaction. The final failure occurs as the applied stress exceeds the residual fracture strength of the composite.

In Composites C and D, the particulate oxidation inhibitors were mixed with a graphite precursor and subsequently applied to the fiber cloths before final SiC infiltration. Both carbon and boron-containing inhibitors are known to exhibit measurable oxidation rates at temperatures ≥ 400°C in air [8,17,18]. Figure 7a shows a representative fracture surface in the tensile surface region of Composite C tested at 950°C/100 MPa with a life of ~ 100 h. SEM observations revealed a substantial formation of boron-containing glass, as a result of the oxidation of particulate inhibitors, with no fiber pullout (brittle fracture). The presence of boron in the glass was confirmed by Auger analysis. The amount of glass formation decreased with an increase in applied stress level and a decrease in test temperature. On the other hand, sponge-like graphite caused by an oxidation reaction was also observed within the fiber bundles in both the tensile and

[5]K. L. More, Oak Ridge National Laboratory, Oak Ridge, TN, unpublished results.

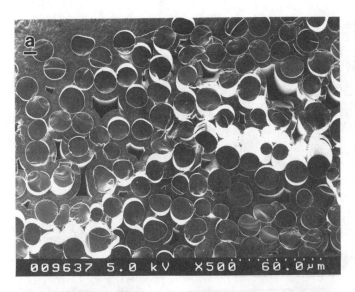

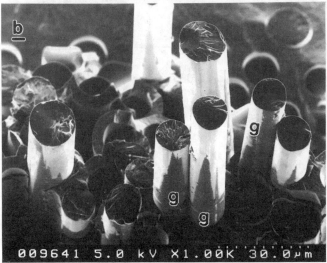

FIG. 6. Fracture surface features of Composite B tested at (a) 950°C showing brittle fracture, and (b) 600°C showing limited fiber pullout with residual graphite.

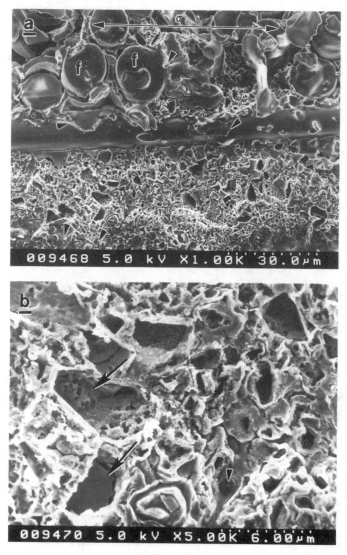

FIG. 7. Fracture surface features of Composite C tested at 950°C. (a) Brittle fracture with substantial formation of boron-containing glass as indicated by small arrows, and (b) Sponge-like graphite observed in fiber bundle associated with particulate-shaped pores due to the oxidation of inhibitors.

compressive regions (Fig. 7b). Oxidation and volatilization of particulate inhibitors [17] also occurred upon exposure to air leaving particulate-shaped pores on the surface (as seen in Fig. 7b). Oxidation of the mixture of graphite and particulate inhibitors within the fiber bundle will cause disintegration of the composite and lead to a continuous decrease in composite strength, resulting in a catastrophic failure. Fatigue results in the present study suggest that various matrix modifications, which were applied to the Nic/SiC composites investigated, can enhance the lifetime response somewhat, but further improvement in the Nic/SiC composites is needed to meet the requirements for very extended lifetime over a wide range of temperature.

SUMMARY

Static fatigue tests in flexure were conducted to study the lifetime response of four commercial Nic/SiC composites with a graphitic interfacial coating as a function of applied stress at temperatures of 600 and 950°C in air. The static fatigue results indicated that all the Nic/SiC composites, in spite of differences in interface thickness and matrix composition, exhibited similar stress-dependent failure at applied stress above the apparent fatigue limit. The lifetimes of Nic/SiC composites in an oxidizing environment increased with a decrease in both stress level and test temperature. The lifetime of Nic/SiC composites appeared to be relatively insensitive to the interface thickness and fiber cloth layup. The fatigue life was also somewhat enhanced by an introduction of particulate oxidation inhibitors. Electron microscopy and oxidation studies indicated that the fatigue life of the Nic/SiC composites investigated was governed by oxidation of the graphitic interface and the formation of glass(es) in the composite as a result of the oxidation of the fiber and matrix and any oxidation inhibitors.

ACKNOWLEDGMENTS

The authors thank Drs. P. F. Tortorelli and C. H. Hsueh for reviewing the manuscript. Research sponsored by the U.S. Department of Energy, Assistant Secretary for Energy, Efficiency and Renewable Energy, Office of Industrial Technologies, Energy Efficiency Division and Continuous Fiber Ceramic Composite Program, under Contract DE-AC05-96OR22464 with Lockheed Martin Energy Reserach Corp.

REFERENCES

[1] Lamicq, P. J., Bernhart, G. A., Dauchier, M. M., and Mace, J. G., "SiC/SiC Composite Ceramics," *American Ceramic Society Bulletin*, Vol. 65, No. 2, 1986, pp. 336-338.

[2]   Stinton, D. P., Caputo, A. J., and Lowden, R. A., "Synthesis of Fiber-Reinforced
      SiC Composites by Chemical Vapor Infiltration," *American Ceramic Society
      Bulletin*, Vol. 65, No. 2, 1986, pp. 347-350.

[3]   Filzer, E. and Gadow, R., "Fiber-Reinforced Silicon Carbide," *American Ceramic
      Society Bulletin*, Vol. 65, No. 2, 1986, pp. 326-335.

[4]   Frety, N and Boussuge, M., "Relationship Between High-Temperature
      Development of Fiber-Matrix Interfaces and the Mechanical Behavior of SiC-SiC
      Composites," *Composite Science and Technology*, Vol. 37, 1990, pp. 177-189.

[5]   Singh, D. and Singh, J. P., "Effect of High-Temperature Loading on Mechanical
      Properties on Nicalon Fibers and Nicalon Fiber/SiC Matrix Composites," *Ceramic
      Engineering & Science Proceedings*, Vol. 14, No. 9-10, 1993, pp. 1153-1164.

[6]   Nair S. V. and Wang, Y. L., "Failure Behavior of a 2-D Woven SiC Fiber/SiC Matrix
      Composite at Ambient and Elevated Temperatures," *Ceramic Engineering &
      Science Proceedings,* Vol. 13, No. 7-8, 1992, pp. 433-441.

[7]   Chulya, A., Gyekenyesi, J. Z., and Gyekenyesi, J. P., "Failure Mechanisms of 3-D
      Woven SiC/SiC Composites Under Tensile and Flexural Loading at Room and
      Elevated Temperatures," *Ceramic Engineering & Science Proceedings*, Vol. 13,
      No. 7-8, 1992, pp. 420-432.

[8]   Goto, K. S., Han, K. H., and St. Pierre, G. R., "A Review on Oxidation Kinetics of
      Carbon Fiber/Carbon Matrix Composites at High Temperature," *Transaction of
      Iron and Steel Institute in Japan*, Vol. 26, 1986, pp. 597-603.

[9]   Tortorelli, P. F., Riester, L., and Lowden, R. A., "Influence of Fiber Coatings on the
      Oxidation of Fiber-Reinforced SiC Composites," *Ceramic Engineering & Science
      Proceedings*, Vol. 14, No. 1-2, 1993, pp. 358-366.

[10] Lowden, R. A., James, R. D., and Stubbins, J. F., *ORNL/TM-11893*, Oak Ridge
      National Laboratory, Oak Ridge, TN, 1991.

[11] Raghuraman, S., Ferber, M. K., Stubbins, J. F., and Wereszczak, A. A., "Stress-
      Oxidation Tests in SiC$_f$/SiC Composites," in Advances in Ceramic-Matrix
      Composites II, Ceramic Transaction Vol. 46, J. P. Singh and N. P. Bansal, eds.,
      American Ceramic Society, Westerville, 1995, pp. 1015-1026.

[12] Lin, H. T., Becher, P. F., and Tortorelli, P. F., "Elevated Temperature Static Fatigue
      of a Nicalon Fiber-Reinforced SiC Composite," in the MRS Symposium
      Proceedings, Vol. 365, Ceramic Matrix Composites/Advanced High-Temperature
      Structural Materials, Materials Research Society, Pittsburgh, Pennsylvania 1995,
      pp. 435-440.

[13] Karnitz, M. A., Graig, D. F., and Richlen, S. L., "Continuous Fiber Ceramic
      Composite Program," *American Ceramic Society Bulletin*, Vol. 70, No. 3, 1991,
      pp. 430-435.

[14] "Flexural Strength of High Performance Ceramics at Ambient Temperature," U.S.
      Army Military Standard MIL-STD 1942 (MR). U.S. Army Materials Technology
      Laboratory, Watertown, MA., 1983.

[15] "Flexural Strength of Advanced Ceramics at Ambient Temperature," ASTM Standard C1161, American Society for Testing and Materials, Philadelphia, PA 1991.

[16] Tortorelli, P. F., Keiser, J. R., Riester, L., and Lara-Curzio, E., in "Continuous Fiber Ceramic Composites Program Task 2 Bimonthly Progress Report for June-July 1994," Oak Ridge National Laboratory, Oak Ridge, TN, 1994, pp. 51-54.

[17] Talley, C. P., "Combustion of Element Boron," *Aerospace Engineering*, Vol. 37, 1959, p. 41.

[18] Rizzo, H. F., "Oxidation of Boron at Temperatures Between 400 and 1300°C in Air," in *Boron-Synthesis, Structure, and Properties*, Proceedings of the Conference on Boron, J. A. Kohn and W. F. Nye, Eds., Plenum Press, New York, 1968, pp. 175-189.

Victoria A. Kramb[1] and Reji John[2]

FATIGUE CRACK GROWTH BEHAVIOR OF A WOVEN HPZ/SILICON CARBIDE CERAMIC MATRIX COMPOSITE

REFERENCE: Kramb, V. A. and John, R., **"Fatigue Crack Growth Behavior of a Woven HPZ/Silicon Carbide Ceramic Matrix Composite,"** Thermal and Mechanical Test Methods and Behavior of Continuous-Fiber Ceramic Composites, ASTM STP 1309, Michael G. Jenkins, Stephen T. Gonczy, Edgar Lara-Curzio, Noel E. Ashbaugh, and Larry P. Zawada, Eds., American Society for Testing and Materials, 1997.

ABSTRACT: This paper discusses the results of an investigation of the fatigue crack growth behavior of a silicon-nitrogen-carbon-oxygen/silicon carbide (HPZ/SiC) ceramic matrix composite containing an 8 harness satin weave fiber architecture. Crack growth during the tests was monitored using optical and scanning electron microscopy as well as specimen compliance. The fatigue crack growth behavior of the composite and the monolithic matrix was used to characterize the fiber bridging mechanism during fatigue loading. A shear lag crack bridging model was used to deduce the fiber/matrix interfacial shear stress during the crack propagation. The effect of fatigue loading on the predicted fiber bridging stresses and crack opening displacements are also discussed.

KEYWORDS: ceramic matrix composite, damage tolerance, fatigue crack growth, fiber bridging, shear lag analysis, woven composite

[1]Graduate Research Assistant, and [2]Research Engineer, Structural Integrity Division, University of Dayton Research Institute, 300 College Park, Dayton, OH 45469-0128.

Ceramic matrix composites (CMC) are considered to be potentially useful as hot-section components in advanced engines. These CMC components typically contain damage initiators such as notches and holes from which cracks emanate during service. Crack growth resulting from the application of cyclic loads must be understood before the implementation of a damage-tolerant-based design.   Crack growth in CMC is characterized by matrix crack growth in the presence of fiber bridging [1-10]. Therefore, the development of component life predictions using a damage tolerant design philosophy requires knowledge of the fiber bridging behavior and stress conditions along the crack. Marshall et al. [1] described the fiber-bridging stresses in a brittle matrix composite using a shear lag model as a function of the crack opening displacement, fiber/matrix interfacial shear stress, τ, and constituent properties of the fiber, matrix, and composite. The overall crack growth behavior of the composite is dominated by the strength of the fiber/matrix interface [2]. Values for τ have been obtained by several experimental methods. Pushout and pullout tests are commonly used for direct determination of τ [3]. Fiber pullout lengths [4-6], matrix crack spacing [6-8], and hysteresis loops [2, 6, 9] have also been analyzed to deduce values of τ for subsequent prediction of fiber bridging behavior. This paper discusses the determination of τ from the crack growth behavior under cyclic loading conditions. This method for deducing τ from crack growth data has been used successfully in metal matrix composites [11], but has not yet been applied to CMC. During this study, the deduced τ was used to calculate the fiber-bridging stress distribution and crack opening displacements. The effect of fatigue loading on τ, fiber-bridging stress, and crack opening displacement are also discussed.

MATERIAL

The ceramic matrix composite consisted of a silicon carbide (SiC) matrix reinforced with a silicon-nitrogen-carbon-oxygen (Si-N-C-O) fiber designated as HPZ. The average radius of the HPZ fiber, R_f, was equal to 6 μm [12]. The HPZ fiber reinforcement consisted of 1000 filament tows woven into an 8 harness satin weave cloth. The weave contained 16 ends per inch in both the warp and fill directions, with a ply lay-up of $[0/\pm60]_s$. The fibers were coated with a layer of pyrolytic carbon before depositing the silicon carbide matrix via chemical vapor infiltration. The composite overall fiber (V_f) and matrix (V_m) volume fractions were measured to be 0.41 and 0.36, respectively. The volume fraction of porosity was approximately 0.23. The modulus of the matrix (E_m), fiber (E_f), and the composite (E_c) was 439, 180 [12], and 204 GPa, respectively.

EXPERIMENTAL PROCEDURE

Fatigue crack growth tests were conducted using an automated servocontrolled hydraulic test system. The single edge notched specimen geometry with clamped ends, shown in Fig. 1(a), was used for all the tests. The specimen ends were rigidly clamped resulting in rotationally constrained end conditions. The notches were cut using a diamond saw resulting in an initial notch length, a_0 = 3.96 mm and notch width = 0.5 mm. Crack mouth opening displacement (CMOD) was measured continuously using an extensometer with quartz rods. Optical measurements of matrix crack extension were made periodically using traveling microscopes mounted to the test frame. The optical measurements were verified using scanning electron microscopy during interrupted tests.

Fatigue crack growth tests were conducted under constant applied maximum stress conditions. An initial fatigue crack growth test was conducted to determine overall composite behavior and notched failure stress. In this test, cycling began at an initial maximum stress of 21 MPa, and the stress level was periodically increased until specimen failure. Matrix crack extension was observed on the specimen surface for cyclic loading at 75 MPa. Maximum stress levels chosen for subsequent fatigue crack growth tests described in this paper were based on the results of the initial test. The crack growth test described in this paper, consisted of 12 checkout cycles conducted at a maximum stress of 18 MPa during which no matrix crack extension was observed. The checkout cycles were followed by 1 524 594 cycles at maximum stress of 75 MPa, followed by 2201 cycles at maximum stress of 85 MPa leading to specimen fracture. Load ratio, R, and cycling frequency was maintained at 0.1 and 3 Hz, respectively, throughout the tests. The overall specimen compliance was used to calculate compliance crack length. Isotropic expressions were used to calculate stress intensity factor and crack length from the compliance measurements [13].

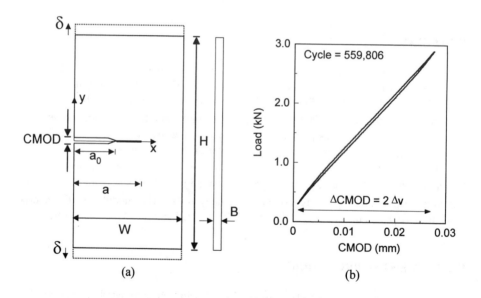

Figure 1.   (a) Schematic of single edge notched specimen with clamped ends with W = 19 mm, B = 2 mm, and H/W = 4. (b) Typical load versus CMOD response.

RESULTS AND DISCUSSION

Fatigue Crack Growth Behavior

A typical load versus CMOD response is shown in Fig. 1(b). Matrix crack extension was observed during the first 400 000 applied cycles, with most of the crack growth occurring in the first few cycles as shown in Fig. 2. Throughout the fatigue crack growth test, the compliance crack length calculated from overall specimen compliance was used to monitor the crack growth behavior as shown by the thin solid line in Fig. 2. The initial value of the compliance crack length is equal to the initial notch length, for a maximum applied stress below that which resulted in matrix cracking. At higher maximum stress levels the matrix crack growth is dominated by fiber-bridging. Therefore, the compliance based crack length was less than optical matrix crack length measured on the specimen surface. The woven nature of the HPZ/SiC composite made continuous optical measurements of matrix crack extension difficult. The compliance crack length was corrected using the periodic optical measurements and is shown as the dashed line in Fig. 2. Slight variations in the experimental data as a result of noise or test interruptions were reduced by smoothing the optically corrected compliance crack length data using a sliding polynomial fit. The smoothed crack length versus cycle data was used to calculate composite crack growth rates as a function of applied stress intensity factor range.

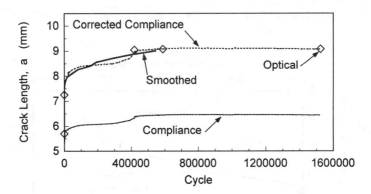

Figure 2.   Surface matrix crack growth progression with cycling at maximum applied stress of 75 MPa.

At the maximum applied stress, $\sigma_{a,max}$ = 75 MPa, a crack arrest condition occurred after about 400 000 cycles. Cycling was continued to 1 524 594 cycles, but no further increase in surface matrix crack extension and specimen compliance were observed. The crack arrest condition was also indicated by the CMOD response as shown in Fig. 3. The minimum value of CMOD ($CMOD_{min}$) shows an initial increase during the first few cycles. The value of $CMOD_{min}$ remained constant during crack growth, followed by a slight decrease during crack arrest. The maximum value of CMOD ($CMOD_{max}$) increased steadily for the first 400 000 cycles then fluctuated about a constant value for the remaining cycles at 75 MPa. The difference between $CMOD_{max}$ and $CMOD_{min}$ ($=\Delta CMOD$) showed an initial drop, because of the increase in $CMOD_{min}$, followed by a gradual increase up to 400 000 cycles. $\Delta CMOD$ remained constant for the last 1 124 594 cycles at 75 MPa consistent with the crack arrest conditions shown in Fig. 2.

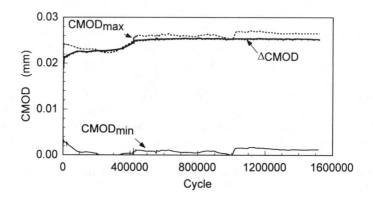

Figure 3.   CMOD progression with cycling at maximum stress of 75 MPa.

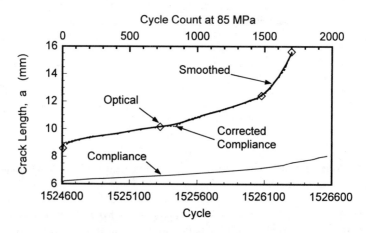

Figure 4.   Surface matrix crack growth during cycling at maximum stress of 85 MPa.

When $\sigma_{a,max}$ was increased to 85 MPa, further matrix crack extension occurred, accompanied by an increase in specimen compliance as shown in Fig. 4. The corrected data is not shown beyond 1700 cycles because optical measurements were unavailable.

The specimen failed after fatiguing at 85 MPa for 2201 cycles. The CMOD response, shown in Fig. 5, supports the crack growth data as the $CMOD_{max}$, $CMOD_{min}$, and $\Delta CMOD$ increased with applied cycles until specimen failure.

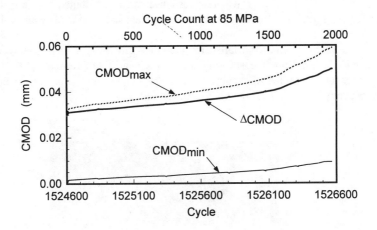

Figure 5.   CMOD progression with cycling at $\sigma_{a,max}$ = 85 MPa.

The smoothed crack length versus cycles data in Figs. 2 and 4 were used to obtain the crack growth rate (da/dN) versus applied stress intensity range (ΔK_a) response of the composite at 75 and 85 MPa, respectively.   The crack growth rate behavior of the composite and monolithic SiC [14] is shown in Fig. 6. The continually decreasing crack growth rate with increasing ΔK_a at $\sigma_{a,max}$ = 75 MPa indicates fully bridged crack growth behavior. Similar bridged crack growth behavior was also observed by Luh et al. [10] in SiC/LAS and Dauskardt et al. [15] in SiC/Al$_2$O$_3$.

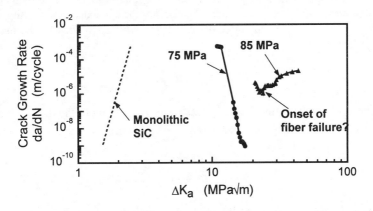

Figure 6.   Fatigue crack growth behavior of HPZ/SiC at $\sigma_{a,max}$ = 75 and 85 MPa.

When the applied stress is increased to 85 MPa, the crack is initially fully bridged, as indicated by the decreasing crack growth rate with increasing ΔK_a up to $\approx$ 22 MPa·m$^{1/2}$, followed by increase in crack growth rate leading to eventual specimen failure. The sudden increase in crack growth rate response can be attributed to the onset of fiber breakage [3,11,12]. The increase in crack growth rate started at cycle count $\approx$ 1 525 000.

The crack profile for a failed fatigue crack growth specimen is shown in Fig. 7. The crack growth from the saw-cut notch was nearly self-similar. The fiber pullout lengths for the ±60° plies were approximately the same as for the 0° plies, indicating that fiber bridging occurred in all the plies of the composite.

$\longleftrightarrow$
2.0 mm

Figure 7.   Crack profile of the failed fatigue crack growth specimen.

<u>Bridging and Effective Stress Intensity Factor Range</u>

As shown in Fig. 6, the HPZ/SiC composite exhibits significantly higher resistance to crack growth compared to monolithic SiC. The additional crack growth resistance in the composite has been attributed to the fiber-bridging mechanism [1-13,15-17]. The fibers bridging the crack reduce the effect of the applied stress intensity factor at the matrix crack tip. Thus, the effective stress intensity factor range at the matrix tip, ΔK_{tip}, can be expressed as,

$$\Delta K_{tip} = \Delta K_a - \Delta K_b \qquad (1)$$

in which ΔK_b = bridging stress intensity factor range as a result of the fibers bridging the crack wake. The crack growth behavior of the composite is correlated with that of monolithic SiC using Eq. 2.

$$\Delta K_{tip} = F_s \Delta K_m \qquad (2)$$

where ΔK_m = stress intensity factor range in monolithic SiC, and F_s is termed as a shielding factor [18]. Various investigations [1,2,10,11,14-18] have used different forms for F_s. In this study, F_s was assumed equal to 1.0, similar to the assumptions in Refs. 10,15, and 17. The crack growth behavior of monolithic SiC shown by the dashed line in Fig. 6, relates ΔK_m to the crack growth rate, da/dN, as given by Eq. 3.

$$da/dN = 8.680 \times 10^{-15} (\Delta K_m)^{27.38} \qquad (3)$$

in which da/dN is in m/cycle and ΔK_m is in $MPa \cdot m^{1/2}$. Using Eqs. 1 to 3, and assuming $F_s = 1$, ΔK_b was deduced and plotted versus cycles in Fig. 8 for $\sigma_{a,max} = 75$ MPa. ΔK_a and ΔK_{tip} are also shown in the figure. Note that logarithmic scale was chosen for the X axis to highlight the rapid changes during the initial loading cycles. ΔK_a increases with applied cycles as the matrix crack length increases. Simultaneously, ΔK_b also increases continuously, consistent with fully bridged crack growth. ΔK_{tip} is very low and decreases with increasing cycles. The decrease in ΔK_{tip} leads to decrease in crack growth rate of the matrix crack tip. Hence, the composite exhibits decreasing da/dN with increasing ΔK_a as shown in Fig. 6.

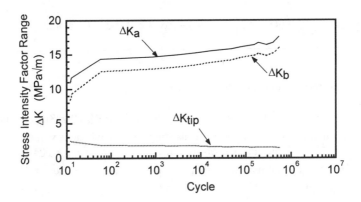

Figure 8. Deduced ΔK_b, ΔK_a and ΔK_{tip} versus cycle for $\sigma_{a,max} = 75$ MPa.

Application of a Shear Lag Model

The weight function method was used to determine ΔK_b according to Eq. 4.

$$\Delta K_b = \int_{a_o}^{a} \Delta \sigma_b(x) \, h(x,a) \, dx \qquad (4)$$

in which $\Delta\sigma_b(x)$ is the bridging stress range along the crack, x, a and a_0 are defined in Fig. 1(a), and h(x,a) is the load-independent weight function. A weight function available [13] for the single edge notched geometry with clamped ends was used for the analysis. Based on the fiber pullout mechanisms, Marshall Cox and Evans [1] derived an expression for the fiber-bridging stress. This expression was modified for cyclic loading [17] as given by Eq. 5,

$$\Delta\sigma_b(x) = \sqrt{\frac{8\,V_{fb}^2\,E_f\,\tau\,E_c}{R_f\,E_m\,V_m}}\sqrt{\Delta v} \tag{5}$$

where $\Delta v(x)$ is the half crack opening displacement range (half-ΔCOD) along the crack, V_{fb} = bridging fiber volume fraction, V_m = matrix volume fraction, E_f = fiber modulus, E_m = matrix modulus, E_c = composite modulus, τ = fiber/matrix interfacial shear stress, and R_f = fiber radius. The expression for $\Delta v(x)$ for a crack subjected to applied stress $\Delta\sigma_a$ and bridging stress range $\Delta\sigma_b$ is given by [19],

$$\Delta v(x) = \frac{1}{E'} \int_x^a \left[\int_0^{a'} h(x',a')\left\{\Delta\sigma_a(x') - \Delta\sigma_b(x')\right\}\,dx' \right] h(x,a')da' \tag{6}$$

in which E' is the orthotropic modulus of the composite.

For the application of the shear lag analysis, the $[0/\pm60]_s$ HPZ/SiC composite was modeled as an unidirectional composite consisting of an equivalent volume fraction of bridging fibers, V_{fb}. Using the rule of mixtures and assuming E_c = 204 GPa obtained from tension tests, the equivalent volume fraction was calculated as $V_{fb} = (E_c - E_m V_m)/E_f$. Thus, we obtain V_{fb} = 0.26. E' was obtained by fitting the predicted Δv at the crack mouth (x = 0) to the experimental data obtained for the first cycle at 75 MPa.

Using Eqs. 4 to 6, τ was deduced as a function of crack length and cycles for the tests conducted at 75 and 85 MPa. The iterative procedure was based on correlating the experimentally deduced ΔK_b (Fig. 8) and ΔK_b predicted using Eq. 4 within 0.5%.

The variation in deduced values of τ with applied cycles is shown in Fig. 9. The initial value of 2.6 MPa for $\sigma_{a,max}$ = 75 MPa is within the range ($2.3 \leq \tau \leq 6.1$ MPa) reported for carbon-coated SiC fiber in a silicon carbide CVI deposited matrix [20]. A rapid decay in τ occurs during the first 100 cycles and stabilizes to about 1.0 MPa. Similar decrease in the magnitude of τ with cycling has been reported in the literature [2,11,18,21,22]. When maximum stress was increased to 85 MPa, τ remained nearly constant with applied cycles. The present analysis assumes the crack is fully bridged beyond a_0. This assumption is valid for continuously decreasing values of da/dN with increasing cycles. Hence, the analysis was stopped at the cycle count corresponding to the onset of increase in crack growth rate.

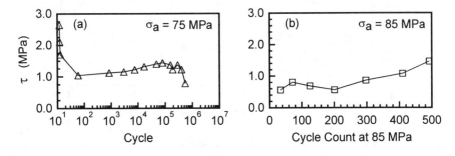

Figure 9.   Deduced τ versus cycles for maximum stress (a) 75 MPa and (b) 85 MPa.

Figure 10(a) shows the effect of increasing applied cycles on the maximum fiber stresses (at $x = a_0$) at $\sigma_{a,max}$ = 75 MPa. Note that the maximum fiber stress, $\sigma_{f,max}$ was calculated as $\sigma_{f,max} = \Delta\sigma_b/[V_{fb}(1-R)]$. As the crack grows, $\sigma_{f,max}$ decreases rapidly from 1520 MPa stabilizing at about 1050 MPa, which is lower than the reported [12] average failure strength of the HPZ fiber of 1650 MPa. Hence, the predicted fiber stresses in Fig. 10(a) are consistent with the assumption of fully bridged crack growth devoid of fiber breakage. Figure 10(b) shows $\sigma_{f,max}$ versus cycles for the test at 85 MPa. $\sigma_{f,max}$ is about the same as the test at 75 MPa up to about 400 cycles when $\sigma_{f,max}$ shows a rapidly increasing trend. Figure 11 shows the fiber-bridging stress σ_f along the crack for three crack lengths. σ_f increases rapidly from zero at the crack tip and continuously increases up to the saw-cut notch tip. Equation (5) shows that $\Delta\sigma_b$ is proportional to $\sqrt{(\Delta v)}$. Consequently, at the crack tip, $\Delta v = \sigma_f = 0$.

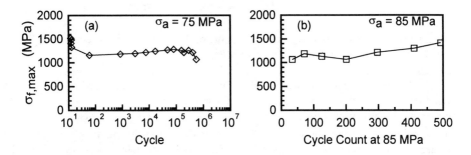

Figure 10.   Predicted maximum fiber bridging stress versus cycles at maximum stress (a) 75 MPa and (b) 85 MPa.

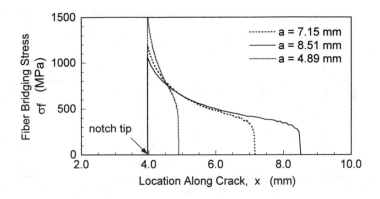

Figure 11. Predicted fiber bridging stress distributions for cycling at maximum applied stress of 75 MPa.

An independent verification of the predicted stress distribution is usually achieved by comparing the predicted and measured COD profile along the crack. The predicted half-COD range, Δv, profile for three crack lengths is shown in Fig. 12. Δv in most of the bridged region is less than 2 μm, while at the crack mouth ($x = 0$) Δv is ≈ 12 μm.

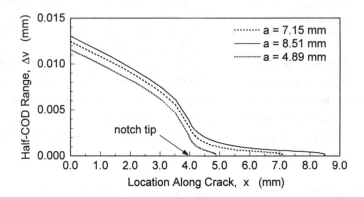

Figure 12. Half-crack opening displacement profiles for various crack lengths at maximum applied stress of 75 MPa.

The predicted and measured values of Δv at $x = 0$ are compared in Fig. 13 as a function of applied cycles. As discussed earlier, the first data point was used to determine E' assuming zero crack extension, that is, $a = a_0$. As the crack grows, the measured values deviate slightly from the predicted values in the middle range of applied cycles, but the trend is correctly predicted. The close agreement appears to validate the predicted σ_f, but the measurements are made about 4 mm away from the first bridged location. Hence, as seen in Fig. 12, Δv at $x = 0$ may not be very sensitive to changes in σ_f in the region $a_0 \leq x \leq a$. The predicted σ_f profile could be verified further if Δv can be measured along the bridged region. Similar measurements have been conducted in metal matrix composites [11,18,23].

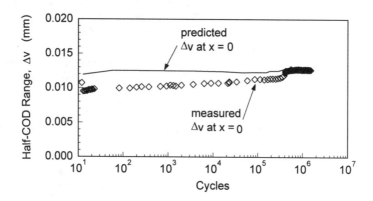

Figure 13.   Predicted and measured half-crack opening displacement range versus cycles.

The fiber-bridging analysis was also used to predict the slip length, l_s, along the crack. The slip length corresponds to the region along the fiber in which a constant τ transfers the load from the matrix to the fiber. Marshall, et al. [1] derived an expression for the slip length as,

$$l_s = \sqrt{\frac{\Delta v \, R_f \, E_f \, E_m \, V_m}{\tau \, E_c}} \qquad (7)$$

l_s calculated using Eq. 7 for different crack lengths is shown in Fig. 14. The predicted values are close to the range of values ($0.8 \leq l_s \leq 1.2$ mm) reported by Lamon et al. [20] for SiC/SiC composites.

During this study, the $[0/\pm60]_s$ woven composite was modeled as an equivalent unidirectional composite with fibers perpendicular to the crack. $\sigma_{f,max}$ and σ_f in Figs. 10 and 11 represent the stress in these unidirectional fibers constituting the volume fraction V_{fb}. To relate the equivalent unidirectional stresses to the axial fiber stresses in the composite, the corresponding stresses in each ply of the composite must be calculated. By requiring the strain in each ply of the composite to be equal to the overall composite strain, the individual ply stresses were calculated. The maximum axial stress for each fiber orientation was then calculated from the in-plane ply stress. The maximum equivalent fiber stress prior to the onset of fiber failure was ≈ 1520 MPa as shown in Fig.

10(b). Therefore, using the ply stress analysis, the axial fiber stresses in the actual composite which are equivalent to a unidirectional fiber stress of 1520 MPa are equal to 1215, 755, and 424 MPa, for fibers oriented at 0, 30, and 60° respectively. For $\sigma_{a,max}$ = 85 MPa, the predicted equivalent $\sigma_{f,max}$ is slightly lower than the reported [12] tensile strength of 1650 MPa. Consequently, the axial stresses in the 0, 30, and 60° fibers will also be lower than the tensile strength. As shown in Fig. 6, da/dN increases after approximately 500 cycles at 85 MPa suggesting the onset of fiber failure. This suggests that either the *in situ* strength of the HPZ fiber is lower than that from single fiber test or the strength of the fiber is degraded as a result of the wear induced during fatigue loading. The maximum value of strain predicted by load equilibrium was 0.015 mm/mm for a = 4.89 mm. From Figs. 12 and 14, we can estimate the strain as $\approx \Delta v/[l_s(1-R)] \approx$ 0.016 which is close to the value obtained from the load equilibrium analysis. The close agreement between these values verifies the fiber stresses estimated from the analysis.

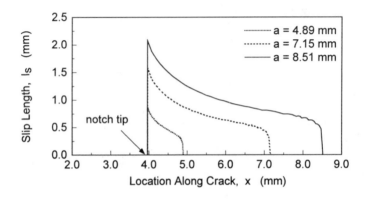

Figure 14. Predicted slip length profile for various crack lengths at a maximum applied stress of 75 MPa.

SUMMARY

The room temperature crack growth behavior of a woven HPZ/SiC composite subjected to fatigue loading at two maximum stress levels was examined. The crack growth rate decreased continuously with increasing applied stress intensity factor range at maximum applied stress of 75 MPa indicating fully bridged crack growth behavior. When the applied stress was increased to 85 MPa, the crack growth rate decreased continuously for approximately 500 cycles, indicating the crack was initially fully bridged. Further cycling at the 85 MPa maximum stress resulted in an increase in crack growth rate leading to eventual specimen failure. A shear lag crack-bridging model was used to analyze the fatigue crack growth behavior of the HPZ/SiC composite simulating the woven composite as a composite with an equivalent volume fraction of unidirectional fibers. The fiber/matrix interfacial shear stress (τ), fiber-bridging stress, slip length, and crack opening displacements were deduced from the measured crack growth behavior. During bridged crack growth, τ decreased rapidly from 2.6 MPa and stabilized at about 1.0 MPa suggesting fatigue-induced degradation of τ. The estimated fiber stresses at the onset of fiber failure were lower than the reported fiber tensile strength implying possible decrease of *in situ* fiber strength as result of wear between the matrix and the fiber during fatigue loading.

The experimental results and analysis discussed in this study demonstrate the feasibility of using the shear lag model to describe crack growth in the woven HPZ/SiC composite. These results, based on an initial test, will be used to define future test conditions and required experimental data. The approximations used to relate the unidirectional fiber bridging model to the woven composite reduce the highly complex state of woven fiber bridging behavior to a simplified unidirectional model which may be used to describe the overall crack growth behavior of the composite. Using these approximations, τ becomes a fitting parameter used to describe the crack growth behavior of the woven composite. The values of τ obtained from the shear lag analysis in this study, agree with the range of values for carbon coated SiC fibers in a SiC CVI matrix, indicating that the effect of off-axis fibers may be modeled as an equivalent volume fraction of unidirectional fibers. Accurate modeling of the crack growth behavior of the woven composite requires a shear lag model based on off-axis fibers.

ACKNOWLEDGMENT

This research was conducted at Wright Laboratory (WL/MLLN), Materials Directorate, Wright-Patterson Air Force Base, OH 45433-7817. R. John was supported under on-site Contract F33615-94-C-5200. V. A. Kramb was supported by a scholarship from the Dayton Area Graduate Studies Institute (DAGSI) and on-site Contract F33615-94-C-5200. Mr. L. P. Zawada, Wright Laboratory (WL/MLLN), provided the specimens, which were fabricated by DuPont-Lanxide, Newark, DE. The authors also gratefully acknowledge technical discussions with Dr. Noel E. Ashbaugh, University of Dayton Research Institute.

REFERENCES

[1]   Marshall, D. B., Cox, B. N., and Evans, A. G., "The Mechanics of Matrix Cracking in Brittle-Matrix Fiber Composites," Acta Metallurgica, Vol. 33, No. 11, 1985, pp. 2013-2021.

[2]   Evans, A. G., Zok, F. W., and McMeeking, R. M., "Fatigue of Ceramic Matrix Composites," Acta Metallurgica Materialia, Vol. 43, No. 3, 1995, pp. 859-875.

[3]   Bright, J. D., Shetty, D. K., Griffin, C. W., and Limaye, S. Y., "Interfacial Bonding and Friction in Silicon Carbide (Filament)-Reinforced Ceramic- and Glass-Matrix Composites," Journal of the American Ceramic Society, Vol. 72, No. 10, 1989, pp. 1891-1898.

[4]   Curtin, W. A., "Theory of Mechanical Properties of Ceramic Matrix Composites," Journal of the American Ceramic Society, Vol. 74, No. 11, 1991, pp. 2837-2845.

[5]   Thouless, M. D. and Evans, A. G., "Effects of Pull-Out on the Mechanical Properties of Ceramic Matrix Composites," Acta Metallurgica, Vol. 36, No. 3, 1994, pp. 517-522.

[6]   Beyerle, D. S., Spearing, S. M., Zok, F. W., and Evans, A. G., "Damage and Failure in Unidirectional Ceramic-Matrix Composites," Journal of the American Ceramic Society, Vol. 75, No. 10, 1992, pp. 2719-2725.

[7]   Zok, F. W., and Spearing, S. M., "Matrix Crack Spacing in Brittle Matrix Composites," Acta Metallurgica Materialia, Vol. 40, No. 8, 1992, pp. 2033-2043.

[8]   Cho, C., Holmes, J. W., and Barber, J. R., "Distribution of Matrix Cracks in a Uniaxial Ceramic Composite," Journal of the American Ceramic Society, Vol. 75, No. 2, 1992, pp. 316-324.

[9]   Cady, C., Heredia, F. E., and Evans, A. G., "In-Plane Mechanical Properties of Several Ceramic-Matrix Composites," Journal of the American Ceramic Society, Vol. 78, No. 8, 1995, pp. 2065-2078.

[10]   Luh, E. Y., Dauskardt, R. H., and Ritchie, R. O., "Cyclic Fatigue-Crack Growth Behavior of Short Cracks in SiC-Reinforced Lithium Aluminosilicate Glass-Ceramic Composite," Journal of Materials Science Letters, Vol. 9, 1990, pp. 719-725.

[11]   John, R., Kaldon, S. G. and Ashbaugh, N. E., "Applicability of Fiber Bridging Models to Describe Crack Growth in Unidirectional Titanium Matrix Composites," in Titanium Metal Matrix Composites II, WL-TR-93-4105, P. R. Smith and W. C. Revelos, Eds., Material Directorate, WL Wright-Patterson AFB, 1993, pp. 270-290.

[12]   Villalobos, G. R., Starr, T. L., Piotrowski, D. P., and Sleboda, T. J., "Advanced Dielectric Fiber Properties," in Ceramic Engineering and Science Proceedings, The American Ceramic Society, Westerville OH, Vol. 14, July-Aug. 1993, pp. 682-689.

[13]   John, R., Kaldon, S. G., Johnson, D. A., and Coker, D., "Weight Function for a Single Edge Cracked Geometry With Clamped Ends," International Journal of Fracture, Vol. 72, 1995, pp. 145-158.

[14] Dauskardt, R. H., "Cyclic Fatigue-Crack Growth in Grain Bridging Ceramics," Transactions of the American Society of Mechanical Engineers, Vol. 115, No. 7, 1993, pp. 244-251.

[15] Dauskardt, R. H., James, M. R., Porter, J. R., and Ritchie, R. O., "Cyclic Fatigue-Crack Growth in a SiC-Whisker-Reinforced Alumina Ceramic Composite: Long- and Small-Crack Behavior," Journal of the American Ceramic Society, Vol. 75, No. 4, 1992, pp. 759-771.

[16] McCartney, L. N., "Mechanics of Matrix Cracking in Brittle-Matrix Fiber-Reinforced Composites," Proceedings of the Royal Society of London, A, Vol. 409, 1987, pp. 329-350.

[17] McMeeking, R. M. and Evans, A. G., "Matrix Fatigue Cracking in Fiber Composites," Mechanics of Materials, Vol. 9, 1990, pp. 217-227.

[18] Larsen, J. M., Jira, J. R., John, R., and Ashbaugh, N. E., "Crack Bridging Effects in Notch Fatigue of SCS-6/Timetal®21S Composite Laminates," in Life Prediction Methodology for Titanium Matrix Composites, ASTM STP 1253, W. S. Johnson, J. M. Larsen, and B. N. Cox, Eds., American Society For Testing and Materials, West Conshohocken, PA, 1996.

[19] Cox, B. N. and Marshall, D. B., "The Determination of Crack Bridging Forces," International Journal of Fracture, Vol. 49, 1991, pp. 159-176.

[20] Lamon, J., Lissart, N., Rechiniac, C., Roach, D.H., and Jouin, J. M., "Micromechanical and Statistical Approach to the Behavior of CMC's," Ceramic Engineering and Science Proceedings, The American Ceramic Society, Westerville OH, Vol. 14, Nos. 9-10, 1993, pp. 1115-1124.

[21] Chan, K. S., "Effects of Interface Degradation on Fiber Bridging of Composite Fatigue Cracks," Acta Metallurgica, Vol. 41, No. 3, 1992, pp. 761-768.

[22] Rouby, D. and Reynaurd, P., "Fatigue Behavior Related to Interface Modification During Load Cycling in Ceramic-Matrix Fiber Composites," Composites Science and Technology, Vol. 48, 1993, pp. 109-118.

[23] John, R., Stibich, P. R., Johnson, D. A., and Ashbaugh, N. E., "Bridging Fiber Stress Distribution During Fatigue Crack Growth in [0]$_4$ SCS-6/Timetal®21S," Scripta Metallurgica et Materialia, Vol. 33, No. 1, 1995, pp. 75-80.

Michael J. Verrilli[1], Anthony M. Calomino[1], and David N. Brewer[2]

CREEP-RUPTURE BEHAVIOR OF A NICALON/SIC COMPOSITE

REFERENCE: Verrilli, M. J., Calomino, A. M., and Brewer, D. N., "**Creep-Rupture Behavior of a Nicalon/SiC Composite,**" Thermal and Mechanical Test Methods and Behavior of Continuous-Fiber Ceramic Composites, ASTM STP 1309, Michael G. Jenkins, Stephen T. Gonczy, Edgar Lara-Curzio, Noel E. Ashbaugh, and Larry P. Zawada, Eds., American Society for Testing and Materials, 1997.

ABSTRACT: A study of the high temperature tensile creep rupture behavior of a commercially available woven [0/90] Nicalon/SiC composite was performed. Tests were performed at temperatures of 500 to 1149°C. At a creep stress of 83 MPa, lives of less than 40 hours for temperatures above 600°C in air were obtained. At the reduced stress level of 69 MPa, lives were twice as long. However, a test conducted at 83 MPa and temperature of 982°C in vacuum yielded a run-out life of more than 1000 hours. Also, the tests performed in air have significantly shorter lives than those reported by the composite manufacturer. Post test investigations focused on identifying the mechanisms responsible for the unexpected difference in life and results are presented. Analytical modeling and supplemental testing revealed an unexpected environmentally assisted material degradation at an intermediate temperature range of 700 to 800°C. Microscopic and chemical analyses indicate that a combination of applied stress and temperature produces an oxidation-embrittlement damage mechanism. The role of the selected specimen geometry and testing conditions, which was instrumental in the detection of this failure mechanism, is thoroughly discussed.

KEYWORDS: Nicalon/SiC composites, creep-rupture, oxidation, test method, continuous fiber ceramic composite, pesting.

[1] NASA Lewis Research Center, Cleveland, OH 44135.
[2] Army Research Lab, Propulsion Directorate, Cleveland, OH 44135.

Continuous fiber ceramic composites (CFCCs) have been proposed for structural aeropropulsion applications in components such as turbine rotors, nozzles, disks, and combustors [1]. In many of these potential applications, material durability at elevated temperature is a key property for economical and safe use. Future aeropropulsion systems will require CFCCs that can retain mechanical properties and structural integrity under both cyclic and creep loading for thousands of hours.

Flexure creep is the test method of choice for CFCCs due to small material requirements and simple specimen and fixturing design. However, the stress state varies through the specimen and data interpretation is not straightforward [2].

From a design point of view, tensile creep data is preferred for stress analysis and lifetime prediction [3]. Tensile creep testing has been used to characterize the time-dependent behavior of glass-ceramic composites reinforced with SiC fibers [4-6], SiC fiber-reinforced Si_3N_4 [7] and SiC/SiC [8].

As part of an effort to characterize the high temperature mechanical performance of a model CFCC, the tensile creep-rupture behavior of a commercially available woven SiC/SiC composite was investigated. Specific objectives of this work were to identify potential failure modes and to provide an experimental database for life modeling efforts.

MATERIAL AND SPECIMEN

The material examined in this investigation is a SiC fiber-reinforced SiC matrix composite manufactured by DuPont Lanxide Composites using a chemical vapor infiltration (CVI) method. The SiC matrix contains a propriety enhancement and is reinforced by [0/90], two dimensional plain weave of ceramic grade Nicalon fibers. The fiber coating used was carbon. The composite contained eight plies.

The specimen design employed [9] is shown in Fig. 1. Note that this design has a 28 mm long gage section and uses a large transition radius (370 mm) from the gage section to the grip end to minimize stress concentrations. Specimens were machined from the Nicalon/SiC plates using diamond grinding and then CVI seal-coated to protect the machined surfaces.

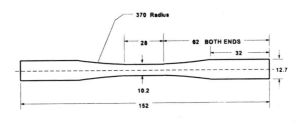

ALL DIMENSIONS ARE IN MM

Fig. 1--Schematic of the tensile creep rupture specimen.

TEST PROCEDURE

Tensile creep-rupture tests were performed in air and vacuum (10^{-5} torr) at temperatures of 500 to 1149°C with applied stress levels from 55 to 83 MPa. Electro-mechanical test machines with water-cooled wedge grips were employed for the testing. To minimize the role of load train misalignment on the creep-rupture behavior, alignment was measured and adjusted using a strain-gaged alignment bar and the recommended procedures in ASTM Standard Test Method for Monotonic Tensile Strength Testing of Continuous Fiber-Reinforced Advanced Ceramics with Solid Rectangular Cross-Section Specimens at Ambient Temperatures (C 1275). The bar, manufactured from a tool steel, contained four strain gages at three locations, one set in the middle of the specimen and the other two spaced 30 mm from the center. For any plane of measurement, the maximum bending strain was less than 5 % at a mean strain of 0.03 %. The test machine alignment was verified before, during, and after the test program.

For tests conducted in air, specimen heating was performed with inductively-heated SiC susceptors (Fig. 2). Specimens tested in vacuum were heated using a single-zone graphite-element furnace. Temperature was measured using Type R (Pt/Pt-Rh) thermocouples and controlled to within ±1°C. Beaded thermocouples, placed adjacent to the center of the specimen (Fig. 2), were used during the tests. Strain was measured using air-cooled axial extensometers of 12.5 mm gage length for air tests and water-cooled extensometers of 25 mm gage length for vacuum tests.

The axial temperature profile of specimens heated with the SiC susceptor was measured in the range of 500 to 1300°C. Eleven beaded thermocouples were used to measure the temperature profile from the center of the specimen to the point where it was gripped. In the gage section of 28 mm in length, the maximum deviation from the nominal test temperature was ±10°C.

For loading up to the creep load, a stress rate of 10 MPa/s was employed. This procedure was used to avoid possible creep life variations associated with transient stress redistribution [10].

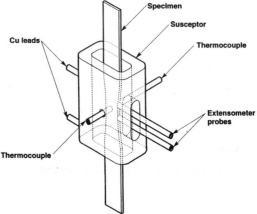

Fig. 2--Schematic of the specimen within the inductively heated susceptor assembly.

Test control and data acquisition were performed using personal computers and in-house developed software. Because the emphasis of the test program was examination of long term material behavior, the software controlled both the test machine controller and the temperature controller to assure that tests are gracefully shutdown due to failure of the specimen, the heating system, or the test machine. The software also shuts off the heating system when a specimen breaks. For a specimen tested at 1149°C, it cools to 300°C in about 5 to 10 minutes.

Standard samples of untested material were prepared in parallel with tested samples for microstructural examination. Sections of tested samples were removed by diamond slicing and placed in metallurgical mounts under vacuum. Samples were typically held under vacuum for several hours to allow pores and cavities to out gas. While still under vacuum, metallurgical samples were then covered with a florescent epoxy, removed from the vacuum chamber, and placed in a high pressure chamber with 10 MPa nitrogen to force epoxy into sample pores and damaged locations. Metallurgical samples were then lapped and polished for examination.

RESULTS AND DISCUSSION

Stress-Strain Behavior

The stress-strain behavior during loading to a creep stress of 83 MPa as a function of temperature is shown in Fig. 3. The various tensile curves are offset along the strain axis for clarity. For all temperatures, the loading curves become nonlinear as the specimens approach the creep stress of 83 MPa (some of the nonlinear nature of the higher temperature tests is due to increasing electronic noise of the data acquisition system with increasing temperature). Tensile data generated in another study by Tosi [11] revealed that the proportional limit is constant from room temperature to 1149°C. Using a strain offset of 0.005 %, the proportional limit was found be 83±6 MPa. Thus, the creep tests conducted at 83 MPa were loaded just to the proportional limit.

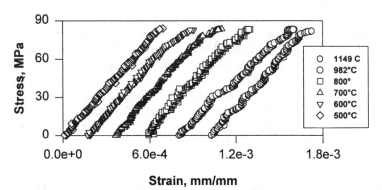

Fig. 3--Initial stress-strain behavior of Nicalon/SiC specimens loaded to a creep stress of 83 MPa.

Stress-Rupture Behavior

The stress-rupture data for the Nicalon/SiC composite between 500 and 1149°C are shown in Table 1. With the exception of one specimen (343-01-178-08), all specimens listed in this table were manufactured during the same production run, however, specimens are cut from several plates (the third number in specimen ID is the plate number). Where multiple tests were performed at a given test condition (e.g., 982°C, 83 and 69 MPa creep stress), relatively small scatter in terms of rupture time was observed. For creep stresses of 83 and 69 MPa at 982°C, the average lives are 19.3 ± 5.0 and 55.7 ± 9.8 hours, respectively. The stress-rupture data at 700, 982 and 1149°C are shown in Fig. 4. For stresses of 69 MPa and above, rupture lives were less that 100 hours, and at a stress of 55 MPa, run-out lives in excess of 1000 hours were obtained for tests conducted in laboratory air. Note that lives for 700 and 982°C are about the same. Tests performed in vacuum at 982°C and a creep stress of 83 MPa yielded run out lives of 1000 hours, but at 1149°C, the rupture time was 36 hours.

Rupture lives for a creep stress of 83 MPa as a function of temperature is shown in Fig. 5. Between 700 and 982°C, rupture time is about 24 hours. Life decreases to 5 hours at 1149°C and gradually increases to 850 hours at 500°C.

Also shown in Fig. 5 is the failure location, as measured from the center of the specimen, as a function of gage section test temperature. Failures which occur within 14 mm of the specimen center are within the straight gage section. For temperatures of 500 to 700°C, failure occurred in the center of the specimen. As the gage section temperature increased, the failure location migrated outside the gage section toward the cooler specimen ends. Failure location (inside or outside the gage section) is listed in Table 1 as well.

Creep Behavior

Creep curves as a function of temperature at a stress of 83 MPa are shown in Fig. 6. Note that most of these strain-time curves show the three regions typically observed during constant-load creep testing of metallic materials. The creep rates generally increase with temperature. The exception is the test conducted at 800°C (spec. 0007-010-24-01). From the stress-strain curve measured during loading to the creep stress, the proportional limit of this specimen was determined to be 60 MPa. As its proportional limit is 23 MPa lower than the average, this specimen contained more extensive matrix microcracking than the others tested at 83 MPa. The proportional limit of 60 MPa is nearly six standard deviations lower than the average. For this reason, data generated for this test is not considered representative of the material's performance.

Fig. 7 is a plot of the secondary creep rate, or minimum creep rate (MCR) versus temperature for a creep stress of 83 MPa. At 500°C, the MCR was about 1×10^{-7} %/sec, and it increased to 9×10^{-7} %/sec at 1149°C . The exception is the data point at 800°C as discussed above.

Creep curves as a function of stress at 982° C are shown in Fig. 8. The MCR for the 83 and 69 MPa tests are about the same, 3×10^{-7} %/sec. The specimen tested using a stress of 55 MPa was stopped at 1000 hours prior to failure, and the MCR was below the

TABLE 1-- Stress-rupture data for [0/90] Nicalon/SiC.

Specimen ID[++]	Gage Temperature [°C]	Creep Stress [MPa]	Time to Rupture [hrs*]	Test Environment	Failure Location [inside or outside gage]
0007-010-23-14	1149	83	5.75	air	outside
0007-010-23-15	1149	83	4.5	air	outside
0007-010-27-03	1149	83	36	vacuum	outside
0007-010-25-16	1100	83	13.77	air	outside
0007-010-21-04	982	83	14.78	air	outside
0007-010-21-03	982	83	23	air	outside
0007-010-21-02	982	83	15.26	air	outside
0007-010-26-18	982	83	24.25	air	outside
343-01-178-08**	982	83	26.53	air	outside
0007-010-23-16	982	83	400+	vacuum	did not fail
0007-010-21-05	982	83	1000+	vacuum	did not fail
0007-010-19-01	982	69	59.75	air	outside
0007-010-21-06	982	69	41.8	air	outside
0007-010-25-18	982	69	64.5	air	outside
0007-010-22-13	982	69	56.75	air	outside
0007-010-27-02	982	55	1000+	air	did not fail
0007-010-27-04	800	83	42.75	air	inside
0007-010-24-01	800	83	18.51	air	outside
0007-010-24-02	700	83	32.5	air	inside
0007-010-24-06	700	69	130.3	air	inside
0007-010-23-17	700	69	66.5	air	inside
0007-010-23-13	700	55	1200+	air	did not fail
0007-010-24-03	600	83	116	air	inside
0007-010-24-05	500	83	845.6	air	inside

*Failure times appended with + denote tests stopped prior to failure.
** This specimen was of the alternative geometry as shown in Fig. 10.
[++] Specimens were numbered by the composite manufacturer, DuPont Lanxide.

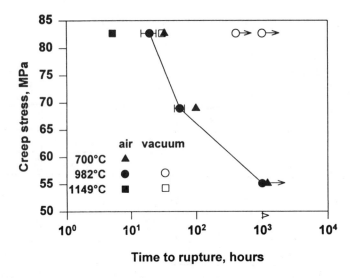

Fig. 4--Stress-rupture data for [0/90] Nicalon/SiC composite at 700, 982 and 1149°C. Arrows indicate tests interrupted prior to failure.

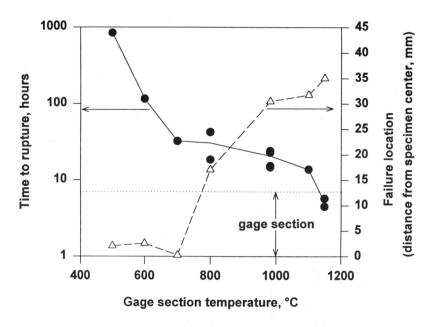

Fig. 5--Stress-rupture data for [0/90] Nicalon/SiC composite as a function of gage section temperature at a creep stress of 83 MPa. Also shown is the failure location (as measured from the center of the specimen) as a function of gage section temperature.

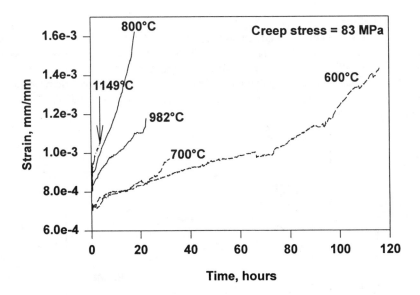

Fig. 6--Creep curves for [0/90] Nicalon/SiC at a stress of 83 MPa as a function of temperature.

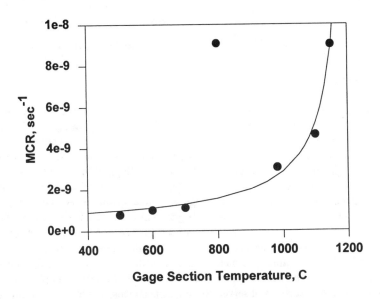

Fig. 7--Minimum creep rate (MCR) as a function of temperature for [0/90] Nicalon/SiC at a stress of 83 MPa.

resolution of the extensometry.

For tests conducted in air, the total strain to failure (that is, initial loading strain plus creep strains) was in the range of 0.08 to 0.15 % for all temperatures and stresses. For the test at 982°C and stress of 55 MPa, the maximum strain attained was 0.16 % when the test was stopped at 1000 hours prior to failure. Also, the specimen tested at 700°C and a stress of 55 MPa reached a maximum strain of 0.04 % before it was stopped after 1200 hours.

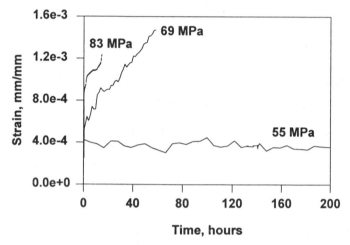

Fig. 8--Creep curves for [0/90] Nicalon/SiC at 982°C as a function of creep stress.

Failure Analysis

Initial creep rupture tests conducted at 982°C and 83 MPa yielded average lives of 19.3 hours with very narrow scatter. The average life was considerably less than that expected based on available published results for the material [3]. Specimens exhibited failure just outside the gage section, which lead to speculation that either test procedure or rig misalignment was the cause for shortened lives. Support for a thermal stress argument came from the observation that the failure location moved predictably along the specimen gage length in response to the gage section temperature. As the gage section temperature increased, the failure location began to migrate outside the gage section toward the cool ends of the specimen. At reduced gage section temperatures, generally below 800°C, specimen failure was predominately within the gage section. Failure surfaces of the creep rupture specimens exhibited brittle behavior, relatively smooth, flat surfaces with little or no observed fiber pull out. The failure surface shown in Fig. 9 is typical of the failure surfaces observed for failed specimens. Although a flat fracture surface with little fiber pull out suggests an embrittlement problem [12], microstructural examination, as discussed below, lends greater support to the existence of environmental degradation at an intermediate temperature.

The test procedure and rig alignment were checked to verify compliance with the standard for tensile testing of CFCCs (ASTM C 1275). The load train alignment was measured several times during the test program with a strain gaged specimen. In each case, a high degree of alignment was maintained, less than 5 % maximum specimen bending. Maximum bending strains were compared to those reported by Holmes for axial creep testing of unidirectional and cross ply ceramic matrix composites, including SiC/SiC [13]. After establishing that rig alignment produced bending strains within the accepted standard (ASTM C 1275), duplicate testing confirmed the initial results of shorter than expected creep life and specimen failures outside the gage section.

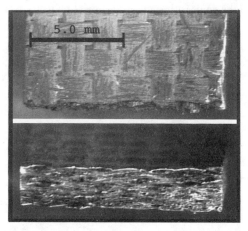

Fig. 9--Typical fracture surface of a specimen tested at 982°C.

Effect of Specimen Design

After the alignment concern was minimized, an investigation that observed lives were an artifact of the specimen design was conducted. Finite-element analyses were used in the design of the specimen to minimize the stresses that would cause failure in the transition between the gage section and the grip region [9]. However, the analysis indicated that the large (370 mm) radius (Fig. 1) could lead to failure in the transition because the net section axial stress decreases gradually from the straight gage section to the grip ends, and specimens could fail in the transition regime due to the presence of pre-existing flaws. To explore specimen geometry effects, a specimen of an alternative design, which was used to characterize the stress-rupture and fatigue behavior of this same material in another study [3], was tested. The alternate specimen was 200 mm long, 12 mm wide at the grip end, and 8 mm wide in the gage section (Fig. 10). The reduced section, including the gage section and the transition region, was 61.5 mm long, with a 40 mm long straight gage section and a transition radius of 30 mm. This specimen was tested at 982°C, using a creep stress of 83 MPa. Even though this specimen was 48 mm longer than the baseline specimen, the additional length was inserted into the grips to yield the same ungripped length. The test result is given in Table 1 (specimen no. 343-01-178-08). Even though this specimen was from a plate manufactured during a different production run, time to rupture and the failure location were the same as seen with the baseline geometry.

A study of the thermal boundary conditions was initiated after the specimen geometry investigation yielded inconclusive results. Elevated temperature testing was accomplished with an induction furnace and susceptor to provide the heating zone. As discussed earlier, the gripped specimen ends were not within the hot zone and were held by water-cooled wedge grips. The fact that the failure location migrated away from the hot gage section toward the cooler grip ends, as gage section temperature increased,

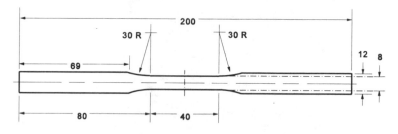

All dimensions are in millimeters.

Fig. 10 -- Schematic of the alternate tensile creep-rupture specimen.

suggested that thermally-induced axial stresses may have played a significant role in specimen life. As discussed above, the thermal profiles of test specimens were experimentally measured with thermocouples to characterize the magnitude of the gradient. The thermal gradient was found to be greatest outside furnace and near the dogbone fillet radius, near the failure location.

Various specimen designs used for CFCC's were analyzed using finite element analysis by Worthem [9]. The optimized design is the baseline employed for this study (Fig. 1). The design of this specimen was based on an isothermal finite element analyses using room temperature material properties. To estimate the thermal stresses arising from the experimentally imposed gradient, additional finite element analyses were conducted for both specimen geometries. Two dimensional, linear elastic finite element analyses were conducted using Abaqus [14]. Pre- and post processing for the finite element analyses were performed using Patran [15]. Constituent material properties used were those of the DuPont Enhanced SiC/Nicalon composite [16]. Based on the measured temperature profiles, from 500°C to 1300°C, several gage section temperatures and external boundary conditions were simulated. The resulting thermal stresses were superimposed on the applied mechanical stresses.

For gage section temperatures and applied tensile stresses used in the experimental program, thermal stresses of 15 to 20 MPa were induced in the baseline specimen, and 40 MPa in the alternate specimen design. For both specimens, the location of the maximum thermal stress varied with gage section temperature. However, the peak stresses occurred outside the observed failure locations. The increase in stress could be used to explain migration of the failure location, but it did not fully explain shorter than expected lives, since the available published results (which reported stress-rupture lives 50 times longer than we obtained under identical conditions [3]) were generated using the second specimen geometry. Furthermore, a test conducted with the second specimen geometry in our laboratory yielded the same shortened life with failure occurring in the specimen at the same temperature range. As a consequence of these tests and the results of the associated finite element modeling, the specimen geometry and the thermal gradient were discounted as the cause for unexpectedly short lives and an investigation for physical evidence of an intermediate temperature effect was initiated.

Examination of Failed Specimens

Fracture surfaces of failed creep rupture specimens were flat and exhibited little or no fiber pull-out. A typical example of a failed surface is shown in Fig. 9. The higher magnification image shown in Fig. 11 demonstrates that most fibers fractured within one or two fiber diameters near the fractured surface. Only isolated examples of modest pull-out greater than two fiber diameters was observed. It can be seen that final fracture surface was contained within one to two transverse fiber tows. Apart from suggesting that final failure was brittle in nature, fractographic examination revealed little information concerning the mechanism producing a time dependent reduction in life.

Subsequent metallurgical examinations of specimens tested in air to failure revealed both the cause for shortened life and the physical mechanisms involved. The first metallurgical examinations were completed on sections taken near the fracture surface. A 3 mm thick cross sectional slice was taken 2 mm behind the fracture surface on several failed specimens. Optical microscopy, conducted after these slices were polished, revealed several instances of fiber-matrix interface damage. The interface material between some of the longitudinal fibers and the surrounding matrix was absent. Since these sections were

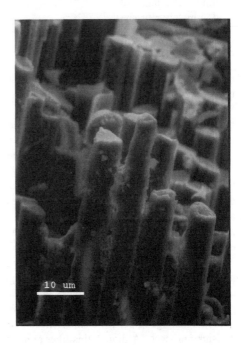

Fig. 11--Fractured fibers on typical failure surface.

taken very near the fracture surface, it was possible that this damage resulted after final failure. The carbon interface would be easily oxidized at elevated temperature after failure. However, not all of the fiber bundles near the fracture surface exhibited a loss of the interface material and previous fractographic examinations revealed that the carbon interface was intact in most of the fiber tows on the surface. Note on these metallurgical slices that fibers absent of interface material were predominately clustered

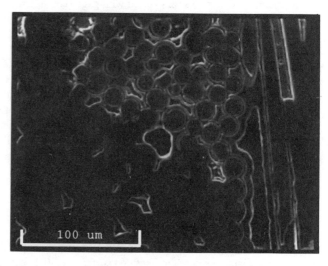

Fig. 12 -- Absence of interface material in the fiber bundle.

together as shown in Fig. 12. It was thus concluded that the removal of interface material occurred during testing, prior to final failure.

The open gap left between the fiber and matrix where interface material had been removed also appeared to be large when compared to the average thickness of the undamaged carbon interface. This observation led to the speculation that either fiber or matrix material had been lost during the test. A loss of fiber material was considered more likely than the matrix material given the difference in the quality of the two SiC materials [17]. A loss of fiber material would produce a loss of fiber radius and a resulting increase in fiber stress, assuming the axial load on the longitudinal fibers remained constant. This argument also provided a physical mechanism which explained the creep rupture failure of the material. A re-examination of the fracture surface also demonstrated evidence of fiber attack. Some of the fibers extending out from the fracture surface in Fig. 11 were also pitted. The fractured ends of several of these fibers also appear to be narrowed and rounded. This was taken as further evidence that a chemical erosion of the fiber radius plays a role in final failure.

Examples of aggressive fiber attack were commonly observed in locations where matrix cracking had occurred and allowed ingress of oxygen. The prevalence of fiber attack near surface connected cracks in the matrix suggests that an oxidation mechanism plays an active part in the damage process. With the loss of support from absent interface material, damaged fiber tows experienced extensive fiber loss during the mechanical polishing process. Although this fiber removal was an obvious artifact of the polishing process, its primary cause was testing damage since similar fiber loss was not observed in any polished samples of untested material. Photographs of a typical damaged tow and undamaged tow are shown in Fig. 13 for a 982°C creep-rupture-tested sample. At closer

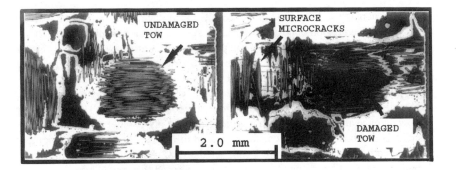

Fig. 13--Damaged and undamaged fiber bundles.

Fig. 14-- Damaged fibers with reduced radii.

examination, fibers within a damaged tow exhibited surface pitting similar to that observed on exposed fibers near the fracture surface. Fig. 14 also shows that fibers near the matrix microcrack have a reduced radius. In light of the physical evidence, the argument that reduced fiber area led to increasing fiber stress and eventual fiber failure by fracture appears reasonable.

Based on the physical metallurgical evidence and the fact that shortened life resulted at a specific temperature region between 700 and 800°C, it was decided to examine the distribution of damage from gage section center to one of the two cooled grip end. Each test specimen has two gripped ends and therefore two cooled locations opposite each other from gage center. It was assumed that both locations experienced similar thermal damage and that final failure resulted from the region which first reached criticality. The cooled region opposite the fracture surface location would provide the best opportunity to observe damage evolution prior to final failure.

Observations of the distribution of damaged fiber tows within the test gage section were taken from samples mounted and polished on planes parallel to the composite ply lay-up. The distance from gage section center to the failure location was used to establish a reference position on the sliced and polished section. The distribution of fiber tow damage along the specimen gage length in the ply-parallel metallurgical samples clearly demonstrated the cause for shortened life and the observed migration of the fracture location. Examinations were conducted on 982, 800 and 700°C samples and all exhibited extensive fiber damage. It was further observed that, as the gage temperature increased, the distribution of damage became more concentrated and migrated away from the gage section toward the cooler grip end. Dramatic evidence of extensive damage for the 700°C sample can be observed in Fig. 15. For the 700°C samples fiber tow damage was observed throughout the gage section with no apparent concentration of damage near the gripped end. Fig. 15 also demonstrates the concentration of damage observed near the cool grip end for failed 982°C samples. For these samples, damage was localized and less damage occurred within the hotter gage section.

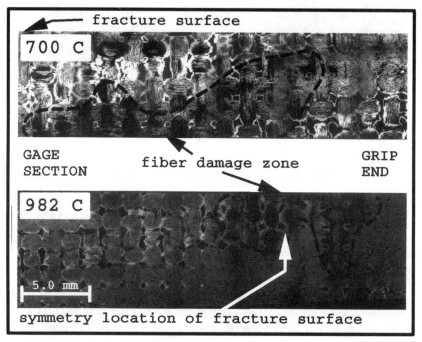

Fig. 15 -- Damage distribution for a 700 and 982°C specimen.

The combination of analytical results, stress-rupture test data, and metallurgical evidence strongly suggests the existence of a pesting phenomenon at temperatures between 700 and 800°C. Pesting is an environmentally-assisted material degradation at an intermediate temperature range. Reduced material performance at intermediate temperatures has been previously reported for other CFCCs [18,19]. In Nicalon/SiC, reduced performance was observed between 600 and 800°C [8,20].

For the DuPont Enhanced CVI SiC/Nicalon material tested here, the pesting manifests itself as oxidation and erosion of the 0° Nicalon fibers. Pesting in Nicalon/magnesium aluminosilicate and Nicalon/Al_2O_3 composites was also attributed to weakening of the fibers [19]. The matrix enhancement in this DuPont Enhanced CVI SiC/Nicalon likely plays a role in the observed pesting phenomena. At this point, the exact mechanism of pesting in this composite is unknown and under investigation. Note that the observed loss of the carbon interface and attack of the Nicalon fiber are consistent with oxidation kinetics of SiC/SiC in the temperature range of 400 to 1000°C [21]. It is suspected that the combination of stress and temperature influence the rate of pesting.

Due to the combination of the existence of the pesting and the specimen design employed, the stress-rupture lives obtained above 800°C are erroneous because failure occurs outside the gage section, at a point where the local specimen temperature is around 700 to 800°C. The measured creep rates are valid regardless of the pesting problem.

SUMMARY

The tensile creep behavior of a woven [0°/90°] SiC/SiC composite was characterized between 500 and 1149°C.

Environmentally assisted material degradation at an intermediate temperature range, or pesting, was detected for this material. Preliminary data suggests that it occurs between 700 and 800°C.

The physical evidence of pesting is an aggressive environmental attack of composite fibers resulting in pitting of exposed fiber surfaces and removal of fiber material. This attack provides a physical mechanism for the time-dependent reduction in material strength principally caused by the time-dependent reduction in fiber radius.

An analysis of test method employed revealed its robustness for investigating creep-rupture behavior. The test set up, including the specimen design, the hot zone used for laboratory air testing, and the gripping system, enabled measurement of creep behavior. This experimental technique enabled the detection of an intermediate temperature pesting phenomena.

ACKNOWLEDGMENT

The authors would like to thank John Zima and John Arnold for their invaluable efforts in setting up the test facility and conducting the tests and Dave Thomas for his support in the finite element analyses.

REFERENCES

[1]   Levine, S. R.,"Ceramics and Ceramic Composites in Future Aeronautical and Space Systems", in Flight-Vehicle Materials, Structures, and Dynamics - Assessment and Future Directions, Vol. 3, Ceramics and Ceramic-Matrix Composites, American Society of Mechanical Engineers, NY, 1992, pp. 1-17.

[2]   Wiederhorn, S. M.,"Creep and Creep Rupture of Ceramic-Matrix Composites"in Flight-Vehicle Materials, Structures, and Dynamics - Assessment and Future Directions, Vol. 3, Ceramics and Ceramic-Matrix Composites, American Society of Mechanical Engineers, NY, 1992, pp. 239-264.

[3]   Headinger, M. H., Gray, P. E., and Roach, D. H.," Lifetime Prediction Data for Enhanced Nicalon Fiber/SiC Matrix Composites," presented at Meeting of American Ceramic Society, Cocoa Beach, FL, Jan. 1995.

[4]   Wu, X. and Holmes, J. W.,"Tensile Creep and Creep-Strain Recovery Behavior of Silicon Carbide Fiber/Calcium Aluminosilicate Matrix Ceramic Composites," Journal of the American Ceramic Society, 76, Vol. 10, 1993, pp. 2695-2700.

[5]   Sutherland, S. and Lewis, M. H.," Creep Deformation of Ceramic Matrix Composites," in High-Temperature Ceramic-Matrix Composites I: Design, Durability, and Performance, A. G. Evans and R. Naslain, Eds., Ceramic Transactions, Vol. 57, 1995, pp. 357-362.

[6]   Doreau, F., Gilbert, F., Vicens, J., and Chermant, J. L.,"On Creep Behavior of SiC_f - YMAS Composites", in High-Temperature Ceramic-Matrix Composites I: Design, Durability, and Performance, A. G. Evans and R. Naslain, Eds., Ceramic Transactions, Vol. 57, 1995, pp. 363-368.

[7]   Holmes, J. W. and Jones, J. W.,"Tensile Creep Behavior of SCS-6 SiC Fiber Si_3N_4-Matrix Composites," HITEMP Review, NASA C.R. 10104, Oct. 1992.

[8]   Schläefer, C. E.,"Mechanical Behavior of SiC/SiC Composites During High Temperature Creep Experiments", Masters thesis, University of California, Santa Barbara, Dec., 1993.

[9]   Worthem, D. W.,"Flat Tensile Specimen Design for Advanced Composites," NASA C.R. 185261, Nov. 1990.

[10] Chermant, J. L., and Holmes, J.," Elevated Temperature Creep and Cyclic Creep Behavior of Fiber Reinforced Ceramics", in High-Temperature Ceramic-Matrix Composites I: Design, Durability, and Performance, A. G. Evans and R. Naslain, Eds., Ceramic Transactions, Vol. 57, 1995, pp. 95-106.

[11]   Tosi, K., Pratt and Whitney, West Palm Beach, FL., 1996, unpublished work.

[12]   Nutt, S. R..,"Environmental Effects on High Temperature Mechanical Behavior of Ceramic Matrix Composites", in High Temperature Mechanical Behavior of Ceramic Composites, S. V. Nair and K. Jakus, Eds., Butterworth-Heinemann, Publisher, 1995, pp.365-406.

[13]   Holmes, J. W.,"A Technique for Tensile Fatigue and Creep Testing of Fiber-Reinforced Ceramics," Journal of Composite Materials, Vol. 26, No. 6, 1992.

[14]   Abaqus, User's Guide, Hibbit, Karlsson and Sorensen, Inc., Pawtucket, RI, 1994.

[15]   PDA/Patran III, User's Guide, PDA Engineering, Santa Ana, CA 1994.

[16]   DuPont Lanxide Composites, Inc., Newark, DE., literature on Enhanced SiC/SiC.

[17]   Brennan, J. J.,"Interfacial Characterization of Glass and Glass-Ceramic Matrix/Nicalon SiC Fiber Composites", in Tailoring Multiphase and Composite Ceramics, Materials Science Research, Vol. 20, 1986, pp. 549-560.

[18]   Prewo, K. M.,"Fatigue and Stress Rupture of Silicon Carbide Reinforced Glass Ceramics", Journal of Material Science, Vol. 22, Aug. 1987, pp. 2695-2701.

[19]   Wetherhold, R.. C. and Zawada, L. P.,"Heat Treatments as a Method of Protection for a Ceramic Fiber-Glass Matrix Composite", American Ceramic Society, Communications, Vol. 24, Aug. 1991, pp. 1997-2000.

[20]   Heredia, F. E., McNulty, J. C., Zok, F. W., and Evans, A. G.," An Oxidation Embrittlement Probe for Ceramic Matrix Composites", Journal of the American Ceramic Society, 78, Vol.8, 1995, pp. 2097-2100.

[21]   Naslain, R., "Two-dimensional SiC/SiC Composites Processed According to the Isobaric-Isothermal Chemical Vapor Infiltration Gas Phase Route", Journal of Alloys and Compounds, Vol. 188, 1992, pp. 42-48.

Kurt L. Munson[1] and Michael G. Jenkins[2]

RETAINED TENSILE PROPERTIES AND PERFORMANCE OF AN OXIDE-MATRIX CONTINUOUS-FIBER CERAMIC COMPOSITE AFTER ELEVATED-TEMPERATURE EXPOSURE IN AMBIENT AIR

REFERENCE: Munson, K. L. and Jenkins, M. G., "Retained Tensile Properties and Performance of an Oxide-Matrix Continuous- Fiber Ceramic Composite after Elevated-Temperature Exposure in Ambient Air," Thermal and Mechanical Test Methods and Behavior of Continuous-Fiber Ceramic Composites, ASTM STP 1309, Michael G. Jenkins, Stephen T. Gonczy, Edgar Lara-Curzio, Noel E. Ashbaugh, and Larry P. Zawada, Eds., American Society for Testing and Materials, 1997.

ABSTRACT: An oxide-matrix continuous-fiber ceramic composite (CFCC) reinforced with Si-C-O (Nicalon™) fibers coated with an oxidation-resistant SiC/BN interphase was investigated for its resistance to elevated-temperature degradation. Tensile specimens at zero load were exposed to ambient air environments at 800 and 1000°C for 1, 24, and 100 h. Room-temperature tension tests of the exposed specimens were conducted per ASTM Test Method for Monotonic Tensile Strength Testing of Continuous Fiber-Reinforced Advanced Ceramics with Solid Rectangular Cross Section Specimens at Ambient Temperatures (C 1275) at 0.003 mm/s to ascertain retained mechanical properties. While elastic constants and strengths decreased on the order of 10 to 55%, the modulus of toughness, a direct measure of the inherent damage tolerance of CFCCs, decreased 90%. For example, elastic modulus decreased with exposure temperature and time from 150 GPa in the as-received condition to ~135 GPa after exposure at 1000°C. Proportional limit stress decreased from 42 MPa in the as-received condition to 22 MPa after exposure to 1000°C. Ultimate tensile strength decreased from 244 MPa in the as-received condition to 107 MPa after exposure to 1000°C. Finally, modulus of toughness decreased from 1062 kJ/m^3 in the as-received condition to 113 kJ/m^3 after exposure to 1000°C. The Nicalon™ fibers showed some degradation effects of elevated-temperature exposure. Fractography revealed damage to both the fibers and matrix. Brittle fracture (accompanied by minimal fiber pullout) was the dominant failure mode at after exposure to all elevated temperatures.

KEYWORDS: continuous fiber ceramic composite, oxide matrix, tensile test, elevated-temperature exposure, bending, proportional limit stress, ultimate tensile strength

Continuous-fiber ceramic composites (CFCCs) are being proposed for numerous industrial applications in which the elevated-temperature properties of ceramics are required along with the inherent damage tolerance (and increased reliability) of CFCCs [1]. CFCCs have the

---

[1] Associate engineer, EG&G Structural Kinematics Inc, Troy, MI 48084.

[2] Assistant professor, Department of Mechanical Engineering, University of Washington, Seattle, WA 98195-2600.

potential of much greater resistance to catastrophic failure than their
monolithic counterparts while retaining the elevated-temperature
strengths, corrosion/erosion resistances, high stiffnesses, and low
densities characteristic of ceramics in general [2-4]. Therefore, CFCCs
offer greater "toughness," increasing reliability by reducing fracture
sensitivity to inherent defects, impact and contact damage, or thermal
shock. "Toughness" in this case is not necessarily the resistance to
the initiation of the fracture process, but rather the ability of the
material to absorb energy without fracturing into pieces.

Figure 1 shows a relative comparison of two stress-strain curves:
one for a monolithic ceramic and the other for a CFCC. While the
strength of the CFCC is not as great as that of the monolith, the
greater "toughness" (i.e., area under the entire stress-strain curve)
and hence inherent damage tolerance of the CFCC is obvious from the
extent of the area under the curve.

Applications of CFCCs cover a wide range of industrial sectors [1]
and tend to encompass those applications that involve elevated
temperatures and corrosive environments. Filters, substrates, piping
and tanks are possible applications for separation/filtration and
chemical reactor areas. Incinerators and combustors can utilize burners
and heat pipes fabricated from CFCCs. Tubes and supports can be used in
heat recovery systems. Combustor liners, vanes, and nozzles are
possible applications in heat engines.

Soon after the development and investigation of CFCCs as a subset
of ceramic matrix composites, researchers noted that the primary
mechanisms of "toughening" required a controlled debonding and pullout
of fibers in the matrix [5-11]. Fibers that did not debond led to
brittle fracture and little to no toughening. Fibers that were not
bonded at all did not bridge matrix cracks and did not absorb fracture
energy since they did not pull out.

Thus, an important aspect of CFCCs, in addition to the reinforcing
fibers and the matrix, is the third major component of ceramic
composites, the interphase. The interphase is typically a low-strength
material that adheres to and separates the matrix and fiber thus,
promoting debonding and pullout of the fibers. In SiC fiber-reinforced
SiC matrix CFCCs, the interphase is generally a pyrolytic carbon that

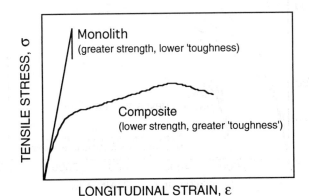

FIG 1--Comparison of stress-strain curves for monolithic and composite
ceramics.

can be a applied to the fiber preform via chemical vapor infiltration (CVI) [12]. However, the carbon interphase is susceptible to oxidation at elevated temperatures (>600°C). The resulting reaction first causes the carbon to oxidize into CO and CO_2 and then causes free Si to form a brittle SiO_2 layer in place of the carbon interphase. The net result is embrittlement of the CFCC and loss of "toughness" at elevated temperatures as shown in Fig. 2. Figure 2 illustrates the truncated stress-strain curves for a SiC/SiC CFCC with a carbon interphase material tested at 1000°C and compared to stress-strain curves for the same material tested at 20°C [13].

Recent work has concentrated on developing oxidation resistant interphase materials [14,15] such as mullite, $AlTiO_5$, Al_2O_3, Sn_2O_3, BN, TiB_2, and porous SiC. In addition, emphasis has also been placed on developing CFCCs with oxidation resistant matrices and fibers such as Al_2O_3 fibers and Al_2O_3 matrices. Commercial materials [16,17] are beginning to appear that hold the promise of oxidation resistant CFCCs by incorporating oxidation-resistant interphases (BN), oxidation-resistant fibers (polycrystalline Al_2O_3 such as Nextel™), and oxidation-resistant matrices (melt-infiltration Al_2O_3 such as DIMOX™). While tests have been conducted on these materials to determine mechanical properties at short-term elevated temperatures [16,17], few studies have been conducted to assess the effects of long-term exposures to elevated temperatures. In this study, the retained mechanical properties and performance of an Al_2O_3 matrix CFCC at room temperature after exposure to elevated temperatures in ambient air are investigated.

The material is briefly described followed by an overview of the experimental procedure. Test results are presented in terms of stress-strain response, proportional limit stress, ultimate tensile strength, and modulus of toughness. The effect of bending on proportional limit stress and ultimate tensile strength is discussed. Fractographic analyses are presented to illustrate aspects of the material performance.

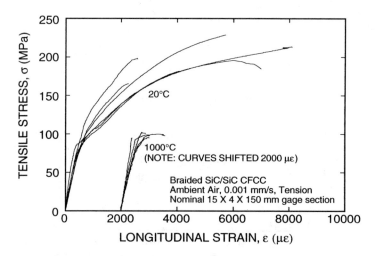

FIG 2--Comparison of engineering stress-strain curves at 20 and 1000°C in tension for an SiC/SiC CFCC with a pyrolytic carbon interphase, showing the embrittlement of the CFCC at elevated temperature [13].

TEST MATERIAL

A non-commercial, trial CFCC was the focus of this study. The reinforcing fibers were a ceramic grade Si-C-O (Nicalon™) fiber. Two-dimensionally reinforced, plain woven cloths were fabricated using fiber bundles (~500 fibers/bundle) by the fiber producer. The fiber preforms were fabricated by the CFCC manufacturer by layering twelve plies of cloth.

Processing the matrix included the following steps [16,17]. First a ~0.3 to 5 μm interfacial duplex layer of BN and SiC was deposited by CVI onto the fiber preform. The inner BN layer provides the weak fiber/matrix interface that is essential for achieving the desired toughness and non-catastrophic failure. The outer SiC coating protects the inner BN layer and/or fiber from oxidation and reaction with the molten aluminum during the subsequent matrix growth processing step.

The second processing step involved the directed oxidation of molten aluminum alloy to provide a three-dimensionally interconnected matrix of Al_2O_3. The Al_2O_3 grew into the open spaces of the coated fiber preform when it was brought into contact with a molten aluminum alloy at temperatures of 900 to 1000°C in air. The growth of the oxide was sustained by the presence of an interconnected network of microscopic metal channels in the matrix phase. In this way, net or near net shape fabrication could be achieved.

Following matrix growth, residual metal normally remained, predominantly in the form of a three-dimensional interconnected network. Usually, this residual metal was removed via a proprietary wicking process that resulted in the formation of fine, uniformly distributed microchannels of porosity comprising ~20 to 25 vol% of the composite. However, the material tested in this study was not only non commercial but also non standard in that an unquantified amount of residual metal unintentionally remained in the matrix. As will be discussed, this residual metal may have.affected the test results. Approximate volume fractions of fibers and matrix were 30 to 35% and 40 to 45%, respectively.

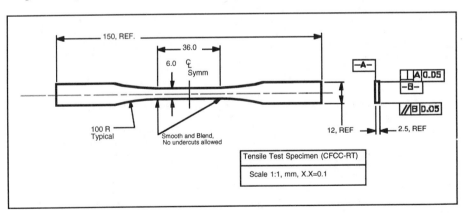

FIG. 3--Reduced gage section tensile specimen fabricated via abrasive water jet cutting.

A previous study [18] has shown no statistically-significant effect (i.e., analysis of variation at 95% significance level) of specimen geometry on the tensile mechanical behaviour of a two dimensionally-reinforced SiC fiber/SiC matrix CFCC. Therefore, in the present study only one specimen geometry was employed. To promote gage section failures, reduced gage section (i.e. dog bone) specimens (Fig. 3) were fabricated to the dimensions shown in the figure. All specimens were twelve plies thick, equivalent to ~2.5 to 3.4 mm.

The novel material-removal technique of abrasive water jet (AWJ) cutting was employed to reduce fabrication costs and times. The AWJ cutting conditions included 80-mesh garnet at 0.22 to 0.33 kg/min and 380 MPa of water pressure through a 0.33 mm orifice and 1 mm nozzle. As will be discussed, an unforeseen complication of the use of AWJ with CFCCs containing hygroscopic constituents such as BN is the degradation of the CFCC at elevated temperatures after impingement with the high pressure water of the AWJ process.

Tapered end tabs comprised of an E-glass fiber/epoxy matrix composite were used to protect the specimens from being damaged (e.g., splitting as a result of the contact of the grip surface with the specimen) at the area within the hydraulic grips. The ratio for the resin and curing agent was so chosen to produce an adhesive with a shear strength greater than ~10 MPa, the maximum interfacial shear stress anticipated at the interface of the tab and specimen.

EXPERIMENTAL PROCEDURE

All tests were conducted at ambient temperatures (20 to 22°C, 55 to 65 %RH) in accordance with ASTM Test Method for Monotonic Tensile Strength Testing of Continuous Fiber-Reinforced Advanced Ceramics with Solid Rectangular Cross Section Specimens at Ambient Temperatures (C 1275). A commercial, single-actuator, electromechanical materials test system (100-kN capacity) having load, stroke, strain, or special channel-limited-channel control capabilities was used with the digital controller and related software assembling all input and output signals.

The test system included an interchangeable specimen grip system capable of 31 kN in monotonic loading. The hydraulically-actuated grip system was independently activated and could maintain an adjustable grip force on the specimen grip face without backlash. Grips were attached to the load frame via a fixed, but adjustable, commercially-available alignment system.

As per ASTM Test Method C 1275 load-train alignment was performed prior to and at the completion of testing to assure less than 5 percent bending (PB) at an average strain of 500 x 10^{-6} m/m in the alignment specimen. The steel alignment specimen was 200 mm in length and had a 35-mm-long reduced gage section with a 6 by 6 mm cross section. Eight longitudinal strain gages were adhered at two longitudinal planes (four strain gages equispaced around the circumference on each plane).

Strain was measured using a dual-arm, strain-gage based extensometer, Axis A and Axis B, at gage lengths of 25 mm with ranges of +50000 x 10^{-6} to -20000 x 10^{-6} m/m strain (see Fig. 4). Separate but continuous strain values were returned for two opposing sides of the specimen. PB (in this case, out-of-plane bending only) was calculated as:

$$PB = 100\frac{(\varepsilon_A - \varepsilon_B)}{(\varepsilon_A + \varepsilon_B)} \tag{1}$$

where PB is percent bending, ε_A is the strain from Axis A, and ε_B is the strain from Axis B.

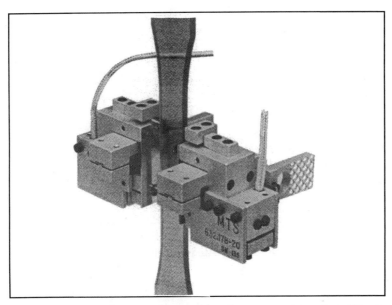

FIG. 4--Dual extensometer mounted on a polymer specimen for illustrative purposes. Note that for tests of CFCCs the extensometer was mounted on the specimen faces.

Elevated temperatures were obtained using a unique "ignitor" furnace. This furnace, which measures ~150 by ~150 mm in width and length and ~100 mm in height, is resistance-heated over a 50-mm hot zone by four commercial "ignitor" elements used in natural gas appliances. These "ignitors" draw a maximum of ~4 A each at 120 V and provide a maximum temperature of ~1400°C at heating rates of 10 to 25 °C/s.

When exposed to temperature, the specimens were held by the top grip only and heated to the exposure temperature in 5 to 10 min, after which time the temperature was held constant to ±2°C for the duration of the test. Hold times were 1, 24, and 100 h. At the completion of the hold time, the furnace power was removed and the specimens were allowed to cool naturally in the ambient air.

Two as-received specimens each were tested in cross-head displacement (0.003 mm/s) and load control (50 N/s) to ascertain the effect of test mode on the tensile behavior. Two specimens at each condition were exposed to elevated temperatures and then tested only in cross-head displacement control (0.003 mm/s) at room temperature.

RESULTS

The stress-strain response is the primary means for obtaining and analyzing performance data. For this study, the stress-strain response was generally linear up to the proportional limit stress, σ_0 (~matrix cracking stress), after which the stress would increase at a much slower rate to the ultimate strength. For the most part the fracture stress corresponded to the ultimate stress. In addition to the proportional limit stress, the elastic modulus, E, ultimate tensile strength, S_u,

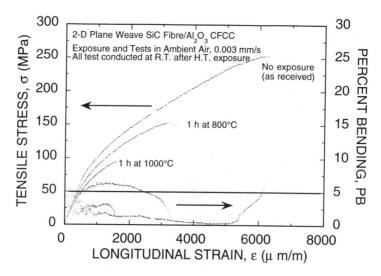

FIG. 5--Actual stress-strain and percent bending-strain curves.

fracture strength, S_F, and corresponding strain values, (ε_O, ε_U, and ε_F), along with the modulus of toughness, U_T, can be extracted from the stress-strain curve as detailed in ASTM Test Method C 1275. Figure 5 shows actual curves of stress versus strain with superposed curves of percent bending versus strain for specimens tested at room temperature in the as-received condition and after 1 h exposure at 800 and 1000°C.

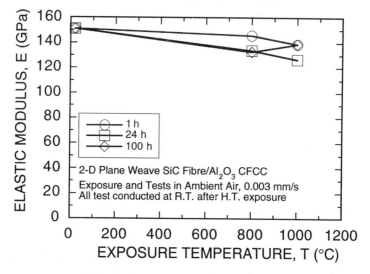

FIG. 6--Elastic modulus versus exposure temperature.

Elastic modulus can be used as an indicator of the cumulative damage within the material. Generally, E decreases as cumulative damage increases, and the life of the material decreases.   In these tests, for consistency, elastic modulus was determined as the slope of the linear, least-squares regression of the stress-strain curve from 0 to 15 MPa. The fixed value of 15 MPa was chosen as it represented the least value at the onset of non linearity observed in the tests. Elastic modulus is plotted as a function of exposure temperature in Fig. 6.   Elastic modulus decreases with increasing exposure temperature, but shows no strong apparent effect of exposure time.

Although ASTM Test Method C 1275 recommends two methods for determining the proportional limit (PL) stress (stress at an offset strain and stress at a prescribed strain), for reasons of consistency [18] the PL stress in this study was calculated as follows:

$$\sigma = \text{PL when } \frac{(\sigma_i - \sigma)}{\sigma} x 100 \geq 10\% \qquad (2)$$

where σ_i is the stress calculated from the elastic modulus, E, and the corresponding strain, ε_i, at the ith datum such that $\sigma_i = E\varepsilon_i$, and σ is the actual stress at the ith strain. The PL is the point at which the difference between the actual stress and the calculated stress is equal to 10%. Although a recent study [19] has shown that matrix cracking measured by acoustic emission may occur at tensile stresses of less than one half of the macroscopically-observed PL stress in a two-dimensionally reinforced SiC fiber / SiC matrix CFCC, it can be argued that the PL is the most important design parameter because it defines the macroscopically observable stress or strain corresponding to the onset of damage in the composite. Thus, the PL stress can be used to define the maximum allowable stress for design purposes.   Figure 7 illustrates the decrease of PL stress with increasing temperature of exposure.   Note that PL stress appears independent of exposure time at 1000°C, indicating that any temperature-dependent damage occurs within the first one hour of exposure.

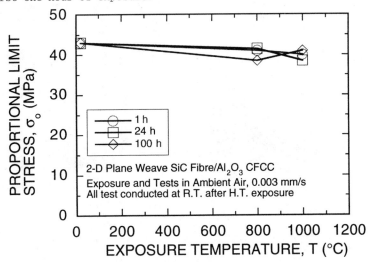

FIG. 7--Proportional limit stress versus exposure temperature.

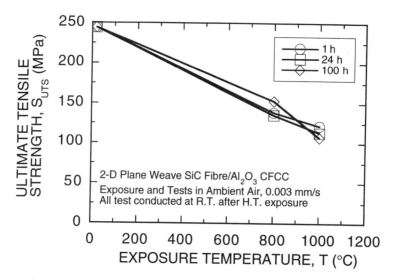

FIG. 8-- Ultimate tensile strength versus exposure temperature.

As was found with the PL stress, the ultimate tensile strength shows a dependence on exposure temperature but not necessarily a dependence on exposure time (Fig. 7). The ultimate strength is an important characteristic when comparing most materials and may be used intuitively to compare and select a material for "engineering" design. At the ultimate tensile strength, the load is carried almost entirely by the fibers and, therefore, often coincides with the fracture strength, S_F, of the composite. Although the load is carried by the fibers at S_U, an accurate measure of the fiber strength within the composite is difficult since physical and chemical degradation may occur during fabrication. The ultimate tensile strength is plotted versus exposure temperature in Fig. 8.

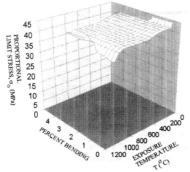

a) Proportional limit stress

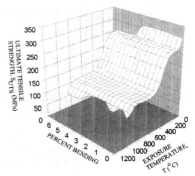

b) Ultimate tensile strength

FIG 9--Strength as a function of percent bending and exposure temperature: (a) proportional limit stress and (b) ultimate tensile strength.

The use of a dual-arm extensometer made it possible to calculate the amount of bending in each specimen. The percent bending was calculated to compare the uniformity of uniaxial tensile stress on the material properties. However, because strengths generally decreased with increasing exposure temperature, it is not possible to evaluate strength as a function of bending alone.

Instead, PL stress and ultimate tensile strengths are plotted as functions of percent bending and exposure temperature as shown in Figs. 9a and 9b, respectively. Interpolated surface plots are used to illustrate the trends. For both PL stress and ultimate tensile strength, a decreasing trend with increasing exposure temperature is obvious although the effect of bending is not obvious for the bending less than 7% observed in these limited tests. Previous tension tests of CFCCs [18] have shown that PL stress, which is the macroscopic manifestation of matrix cracking stress, decreases with increasing percent bending, as expected for the fracture stress of a brittle matrix. Ultimate tensile strengths showed little effect of increasing percent bending, as expected for the fiber-dominated ultimate tensile strength [18].

Figure 10 shows the effect of exposure temperature on modulus of toughness, U_T where:

$$U_T = \int_0^{\varepsilon_f} \sigma \, d\varepsilon \qquad (3)$$

in which ε_f is the strain at fracture and σ and ε are the stress and strains from the stress-strain curves, respectively. U_T is the area under the stress-strain curve and, therefore, represents the energy absorbed during the tensile deformation and failure of the material. Note in Fig. 10, that after exposure to 1000°C U_T decreases to only 10% of its value at room temperature. Decrease in U_T indicates loss of damage tolerance, with subsequent embrittlement of the CFCC.

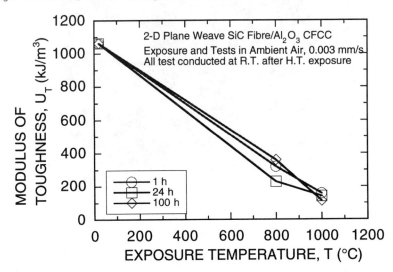

FIG 10--Modulus of toughness versus exposure temperature.

DISCUSSION

Material availability limited the number of replicate tests at each condition. Thus, data points in Figs. 6 through 10 represent averages or single data points. Error bars are not shown for clarity in these plots. Note that significant scatter (ranges of up to ± 20% about the mean for strengths and ranges up to ±50% about the mean for modulus of toughness) was noted at conditions where replicate tests were conducted. Therefore, only the trends of decreasing properties with increasing exposure temperature as shown in Figs. 6 through 10 should be viewed as significant. Any trends associated with exposure time at each of the temperatures cannot be discerned or inferred.

Extensive scanning electron microscope (SEM) fractography was conducted to link failure mechanisms with the trends in Figs. 6 through 10. Figure 11 shows evidence of extensive fiber debond and pullout as well as transgranular, cleavage fracture of the fibers for the room temperature tests. Such mechanisms are reflected in the high elastic modulus, proportional limits, ultimate tensile strength and modulus of toughness all at room temperature in Figs. 6 through 10.

Figures 12 and 13 (after 100 h at 800 and 1000°C) show almost no fiber pullout, extensive matrix cracking, and intergranular fracture of fibers point to generalized degradation of the composite, including fibers, matrix, and interphase. Such evidence supports the trends of decreasing properties with increasing exposure temperature as shown in Figs. 6 through 10. The fiber coating appears to have remained intact, not permitting debonding and leading to embrittlement of the of CFCC and fibers.

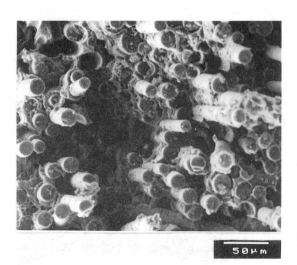

FIG 11--SEM micrographs of a fracture surface at room temperature.

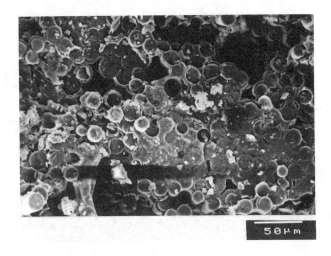

FIG 12--SEM micrographs of a fracture surface after 100 h at 800°C.

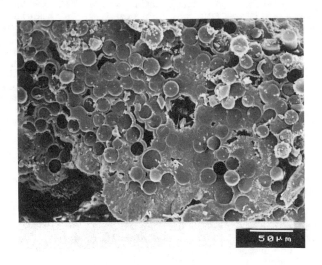

FIG 13--SEM micrographs of a fracture surface after 100 h at 1000°C.

It is worth noting that oxide matrices and BN coatings have been shown in recent unpublished studies to be highly hygroscopic. This tendency would be expected to be exacerbated by the AWJ cutting employed to fabricate the tensile specimens. The extensive matrix cracking and apparent brittle fracture of the fibers (lack of fiber dedonding) supports the notion of hygroscopic materials degrading upon exposure to elevated temperatures. Further materials analyses are necessary to confirm this conclusion.

In addition, rudimentary micromechanical modeling [20] of this material system shows that the matrix microcracks during processing as a result of thermal coefficient mismatch between the matrix and fiber. These microcracks open when the material is reheated during the elevated-temperature tests, exposing the interphase and fiber to the molten, unintentional residual metal in this non standard material. This molten metal (aluminum) is highly reactive at the exposure temperatures of 800 to 1000°C and could degrade the matrix and fibers, leading to loss of structural integrity and decreases in performance.

However, it is not clear from the present study which scenario (degradation of the hygroscopic BN interphase due to AWJ cutting or reaction of molten, residual metal with the interphase and matrix) led to the degradation of this material and the subsequent decrease in tensile properties and performance. Planned, future studies of this material systems are planned to clarify these issues.

CONCLUSIONS

Basic information about the tensile mechanical behavior of an non standard oxide-matrix CFCC was obtained. In general, retained mechanical properties after elevated-temperature exposure showed decreasing trends with increasing exposure temperature. Limited replicate tests and scatter in the data prevented any definite conclusions from being made about the effect of exposure time at temperature on mechanical properties and performance. However, fractography revealed that as exposure temperature increased, fiber pullout decreased while matrix cracking and embrittlement of fibers increased. Recent unpublished studies have shown the matrix and fiber coating to be highly hygroscopic, a tendency exacerbated by the abrasive water jet cutting of the tensile specimens. Therefore, the water-exposed oxide-based matrix when combined with the SiC fibers and BN interphase appeared to be degraded during exposure to elevated temperature in an ambient air environment. In addition, the molten, unintentional residual metal in the matrix would be expected to be highly reactive at the exposure temperatures, thus adding to the degradation of the interphase and matrix via microcracks in the matrix introduced from thermal coefficient mismatch between the matrix and fibers. Additional studies are needed to clarify which of these scenarios was responsible for the degradation of the constituent materials and the subsequent decrease of properties and performance of this CFCC after exposure to elevated temperatures.

ACKNOWLEDGMENTS

Research sponsored by the U.S. Department of Energy, Assistant Secretary for Energy Efficiency and Renewable Energy, Office of Industrial Technologies, as part of the CFCC Program under Contract DE-AC05-96OR22464 with Lockheed Martin Energy Systems, Inc. The Department of Mechanical Engineering at the University of Washington is acknowledged for providing part of K. L. Munson's support during the course of this investigation.

REFERENCES

[1] Karnitz, M. A., Craig, D. A., and Richlen, S. L., Ceramic Bulletin, Vol. 70, No. 3, 1991, pp. 430-435.

[2] Inghels, E., and Lamon, J., Journal of Materials Science, Vol. 26, 1991, pp. 5403-5410.

[3] Donald, I. W., and McMillan, P. W., Journal of Materials Science, Vol. 11, 1976, pp. 949-972.

[4] Cao, H. C., Bischoff, E., Sbaizero, O., Ruhle, M., and Evans, A. G., Journal of the American Ceramic Society, Vol. 73, No. 6, 1990, pp. 1691-1599.

[5] Aveston J., and Kelly, A., Journal of Materials Science, Vol. 8, 1973, pp. 352-362.

[6] Curtin, W. A., Journal of the American Ceramic Society, Vol. 74, No. 11, 1991, pp. 2837-2845.

[7] Curtin, W. A., Journal of the American Ceramic Society, Vol. 77, No. 4, 1994, pp. 1075-1078.

[8] Marshall, D. B. and Evans, A. G., Journal of the American Ceramic Society, Vol. 68, No. 5, 1985, pp. 225-231.

[9] Davidge, R. W., and Briggs, A., Journal of Materials Science, Vol. 24, 1989, pp. 2815-2819

[10] Budiansky, B., Hutchinson, J. W. and Evans, A. G., Journal of Mechanics and Physics of Solids, Vol. 34, No. 2, 1986, pp. 167-189.

[11] Evans, A. G. and Marshall, D. B., in Fiber Reinforced Ceramic Composites, K. S. Mazdiyasni, Ed., Noyes Publications, Park Ridge, NJ, 1990.

[12] Evans, A. G., Materials Science and Engineering, Vol. A143, 1991, pp. 63-76.

[13] Jenkins, M. G., Piccola, J. P., Jr., Mello, M. D., Lara-Curzio, E., and Wereszczak, A. A., Ceramic Engineering and Science Proceedings, Vol. 15, No. 4, 1994, pp. 209-218.

[14] Shanmugham, S., Stinton, D. P., Rebillat, F., Bleier, A., Besmann, T. M., Lara-Curzio, E., and Liaw, P. K., Ceramic Engineering and Science Proceedings, Vol. 16, No. 4, 1995, pp. 389-399.

[15] Griffin, C.J. and Kieschke, R. R., Ceramic Engineering and Science Proceedings, Vol. 16, No. 4, 1995, pp. 425-432.

[16] Fareed, A. S. and Schiroky, G. H., Ceramic Engineering and Science Proceedings, Vol. 15, No. 4, 1994, pp. 344-352.

[17] Fareed, A. S., Sonuparlak, B., Lee, C. T., Fortini, A. J., and Schiroky, G. H., Ceramic Engineering and Science Proceedings, Vol. 11, No. 8, 1990, pp. 782-794.

[18] Piccola, J. P., Jr., "Effects of Test Parameters on Tensile Mechanical Behaviour of a Continuous Fiber Ceramic Composite (CFCC)," Master of science thesis, University of Washington, 1994

[19] Jenkins, M. G., Piccola, J. P., Jr., and Lara-Curzio, E. "Onset of Cumulative Damage (First Matrix Cracking) and the Effects of Test Parameters on the Tensile Behaviour of a Continuous Fiber-Reinforced Ceramic Composite (CFCC)," in Fracture Mechanics of Ceramics, Vol. 11 and 12, Plenum Press, New York (in press 1996 expected).

[20] Munson, K. L., "Retained Tensile Properties of an Oxide-Matrix Continuous Fiber Ceramic Composite after High-Temperature Exposure in Ambient Air," Master of science thesis, University of Washington, 1995.

Nondestructive Characterization

Reji John[1], Dennis J. Buchanan[2], David A. Stubbs[3], ánd Julie A. Herzog[4]

CHARACTERIZATION OF DAMAGE PROGRESSION IN CERAMIC MATRIX COMPOSITES USING AN INTEGRATED NDE/MECHANICAL TESTING SYSTEM

REFERENCE: John, R., Buchanan, D. J., Stubbs, D. A., and Herzog, J. A., **"Characterization of Damage Progression in Ceramic Matrix Composites Using an Integrated NDE/Mechanical Testing System,"** Thermal and Mechanical Test Methods and Behavior of Continuous-Fiber Ceramic Composites, ASTM STP 1309, Michael G. Jenkins, Stephen T. Gonczy, Edgar Lara-Curzio, Noel E. Ashbaugh, and Larry P. Zawada, Eds., American Society for Testing and Materials, 1997.

ABSTRACT: This paper discusses the use of an unique integrated Nondestructive Evaluation (NDE)/Mechanical test system to characterize the damage progression in a ceramic matrix composite (CMC) under tensile and fatigue loading conditions. During the tests, the effects of damage were characterized *in situ* using conventional extensometry, and ultrasonic surface and longitudinal wave transducers. The surface wave technique clearly identified the proportional limit of the composite, while the longitudinal wave technique captured the overall deformation behavior during the tension tests. Both ultrasonic NDE techniques showed equal or greater sensitivity to damage progression in the CMC compared to conventional extensometer-based modulus data.

KEYWORDS: ceramic matrix composite, damage progression, *in situ*, longitudinal wave, mechanical testing, nondestructive evaluation, surface wave, ultrasonic

[1] Research Engineer, [2]Assistant Research Engineer, [3]Associate Research Engineer and [4] Undergraduate Student Assistant, Structural Integrity Division, University of Dayton Research Institute, 300 College Park, Dayton, OH 45469-0128.

Ceramic matrix composites (CMC) are considered to be potentially useful as hot-section components in advanced engines and structures in aerospace vehicles. The enhanced behavior of the CMC compared to unreinforced matrix is attributed to mechanisms such as crack arrest, retardation of crack growth, and distribution of damage by the reinforcing fibers [1]. Damage-tolerance based design of the CMC components requires the knowledge of damage initiation and progression under service load conditions. Implementation of the damage-tolerance based design procedure requires reliable methods of detecting the matrix cracks in CMC components.

Conventional displacement gages are not very sensitive to hairline cracks observed on the surface of CMC components. However, the distributed damage affects the characteristics (wave speed, amplitude etc.) of longitudinal and surface waves propagating across the composite component. Based on this concept, many investigators [2-9] have used various NDE techniques to detect and monitor damage progression in composites under tension and fatigue loading conditions. The proposed NDE techniques include acousto-ultrasonic (AU) [2,3,6], surface wave [4,8], longitudinal wave [5], acoustic emission[5] [9], and internal heating measurements [7]. In these investigations [2-9], the applicability of the NDE methods were demonstrated using experiments conducted at room temperature. The use of CMC in high-temperature applications requires techniques to monitor damage initiation and progression at elevated temperatures. Recently, the University of Dayton Research Institute[6] and the Wright Laboratory [8,10] have been involved in developing automated damage measurement methods using NDE techniques, which can be used over a wide range of temperatures. This paper discusses the development of an integrated NDE/mechanical testing system with simultaneous damage characterization using NDE and conventional extensometry techniques, which can be used at room and elevated temperatures.

EXPERIMENTAL PROCEDURE

A glass-ceramic matrix composite was used as a model material to demonstrate the feasibility of the test technique. The composite consisted of barium-magnesium aluminosilicate (BMAS) matrix reinforced with silicon carbide fibers[5] [11] forming a $[0/90]_{3s}$ layup. The microstructural details of the SiC/BMAS composite can be found in Ref. 11. The volume fraction of fibers in the composite was $\approx 40\%$.

The schematic of the test setup is shown Fig. 1(a). Dog-bone shaped specimens, as shown in Fig. 1(b), were used during this study. The horizontal test frame was specially designed [12] for conducting closed-loop controlled tension, creep, and thermomechanical fatigue tests of brittle and metal matrix composites. The test control

---

[5] D. Murphy, "Fatigue Testing and Damage Monitoring of UT-22," Private communication to Larry P. Zawada, Dec. 1993.

[6] R. John, P. Karpur, G. A. Hartman, D. A. Stubbs, and D. J. Buchanan, Internal communications, University of Dayton Research Institute, Dayton, OH, Oct. - Sept. 1991.

and data acquisition were achieved using personal computers. The specimens were loaded using friction grips similar to that shown in Fig. 1(a). For this study, the friction grips were redesigned to include a chamber for housing the longitudinal wave transducers. The transducers were held in place using a spring-loaded attachment and

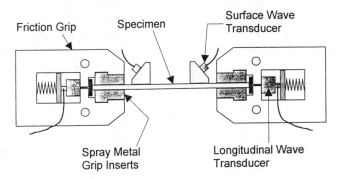

(a) Test set up with ultrasonic longitudinal and surface wave transducers

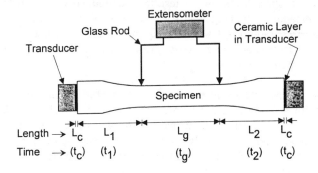

(b) Lengths of different specimen sections and the corresponding wave propagation time

Figure 1.   Schematic showing (a) test set up with ultrasonic longitudinal and surface wave transducers and (b) Lengths of different specimen sections and the corresponding wave propagation time.

passed through a hole establishing full contact with the specimen ends. Evaluation tests confirmed that this simple attachment was stable for more than a million cycles. The surface wave transducers were attached to the top of the specimen using spring clips and conventional couplants were used between the transducers and the specimen. The frequency of the longitudinal and surface wave transducers was centered around 5 and 10 MHz, respectively. The arrangement shown in Fig. 1(a) enables using the longitudinal and surface wave transducers in either through-transmission or pulse-echo modes.

During this study, the through-transmission mode was adopted. The location of the longitudinal wave transducers at the specimen ends inside the water-cooled grips ensures that the transducers can also be used during elevated temperature tests.

Special quartz rod, resistive-type extensometers were used to measure the displacement in the gage section. As shown in Fig. 1(b), the quartz rods were bent to enable measurement of displacement across the entire gage length of the specimen. Typical specimen dimensions were: $L_1 = L_2 = 50.7$ mm, $L_g = 46.7$ mm, gage section width = 5.68 mm, and thickness = 2.73 mm. L_g denotes the gage length between the extensometer rods and L_c the ceramic wear surface on the transducers.

Tension and fatigue tests were conducted using the dog-bone specimens. The tension tests were crosshead-displacement controlled. In the first tension test, longitudinal and surface wave signals were acquired at periodic intervals while the specimen was monotonically loaded. At the required stress level, the test was put on hold for ≈ 40 seconds, ultrasonic through-transmission wave signals acquired, and the test restarted. This procedure was continued until failure. In the second tension test, the specimen was loaded to predetermined stress levels, unloaded to near-zero load and loaded to the next stress level. In this test, the longitudinal wave signals were acquired just prior to unloading. The fatigue tests were conducted using maximum stresses of 100 and 155 MPa, stress ratio, R = 0.05, and frequency of 5 Hz. Specimen deformation was measured during tension and fatigue tests. All the tests for this study were conducted in laboratory air at room temperature.

The ultrasonic data acquisition system consisted of a standard commercial spike-type pulser with a 35 MHz bandwidth receiver. Commercial broad band ultrasonic transducers were used for the longitudinal and surface wave generation and reception. Surface wave mode conversion wedges were used to generate the surface waves on the specimen. The ultrasonic wave signals were converted to digital data using a personal computer-based 8-bit 100 MHz analog-to-digital converter.

RESULTS AND DISCUSSION

Tension Tests

Stress-Strain Response--The stress versus strain responses of the two tension tests are shown in Fig. 2. Both specimens failed within the gage section. The stress levels at which the interrupted monotonic tests were temporarily put on hold correspond to the discontinuities in curve (a). The peak stress was $\approx$ 200-220 MPa and the failure strain ranged between 0.006 and 0.009 m/m, similar to those reported by Brennan et al. [11]. The data in Fig. 2 show three linear regions with the breakpoints at $\approx$ 70 and 170 MPa. The stress-strain data near the first breakpoint, usually identified as the proportional limit (PL), is magnified in Fig. 3. Also shown is a dashed line corresponding to the initial tangent modulus, E of 120 GPa. As seen in Fig. 3, the PL is ≈ 65 MPa, which corresponds to the onset of deviation of the data from the dashed line. This value for PL, based on the data from the extensometer, corresponds to 80 MPa reported by Murphy[5] using acoustic emission measurements.

Longitudinal and Surface Wave Signals--The longitudinal and surface wave signals transmitted through the specimen at different stress levels are shown in Figs. 4 and 5, respectively. The stress levels were chosen to highlight the changes in the wave

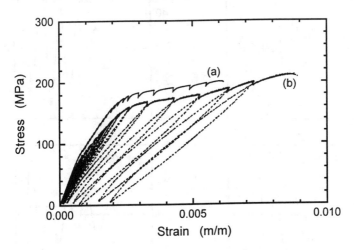

Figure 2.   (a) Monotonic and (b) Load-unload tensile stress versus strain response.

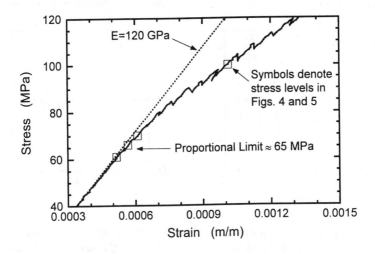

Figure 3.   Monotonic tensile stress versus strain response highlighting the proportional limit.

characteristics at the PL and at near-failure stresses. A schematic of a typical time-domain signal is shown in Fig. 6. The time of propagation of the longitudinal wave as measured by the receiving transducer is denoted as t_s, and the maximum difference between successive peaks is denoted as peak to peak (p-p) amplitude. Figure 4 shows that the longitudinal wave propagation time, t_s increases and p-p amplitude decreases

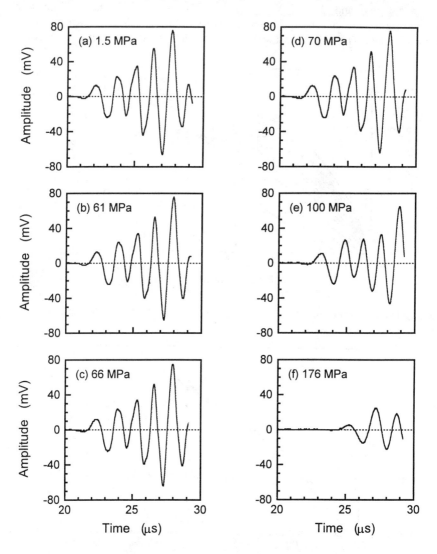

Figure 4.   Longitudinal waveforms transmitted through the specimen at stress levels of (a) 1.5 MPa, (b) 61 MPa, (c) 66 MPa, (d), 70 MPa, (e) 100 MPa, and (f) 176 MPa. Some stress levels are indicated by data symbols in Fig. 3.

with increase in applied stress. The change in t_s and p-p amplitude appears to be gradual up to 100 MPa. Figure 5 shows that significant changes occur in the surface wave signals in the stress range between 70 and 100 MPa. In addition, the frequency of the wave also appears to change after 70 MPa, as discussed later.

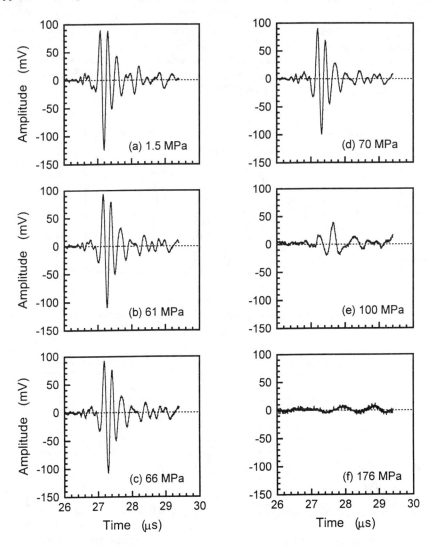

Figure 5.   Surface waveforms transmitted through the specimen at stress levels of (a) 1.5 MPa, (b) 61 MPa, (c) 66 MPa, (d), 70 MPa, (e) 100 MPa, and (f) 176 MPa. Some stress levels are indicated by data symbols in Fig. 3.

Fast Fourier Transform (FFT) analysis of the longitudinal and surface wave signals was conducted to determine the effect of applied stress on the frequency of wave propagation. Figure 7 shows the frequency spectrum for the longitudinal and surface wave signals acquired at 61 and 100 MPa. Even though the longitudinal wave transducers were centered around 5 MHz, the transmitted energy was centered around 0.73 MHz, indicating that the composite severely attenuated the higher frequencies of the signal in the through transmission mode. The initial surface wave propagation was centered around 4.2 MHz and decreased to about 2 MHz at 100 MPa. Figure 8 shows the results of the FFT analysis of all the signals obtained during the tension test. The dominant frequency is plotted versus the stress level. Note that the frequency data for the surface wave shows no change until about 65 MPa.

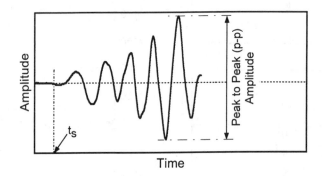

Figure 6.   Schematic showing definition of wave characteristics.

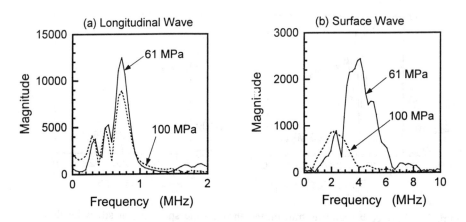

Figure 7.   Frequency spectrum during (a) longitudinal and (b) surface wave propagation at different stress levels.

Figure 8 shows that as the stress increases to higher values, the frequency gradually decreases until 90 MPa, at which a significant drop is observed. In contrast, the longitudinal wave reveals near-constant frequency of ≈ 0.73 MHz until 120 MPa, followed by a gradual decrease to about 0.4 MHz at specimen failure. The onset of decrease in the transmission frequency of the surface wave has been associated with the formation of surface breaking cracks in the surface ply (0°) [8]. Further increase of applied stress results in an increase in the number of matrix cracks in the 0° ply[5] [1]. Consequently, these cracks filter the higher frequency content of the surface wave, and the dominant frequency continues to decrease with increase in applied stress as shown in Fig. 8.

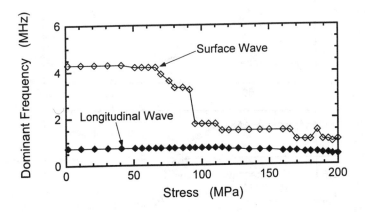

Figure 8.   Effect of stress on frequency of the transmitted waves.

The surface waves are generally sensitive to surface cracks as the energy of the surface wave is confined to a depth of approximately one wavelength [4,8]. For the CMC used in this study the wavelength of the surface wave is ≈ 0.7-1.0 mm. This depth corresponds to the first 4 layers corresponding to the 0°, 90°, 0° and 90° plies. Hence, in addition to frequency, wave characteristics such as energy of propagation of the surface waves can be expected to be influenced by the formation of matrix cracks in the 0° plies, debonding at the fiber/matrix interface in the 90° plies and matrix cracks in the 90° plies. This is evident in Fig. 9(a), in which the normalized p-p amplitude of the surface wave is plotted as a function of the applied stress. The p-p amplitude remains constant until ≈ 65-70 MPa, followed by a steep decrease between 70 and 110 MPa, and remains near-constant from 110 MPa until failure. The steep decrease in the p-p amplitude coincides with the decrease in dominant frequency as shown in Fig. 8 and the proportional limit as shown in Fig. 3. Hence, the surface wave technique can be used to identify the PL of CMC in which the PL is determined by the onset of surface and near-surface cracks. Comparing Figs. 8 and 9(a) we see that the dominant frequency and the p-p amplitude of the surface wave decrease between 70 and 110 MPa. Interestingly, this stress range corresponds to the transition range in terms of slope of the stress-strain curve as shown in Figs. 2 and 3. Hence, the formation of through matrix cracks is probably completed at about 110 MPa. Additional experiments are required to confirm the correlation between the formation of surface and near-surface cracks and the decrease in surface p-p amplitude beyond 70 MPa.

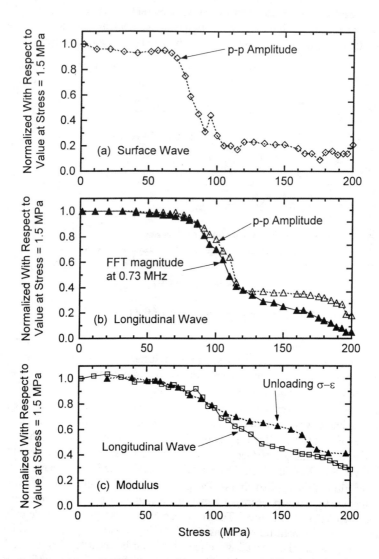

Figure 9.   Effect of applied stress on (a) surface wave characteristics (b) longitudinal wave characteristics, and (c) modulus during the tension test.

Figure 9(b) shows the effect of stress level on the normalized p-p amplitude and magnitude of the dominant frequency (=0.73 MHz) of the longitudinal wave. The frequency of 0.73 MHz was chosen as the near-constant value from Fig. 8. The longitudinal p-p amplitude shows a gradual decrease between 70 and 110 MPa in contrast to the steep decrease in the surface p-p amplitude. This implies that the longitudinal wave is not as sensitive to the near-surface cracks. Figure 9(b) shows that the magnitude of the frequency decreases with increase in stress similar to the p-p amplitude except for stresses > 130 MPa. The difference between the trends in frequency magnitude and p-p amplitude may be related to the change in dominant frequency for stresses > 130 MPa as shown in Fig. 8.

As discussed earlier and illustrated in Fig. 4, the time of propagation of the longitudinal wave, t_s increases with increase in applied stress. The time required by the longitudinal wave to travel from one transducer to the other can be split into several components as shown in Fig. 1(b). The average time required to propagate through the ceramic wear layers in the transducers is denoted as t_c, time required to propagate through the gage length is t_g, and the time required to propagate through the specimen sections on either side of the gage length is t_1 and t_2. Hence, t_s is given by,

$$t_s = t_g + t_1 + t_2 + 2t_c \qquad (1)$$

After the test, the sections corresponding to L_1 and L_2 (see Fig. 1(b)) were cut, and t_1 and t_2 measured independently. Using an ultrasonic pulse-echo technique, t_c was measured for the transducers. Thus, knowing t_s, t_1, t_2 and t_c, t_g was determined for each wave signal. Using t_g, the average longitudinal wave velocity in the gage section, v_g was calculated as,

$$v_g = \frac{L_g}{t_g} \qquad (2)$$

The average wave velocity was used to calculate an effective modulus, E_{eff} of the composite using the expression [13] for an infinitely wide plate,

$$E_{eff} = v_g^2 (1 - \upsilon^2)\rho \qquad (3)$$

in which ρ = density and υ = Poisson's ratio of composite. For SiC/BMAS used in this study, $\rho \approx 2655$ kg/m^3 and $\upsilon = 0.2$. E_{eff} calculated using Eq. 3 was normalized with respect to the value calculated at stress = 1.5 MPa and plotted as a function of applied stress in Fig. 9(c). Also shown in Fig. 9(c) are the results from the unload-load tests (curve b in Fig. 2). The data for each unload-load cycle were used to calculate the current modulus corresponding to the initial unloading portion identified as "unloading σ-ε" in

Fig. 9(c).   The range of stress used was 25 MPa.   The trend obtained using the longitudinal wave is close to that from the initial unloading response, demonstrating the correlation between the longitudinal wave propagation velocity and the stiffness of the composite.

<u>Fatigue Tests</u>

The results of the fatigue tests at 100 and 155 MPa are discussed in this section. As seen in Figs. 2 and 3, 100 MPa is slightly above the proportional limit and 155 MPa is in the middle of the second linear region of the stress-strain response. During the fatigue tests, the stress-strain response was acquired at predetermined cycles, including the first ten cycles. Just prior to the stress-strain data acquisition, the longitudinal wave signals were obtained at the maximum stress level. The effective modulus calculated using Eqn. (3) is normalized with respect to the value at the first cycle and plotted as a function of cycles in Fig. 10 for the 100 and 155 MPa tests.   Note that the X-axis is in logarithmic scale. The initial unloading modulus calculated using the stress-strain response is also plotted in Fig. 10. The longitudinal wave signal exhibits a trend similar to that shown by

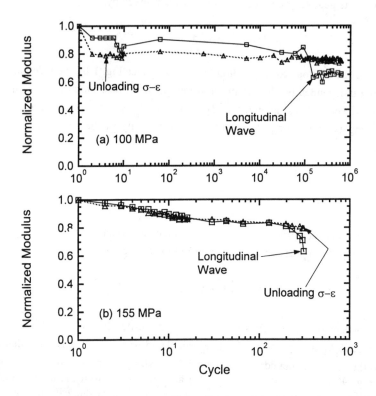

Figure 10.   Effect of applied cycles on normalized modulus during fatigue loading at (a) 100 MPa and (b) 155 MPa.

the modulus from the stress-strain data. The difference in normalized modulus obtained using ultrasonic wave and extensometer techniques is generally within 10%. As discussed earlier, the 100 MPa test was stopped after ≈ 630,000 cycles and the stress level gradually increased to 155 MPa. The specimen failed after fatiguing for about 310 cycles at 155 MPa. As seen in Fig. 10, both 100 and 155 MPa tests revealed only a 30% reduction in modulus at the end of the test.

Figure 11 shows the effect of fatigue cycles on the p-p amplitude of the through-transmitted longitudinal.wave corresponding to 100 and 155 MPa tests. Comparing Figs. 10 and 11, we can conclude that the p-p amplitude is more sensitive to the damage progression in the CMC than the modulus. The p-p amplitude decreased 40% at 100 MPa and 70% at 155 MPa. The decrease in the p-p amplitude is larger than that shown in the modulus data, especially at the higher stress level. Hence, the p-p amplitude may be a better indicator of the damage progression in the CMC and provide adequate warning prior to failure.

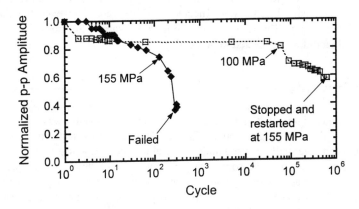

Figure 11. Effect of applied cycles on normalized longitudinal p-p amplitude during fatigue loading at 100 and 155 MPa.

Advantages of the NDE/Mechanical Integrated Testing System

The results from this study show that the surface wave technique potentially is a valuable tool for determining the onset of surface and near-surface matrix crack initiation. The trend in the frequency spectrum of the surface wave appears to be related to the matrix crack formation in the CMC. Additional work is required to verify the relationship between the surface wave characteristics and the evolution of the damage mechanisms such as crack spacing and crack depth. The p-p amplitude of the longitudinal wave and the time to propagate through the critical section can be used to characterize the overall deformation behavior of the composite. The results from the tension and fatigue tests show that the p-p amplitude of the longitudinal wave could be a better indicator of the onset of failure than the modulus from the stress-strain data. The proposed technique with modified grips is also well suited for conducting tests at elevated temperatures with off-the-shelf longitudinal wave transducers. This test system can be easily used for testing under general thermomechanical loading conditions. The information from the NDE techniques can be coupled with the conventional extensometry data to better characterize the damage progression in any material.

Ultrasonic Wave Propagation in Rectangular CMC Specimens

Equation 3 is applicable for an infinitely-wide homogeneous isotropic plate, if the ratio of plate thickness to wavelength is less than 0.1 [13]. The specimen used during this study was not infinitely wide but had a finite width with a ratio of wavelength to width $\approx$1.6-2.0. During this investigation, the wavelength of the longitudinal wave ranged between 9-11 mm. This resulted in specimen thickness to wavelength ratio of 0.25 to 0.3 which is greater than the 0.1 requirement. In addition, the material was anisotropic with alternating layers of longitudinal and transverse fibers. Hence, the absolute value of modulus calculated using Eq. 3 is not expected to be accurate. However, the changes in the specimen modulus (stiffness) will be accurately measured. So the deduced trend of the normalized modulus is expected to be valid.

CONCLUSIONS

An unique integrated NDE/mechanical testing system was developed to characterize the damage progression in CMC. The feasibility tests indicate that the testing system can potentially be used under general thermomechanical testing conditions. *In situ* measurement of ultrasonic surface and longitudinal wave propagation characteristics enabled direct comparison with corresponding extensometer measurements. Surface waves were used to identify the onset of surface and near-surface cracks in SiC/BMAS with $[0/90]_{3s}$ layup. Longitudinal wave propagation was successfully used to monitor the changes in the stiffness of the composite during tension and fatigue loading conditions. The decrease in wave propagation velocity and attenuation in transmitted energy can be attributed to damage induced by increasing stress and/or fatigue cycles. The changes in the peak-to-peak amplitude of the transmitted wave signal appears to be an equal or better indicator of impending failure of the composite than the modulus data.

ACKNOWLEDGMENT

This research was conducted at Wright Laboratory (WL/MLLN), Materials Directorate, Wright-Patterson Air Force Base, OH 45433-7817. R. John, D. J. Buchanan, and D. A. Stubbs were supported under on-site contract number F33615-94-C-5200. J. A. Herzog was supported under AFOSR/AASERT Program (Contract No. F49620-95-1-0500). Mr. L. P. Zawada, Wright Laboratory (WL/MLLN), provided the machined specimens. Mr. G. A. Hartman, University of Dayton Research Institute, provided the machine design for the modified grips. The authors also gratefully acknowledge the assistance of Mr. A. F. Lackey in machining the spring attachment for the transducers.

REFERENCES

[1]   Evans, A. G. and Marshall, D. B., "The Mechanical Behavior of Ceramic Matrix Composites," Acta Metallurgica, Vol. 37, No. 10, 1989, pp. 2567-2583.

[2]   Vary, A., Materials Analysis by Ultrasonics, Noyes Data Corporation, Park Ridge, NJ, USA, 1987.

[3]   Kautz, H. E. and Bhatt, R. T., "Ultrasonic Velocity Technique for Monitoring Property Changes in Fiber-Reinforced Ceramic Matrix Composites," Ceramic Engineering and Science Proceedings, The American Ceramic Society, Westerville, OH, USA, Vol. 12, July-August 1991, pp. 1139-1151.

[4]   Achenbach, J. D., Fine, M. E., Komsky, I., and McGuire, S., "Ultrasonic Wave Technique to Assess Cyclic-Load Fatigue Damage in Silicon-Carbide Whisker Reinforced 2124 Aluminum Alloy Composites," Cyclic Deformation, Fracture, and Nondestructive Evaluation of Advanced Materials, ASTM STP 1157, M.R. Mitchell and O. Buck, Eds., American Society for Testing and Materials, Philadelphia, 1992, pp. 241-250.

[5]   Kasap, S. O., Yannacopoulos, S., Mirchandani, V., and Hildebrandt, J. R., "Ultrasonic Evaluation of Fatigue of Composites," Journal of Engineering Materials and Technology, Transactions of the ASME, Vol. 114, April 1992, pp. 132-136.

[6]   Tiwari, A., Henneke, E. G., and Reifsnider, K. L., "Damage Characterization of a Cross-Ply Ceramic Composite Under Fatigue Loading Using a Real-Time Acousto-Ultrasonic NDE Technique", Journal of Composites Technology and Research, JCTRER, Vol. 17, No. 3, July 1995, pp. 221-227.

[7]   Holmes, J. W. and Sorensen, B. F., Fatigue Behavior of Continuous Fiber-Reinforced Ceramic Matrix Composites, in High-Temperature Mechanical Behavior of Ceramic Composites, S.V. Nair and K. Jakus, Eds., Butterworth-Heinemann, Newton, MA, USA, 1995.

[8]   MacLellan, P. T., Stubbs, D. A., and Karpur, P., "In Situ Ultrasonic Surface Wave Assessment of Mechanical Fatigue Damage Accumulation in Metal Matrix Composites," Composites Engineering, Vol. 5, No. 12, To be published, November 1995.

[9] Kim, R. Y. and Pagano, N. J., "Crack Initiation in Unidirectional Brittle-Matrix Composites," Journal of American Ceramic Society, Vol. 75, No. 4, May 1991, pp. 1082-1090.

[10] Stubbs, D. A. and Buchanan, D. J., "In Situ Ultrasonic Monitoring of Damage in Ceramic Matrix Composites Undergoing Creep and Tension Testing," Final Report, University of Dayton Research Institute, Dayton, OH, USA, Prepared for United Technologies Research Center, East Hartford, CT, May 1995.

[11] Brennan, J. J., Nutt, S. R., and Sun, E. Y., "Interfacial Microstructure and Stability of BN Coated Nicalon Fiber/Glass-Ceramic Matrix Composite," High-Temperature Ceramic Matrix Composites II: Manufacturing and Materials Development, A.G. Evans and R. Naslain, Eds., Ceramic Transactions, Vol. 58, The American Ceramic Society, Westerville, OH, USA, 1994, pp. 53-64.

[12] Zawada, L. P., Butkus, L. M., and Hartman, G. A., "Room Temperature Tensile and Fatigue Properties of Silicon Carbide Fiber-Reinforced Alumino Silicate Glass," Ceramic Engineering and Science Proceedings, The American Ceramic Society, Westerville, OH, USA, Vol. 11, September-October 1990, pp. 1592-1606.

[13] Kolsky, H., Stress Waves in Solids, Dover Publications, Inc., New York, NY, USA., 1963.

Sanjay Ahuja[1], William A. Ellingson[1], J. Scott Steckenrider,[2] and
Steven J. Koch[3]

INFRARED-BASED NDE METHODS FOR DETERMINING THERMAL PROPERTIES AND DEFECTS IN CERAMIC COMPOSITES[*]

REFERENCE: Ahuja, S., Ellingson, W. A., Steckenrider, J. S.,
and Koch, S. J., **"Infrared-Based NDE Methods for Determining
Thermal Properties and Defects in Ceramics,"** Thermal and
Mechanical Test Methods and Behavior of Continuous-Fiber Ceramic Composites, ASTM
STP 1309, Michael G. Jenkins, Stephen T. Gonczy, Edgar Lara-Curzio, Noel E.
Ashbaugh, and Larry P. Zawada, Eds., American Society for Testing and Materials, 1997.

.**ABSTRACT:** Continuous-fiber ceramic matrix composites are
currently being developed for various high temperature
applications, including use in advanced heat engines. In the
material classes of interest for such applications, i.e., silicon
carbide (SiC)-fiber-reinforced SiC ($SiC_{(f)}$/SiC), Al_2O_3/Al_2O_3, etc.,
the condition of the interface between the fibers and matrix is
critical to the mechanical and thermal behavior of each component.
A nondestructive evaluation method developed at Argonne National
Laboratory (ANL) uses infrared thermal imaging to provide "single-
shot" full-field measurement of the distribution of thermal
diffusivity in large components. By applying digital filtering,
interpolation, and least-squares-estimation techniques for noise
reduction, we have achieved acquisition and analysis times of
minutes or less with submillimeter spatial resolution. The system
has been used to examine the effects of thermal shock, oxidation
treatment, and variations in density and fiber coatings in a full
array of test specimens.

KEYWORDS: infrared imaging, thermal diffusivity, continuous-
fiber ceramic composites, nondestructive evaluation

[*]Work supported by the U.S. Department of Energy, Energy
Efficiency and Renewable Energy, Office of Industrial
Technologies, under Contract W-31-109-ENG-38.

[1]Materials Scientist and Senior Scientist respectively,
Energy Technology Division, Argonne National Laboratory, Argonne,
IL 60439.

[2]Materials Scientist, Cabot Corporation, Aurora, IL 60504.

[3]Graduate student, University of Michigan, Ann Arbor, MI.

Continuous-fiber ceramic matrix composites (CFCCs) have high strength and stability at high temperatures because of the incorporation of continuous fibers in the monolithic ceramic matrix. CFCCs are ideal replacements for traditional materials in numerous applications, including gas turbines, because of their relatively high strength and toughness at high temperatures (>1250°C) and their lower density.

Specific materials systems are desired specifically for their thermal properties, and therefore any variation in thermal diffusivity or thermal conductivity will significantly affect their ability to transfer heat properly. Such variations result from processing defects, thermal shock, or thermally induced degradation of the fiber/matrix interface and reduce the advantages for which these materials were chosen. The critical issue in most CFCC applications is therefore the distribution of thermal properties within a given component.

When using infra-red (IR) imaging technology, the method used for thermal excitation can be very important. Of the several methods existing and used extensively in the study of both ceramic and nonceramic materials systems, three thermal excitation methods were evaluated to determine which method is best suited for characterizing CFCC materials [1-4]: (a) photothermal, (b) electrical-resistance heating, and (c) mechanical excitation. Research at ANL has focused on photothermal excitation because it has been the most successful and allows measurement of thermal diffusivity that can be correlated to mechanical properties. In this paper, we describe a portable and inexpensive infrared (IR) imaging system and a reliable technique for measuring thermal diffusivity of $SiC_{(f)}/SiC$ and $Al_2O_3{(f)}/Al_2O_3$ CFCC specimens and components.

EXPERIMENTAL AND THEORETICAL DETAILS

The thermal imaging system is shown in Fig. 1 and is described in earlier papers [5-7]. The system uses Parker's method [8] to calculate thermal diffusivity, requiring a thermal pulse of short duration to be incident upon the front surface of a specimen and the temperature of the back surface to be monitored as a function of time. In our work, this was done by heating the front surface of the specimen with a photographic flash lamp and then monitoring the back surface temperature with a commercially available scanning radiometer IR camera. Images were acquired using a Mac II with an on-board frame grabber receiving standard RS-170 signals from the IR camera, digitizing each received image and then processing each image. The locally developed software extracted the average gray-scale value that represented the specimen temperature.

The theoretically predicted back-surface temperature T as a function of time t and specimen thickness L according to Parker et al.[8] is given by

$$T(L,t) = \frac{Q}{\rho CL}\left[1 + 2\sum_{n=1}^{\infty}(-1)^n \exp\left(\frac{-n^2\pi^2}{L^2}\alpha t\right)\right].$$
(1)

where Q is the radiant energy incident on the front surface, ρ is density, C is specific heat, and α is thermal diffusivity. The common "half-rise time" method of determining α is to take V, the normalized back-surface temperature, as: V = T/T_M = 0.5 (when the

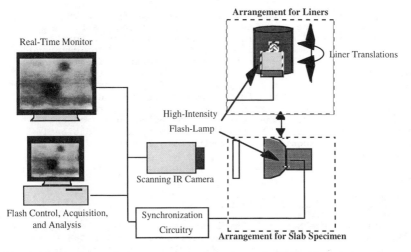

FIG. 1--Experimental arrangement for thermal diffusivity imaging.

back-surface temperature rise has reached half of its maximum, T_M, value) and the normalized time, $\omega = \alpha t \pi^2 / L^2 = 1.37$, obtaining

$$\alpha = 1.37 L^2 / \pi^2 t_{\frac{1}{2}} . \qquad (2)$$

Any noise in the temperature signal significantly alters the computed thermal diffusivity value. Because of the high noise level in scanning radiometers, a noise-reduction method was considered. For the current work, to minimize the time necessary to measure thermal diffusivity, a linear least-squares fit was used to interpolate the value of $t_{1/2}$. By imaging the components at higher resolution than required, spatial averaging was permissible without loss of sensitivity to the minimum defect size.

     For the results presented here, a 10- by 10-pixel block was used and a 512- by 413-pixel digitized image was transformed into a 51- by 41-pixel reduced image providing substantially better signal-to-noise ratio. Also, the quarter-rise time ($t_{1/4}$) and three-quarter-rise time ($t_{3/4}$) were also determined for each block, where $\omega(t_{1/4}) = 0.92$ and $\omega(t_{3/4}) = 2.08$, according to the procedure suggested in the ASTM Test Method for Thermal Diffusivity of Solids by the Flash Method (E 1461). The thermal diffusivity values obtained at these locations were averaged with that of the $t_{1/2}$ value to determine effective thermal diffusivity. This permitted determination of thermal diffusivity from a single thermal cycle, thereby reducing the total acquisition time. The resulting thermal diffusivity values for all 10- by 10-pixel subsets were assembled into diffusivity images and were stored with 16-bit resolution. This avoided the need to scale each image independently and allowed better comparison between images while retaining flexibility for image enhancement in the display.

     The system was further modified by incorporating a locally developed autotrigger circuit to fire the flash repeatedly and to simultaneously acquire the image giving a dependable time for the diffusivity calculations. This autotrigger circuit has eliminated

the need to locate the frame of the flash manually thereby
providing a more precise value for the time of the flash.

Also employed in the present work was a fully integrated,
self-contained IR camera equipped with a 3- to 5-µm optical band-
pass lens system and based on the second-generation focal plane
technology. The electronics of this camera allowed for user-
selectable intensity transform algorithms for contrast enhancement
of the output image. Nonuniformity correction was selected to
eliminate variations in pixels in the focal plane array.
Automatic gain control dynamically optimized the video contrast
and brightness on a frame-by-frame basis, providing additional
resolution in the acquired images without affecting any data
characteristics.

RESULTS

Standard Reference Material (SRM)

SRMs from the National Institute of Science and Technology
(NIST), especially NIST thermal properties calibration SRM (8426
graphite) with a stated thermal diffusivity value of 72×10^{-6}
m^2/s, were used to determine the accuracy of the IR image analysis
system. The absolute value of the measured thermal diffusivity
using this system deviated from the calibration value by <5% as a
result of thermal losses and approximations in the determination
of $t_{1/2}$.

Thermal Shock Damage Detection

A set of 2-D weave Nicalon fiber/CVI SiC composites,
subjected to thermal shock testing at the University of Cincinnati
[9], were studied. The set consisted of six specimens that had
been shocked once at quench ΔT values of 0 (unquenched), 200,
400, 600, 800, and 1000°C, one specimen that had been quenched
four times at 800°C, and a final specimen that had been air-cooled
from 1000°C.

Figure 2 shows the behavior of average thermal diffusivity
over the center 80% of each specimen as a function of quench ΔT,
while Fig. 3 shows the behavior of the two specimens quenched at
800°C as a function of number of quench cycles. Although there is
no obvious trend in either curve, each specimen shows a different
diffusivity value. The variability rather than the quench history
may be highly dependent on the specimens, as evidenced by the
higher thermal diffusivity of the 800°C specimen quenched four
times than that of the specimen quenched only once.

Al_2O_3/Al_2O_3 CFCCs

We also measured the thermal diffusivity of Al_2O_3/Al_2O_3
CFCCs. An Al_2O_3/Al_2O_3 c-ring, ≈75 mm in diameter, was divided
into small segments ≈12 mm wide and each section was then imaged
separately. Because the oxide material is very translucent to the
optical thermal excitation pulse, as shown in Fig. 4, it became
heated volumetrically, creating a distortion from the
theoretically predicted behavior in the temperature/time curve
(which assumes only surface heating). Figure 5 shows temperature/
time curves for the Al_2O_3/Al_2O_3 and for the same material that was
painted on the flashed side to render it opaque.

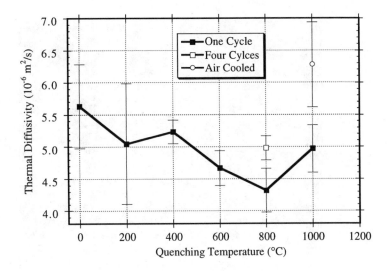

FIG. 2--Effect of quench temperature on thermal diffusivity of thermally shocked 2-D weave Nicalon/CVI SiC CFCC.

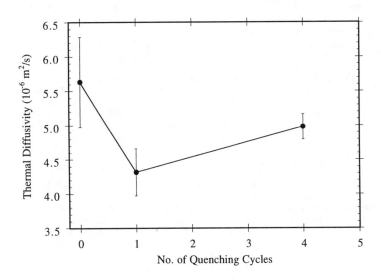

FIG. 3--Effect of number of quench cycles (@ ΔT = 800°C) on thermal diffusivity of 2-D weave Nicalon/CVI SiC CFCC.

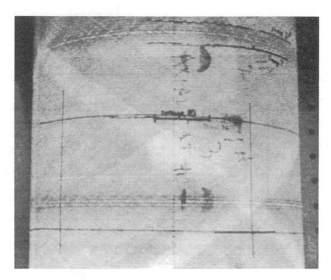

FIG. 4--Visible image of Al_2O_3/Al_2O_3 combustor liner showing optical translucency, with interior illuminated by a glow-lamp. 50x magnification.

The Al_2O_3/Al_2O_3 volumetric heating curve shown in Fig. 5 reached a maximum temperature much later than would be expected based on the initial thermal response. To eliminate volumetric heating, the specimens on the flashed side were sprayed with a graphite-based optically opaque paint. This method provided a more accurate measure of the change in thermal diffusivity in the specimens and overall thermal diffusivity was seen to vary by more than a factor of 2.

The technique of coating the inside of an Al_2O_3/Al_2O_3 liner with a graphite spray was used on a SRM specimen made by the Babcock & Wilcox (B&W) Research Center (Fig. 6). A diagram provided by Babcock & Wilcox showing the locations of the defects is given in Fig. 7. The compiled thermal diffusivity image (Fig. 8) corresponded directly to the defects shown in Fig. 7.

$SiC_{(f)}/SiC$ CFCC Specimens

The system's capability was further tested to distinguish defects of various sizes in 32 "seeded-defect" $SiC_{(f)}/SiC$ composite panels made by varying several parameters such as Graphoil section thicknesses, defect sizes, fiber coatings, defect depth, and infiltration density. A diagram of one such panel, made from twelve layers of 2-D plain weave Nicalon fabric, is shown in Fig. 9. The simulated defects were created by (a) cutting out small sections of two inner plies, (b) replacing the fabric with Graphoil sections, and (c) infiltrating the weave with SiC by CVI.

Figure 10 shows images generated for one $SiC_{(f)}/SiC$ panel. The black and white regions of the images show varying thermal diffusivity values and the normalized scale, with no units, is shown on the right side of Fig. 10. Figure 10a is the raw thermal image taken at the point of maximum thermal contrast between

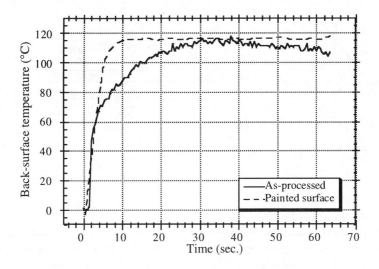

FIG. 5--Surface temperature versus time for an Al_2O_3/Al_2O_3 CFCC in as-processed condition (volumetric heating) and with flashed surface painted to render it opaque (surface heating).

FIG. 6--Al_2O_3/Al_2O_3 NDE SRM specimen fabricated by Babcock & Wilcox Research Center for ANL. Inside of the liner was coated with graphite-based optically opaque paint.

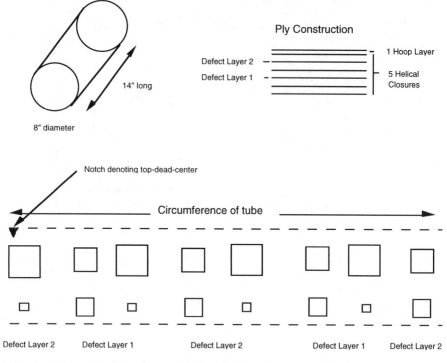

FIG. 7--Schematic diagram of Al_2O_3/Al_2O_3 NDE SRM specimen fabricated by the Babcock & Wilcox Research Center.

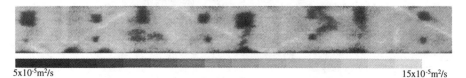

$5 \times 10^{-5} m^2/s$ $15 \times 10^{-5} m^2/s$

FIG. 8--Diffusivity map of Al_2O_3/Al_2O_3 NDE SRM specimen fabricated by the Babcock & Wilcox Research Center.

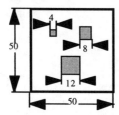

FIG. 9--Schematic diagram of seeded defect $SiC_{(f)}/SiC$ composite panels used for defect detection (dimensions in millimeters).

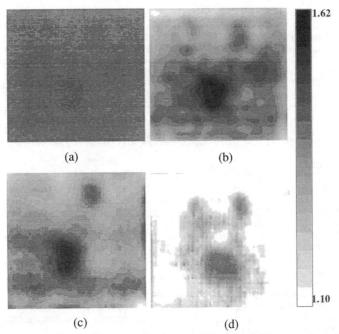

(a)   (b)

1.62

(c)   (d)

1.10

FIG. 10--Normalized images of SiC(f)/SiC composite panel. Image
(a) raw thermal image, (b) processed thermal image, (c) thermal
diffusivity image, and (d) thermal diffusivity image with second-
generation focal plane technology and user-selectable intensity
transform algorithms for contrast enhancement of output image.

defect and nondefect regions. Figure 10b is the same image after
substantial image processing but the seeded defects are not well-
defined in the processed image, the extent of "damage" is unknown,
and the image processing requires expert-user interaction. Figure
10c is a thermal diffusivity image of the specimen with
considerably better contrast than the processed thermal images,
but with average spatial resolution. Because of the quantitative
nature of the thermal diffusivity images, it is possible to
compare directly defect and nondefect regions with respect to
different diffusivities and porosities. Figure 10d was acquired
by dynamically adjusting the gain control to optimize video
contrast and brightness and provide additional resolution in the
acquired image.

CONCLUSIONS

The applications of the thermal diffusivity imaging system
are primarily of interest in materials characterization. During
examination of actual components, the distribution of properties
becomes critical, and what constitutes a potentially dangerous
defect in one location might be an acceptable variation in
another, less-hazardous location. We have developed a thermal
diffusivity imaging method that is applicable to a wide variety of
large continuous-fiber ceramic matrix composite components. Many
specimens have been inspected for manufacturing-related defects.

The data obtained by the thermal imaging method have been correlated to thermal shock, delaminations and density variations.
By applying digital filtering, interpolation, and least-squares-estimation techniques for noise reduction, acquisition and analysis times of minutes or less have been achieved with sub-millimeter spatial resolution. Images were also acquired by user-selectable intensity transform algorithms for contrast enhancement of the output image, and gain control was dynamically adjusted to optimize video contrast and brightness on a frame-by-frame basis, thus providing additional resolution in the acquired image. In the future, fatigue damage will be correlated and methods investigated to allow high-temperature diffusivity measurements.

REFERENCES

[1]   Ramirez, A.L. and Daily, W.D., "Monitoring radio-frequency heating of contaminated soils using electrical resistance tomography," Lawrence Livermore National Laboratory Report, UCRL-ID-11537, 1993.

[2]   Hafidi, A., Billy, M., and Lecompte, J. P., "Influence of microstructural parameters on thermal diffusivity of aluminium nitride-based ceramics," Journal of Materials Science, Vol. 27 (12), pp. 3405-3408 (1992).

[3]   Enguehard, F., Boscher, D., Déom, A., and Balageas, D., "Measurement of the thermal radial diffusivity of anisotropic materials by the converging thermal wave technique," Journal of Materials Science and Engineering, Vol. B5 (2), pp. 127-134 (1990).

[4]   Rantala, J., Wei, L., Kuo, P. K., Jaarinen, J., Luukkala, M., and Thomas, R. L., "Determination of thermal diffusivity of low-diffusivity materials using the mirage method with multiparameter fitting," Journal of Applied Physics, Vol. 73 (6), pp. 2714-2723 (1993).

[5]   Ellingson, W. A., Rothermel, S. A., and Simpson, J. F., "Nondestructive Characterization of Ceramic Composites used as Combustor Liners in Advanced Gas Turbines," Transactions of the ASME, 95-GT-404, American Society of Mechanical Engineers, New York, NY, 1995.

[6]   Steckenrider, J. S., Ellingson, W. A., and Rothermel, S. A., "Full-Field Characterization of Thermal Diffusivity on Continuous-Fiber Ceramic Composite Materials and Components," Thermosense XVII: An International Conference on Thermal Sensing and Imaging Diagnostic Applications, SPIE Proceedings, Vol. 2473, S. Semanovich, Ed., Bellingham, WA, 1994.

[7]   Ahuja, S., Ellingson, W. A., Steckenrider, J. S., and King, S., "Thermal Diffusivity Imaging of Continuous Fiber Ceramic Composite Materials and Components," Proceedings of the 23rd International Thermal Conductivity Conference, Nashville, TN, 1995.

[8]   Parker, W. J., Jenkins, R. J., Butler C. P., and Abbott, G. L., "Flash method of determining thermal diffusivity, heat capacity, and thermal conductivity," Journal of Applied Physics, Vol. 32 (9), pp. 1679-1684, 1961.

[9]   Singh, R. and Wang, H. Fracture and Damage: Thermal Shock Damage of CFCCs, Bi-monthly Periodical, Continuous Fiber Ceramic Composites Program, Oak Ridge National Laboratory, pp. 70-75, April-May, 1994.

Masaru Sakata[1] and Hisaichi Ohnabe[2]

MEASUREMENT OF ORTHOTROPIC ELASTIC CONSTANTS OF CERAMIC MATRIX COMPOSITES FROM IMPACT SOUND

REFERENCE: Sakata, M. and Ohnabe, H., "**Measurements of Orthotropic Elastic Constants of Ceramic Matrix Composites from Impact Sound,**" Thermal and Mechanical Test Methods and Behavior of Continuous-Fiber Ceramic Composites, ASTM STP 1309, Michael G. Jenkins, Stephen T. Gonczy, Edgar Lara-Curzio, Noel E. Ashbaugh, and Larry P. Zawada, Eds., American Society for Testing and Materials, 1997.

ABSTRACT: The isotropic and/or orthotropic elastic constants of ceramic matrix composites are measured from the impact sound of a small rectangular bar specimen which is suspended by thin ceramic threads in a furnace. The natural frequencies at high temperatures of the flexural and torsional vibration modes are measured from the impact sound using a fast Fourier transform analyzer and elastic constants are computed from these frequencies using Timoshenko's beam theory and Saint-Venant's torsion theory. The natural frequencies of a rectangular silicon carbide/silicon carbide (SiC/SiC) plate are also measured at high temperatures and its elastic constants are determined using an iteration technique employing a finite element method. This technique is extended to measure the natural frequencies of a jet engine nozzle flap made of SiC/SiC composite panel from the impact sound before and after engine operation, and thus the damage of the flap is evaluated as the reduction of the Young's modulus of the material.

KEYWORDS: ceramic matrix composite, orthotropic elastic constant, impact sound, natural frequency, Auger electron microscopy, damage evaluation, nondestructive testing

Ceramic matrix composites (CMCs) are now considered to be one of the most attractive and potentially useful materials, and therefore a key technology in supersonic,

[1]Professor, Department of Mechanical System Engineering, Takushoku University, Hachioji, Tokyo 193, Japan.

[2]Director, Composite Materials Center, Aero-Engine & Space Operations, Ishikawajima-Harima Heavy Industries Co., Ltd., Tanashi-shi, Tokyo 188, Japan.

hypersonic, and space transportation systems and in advanced aeroengines [1,2]. The application of CMCs to the hot structures in an aeroengine is expected to increase the turbine inlet temperatures and thrust-weight ratios. In addition CMCs are applied to land and sea gas generators as well as air [3].

The elastic constants of these composites as functions of temperature must be known for optimal design of hot sections subjected to thermal stresses. Conventional methods for measuring elastic constants of ceramic materials are based on the resonant frequencies or on the velocities of ultrasonic waves [see ASTM Test Method for Young's Modulus, Shear Modulus, and Poisson's Ratio for Glass-Ceramics by Resonance (C 623) and Japanese Testing Association Testing Methods for Elastic Modulus of High Performance Ceramics at Elevated Temperature (JIS R1605)]. Recently, an ultrasonic method has been developed for characterizing the damage of long fiber ceramic matrix composites by measuring the Young's modulus of a bar specimen under tensile stresses at high temperatures [4,5]. Moreau and Jones [6] used the remote laser-ultrasonic technique to measure simultaneously the shear and longitudinal acoustic wave velocities in a silicon carbide (SiC)-reinforced alumina sample at temperatures greater than 1000°C to determine the shear and Young's moduli. However, few convenient methods are reported for measuring the shear modulus at elevated temperatures. To overcome these difficulties, a simple instrumentation system was developed for measuring the elastic constants by monitoring the impact sound of a bar of a rectangular cross section suspended by thin ceramic threads [7,8]. The natural frequencies of the flexural and torsional modes of vibration were determined by using a fast Fourier transform (FFT) spectrum analyzer. Elastic constants were then computed using Timoshenko's beam theory and Saint-Venant's torsion theory.

For orthotropic materials, five elastic constants E_x, E_y, G_{xy}, G_{yz}, and G_{zx} are determined by the present method using two specimens taken from the principal direction of the specimen blank. (Only one specimen is required for isotropic materials.)

The present method is extended to include the measurement of orthotropic elastic constants of a plate specimen. The natural frequencies of a rectangular plate of SiC/SiC composite were measured from the impact sound, and the elastic constants were determined by using an iteration technique employing a finite element method (FEM). The damage of the material at high temperatures was estimated from the variation of Young's modulus. As an application example, the natural frequencies of a jet engine nozzle flap made of an SiC/SiC composite panel were measured from the impact sound before and after engine operation, and the damage of the flap was evaluated from the reduction of Young's modulus of the material.

It is shown that the present method is capable of measuring the orthotropic elastic constants at high temperatures by a simple and cost-effective procedure using small specimens and is useful as a nondestructive testing for material evaluation at the development and operation stages.

EXPERIMENTAL PROCEDURE

A brief description will be provided here since details of the method for measurement and computation of isotropic and orthotropic elastic constants from the impact sound of a rectangular bar specimen are given elsewhere [7,8]. The general arrangement of the experimental apparatus and the flow chart for the instrumentation system are shown in Fig. 1. A beam of a rectangular cross section is suspended in a furnace by thin ceramic threads so that it can vibrate without significant constraint. A steel or ceramic ball of 3 mm in diameter is dropped onto the specimen using a guide tube. The ringing noise emitted from the impacted specimen is measured by a microphone which is set outside the furnace as shown in the figure. The signal from the microphone goes to the FFT spectrum analyzer. A Fourier spectrum is obtained as shown in Fig. 2, in which ω_{Hn}, ω_{Vn}, and ω_{Tn} represent the frequency peaks corresponding to the nth mode of flexural vibration in the horizontal direction, those of flexural vibration in the vertical direction, and those of torsional vibration, respectively. The correspondence of each frequency peak to the specific vibration mode is determined from the preliminary calculation, and the elastic constants are determined from the measured frequencies using the least squares fit method. A thermocouple attached to a dummy specimen of the same size and material as the test specimen as shown in Fig. 1 is used to measure and control the test temperature. Natural frequencies of the specimen are not affected by the dummy specimen and the temperature of the test specimen agrees with that of the dummy specimen within $\pm10°K$ at $1000°C$.

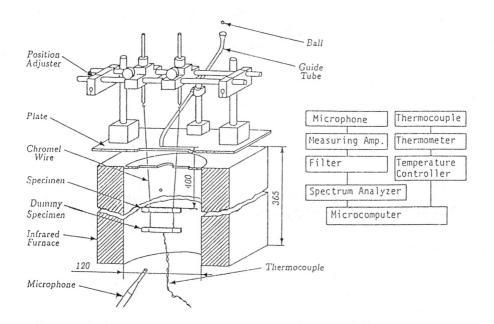

FIG. 1—Experimental apparatus (dimensions in mm) and flow chart for instrumentation system.

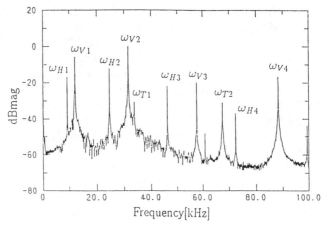

FIG. 2—Fourier spectrum of sound pressure emitted from the impacted beam.

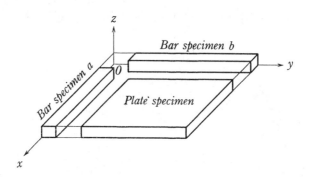

FIG. 3—Specimen and Coordinate system.

MEASUREMENT OF ORTHOTROPIC ELASTIC CONSTANTS USING RECTANGULAR BAR SPECIMENS

Calculation of Natural Frequencies

Flexural Vibrations—Consider a specimen cut out from the x-direction which coincides with the principal direction as shown in Fig. 3. Timoshenko's beam theory [9] is used for calculating the natural frequencies of flexural vibration of a rectangular bar with free ends in order to take the effect of rotary inertia and shear into account. We assume that the interaction of vibrations in the y and z-direction can be neglected. The equation of motion in the z-direction is written as [10]:

$$E_x I_y \frac{\partial^4 w}{\partial x^4} + \rho A \frac{\partial^2 w}{\partial t^2} - \rho I_y (1 + \frac{E_x}{\kappa G_{zx}}) \frac{\partial^4 w}{\partial x^2 \partial t^2} + \frac{\rho^2 I_y}{\kappa G_{zx}} \frac{\partial^4 w}{\partial t^4} = 0 \qquad (1)$$

where w is the displacement in the z-direction, E_x is Young's modulus, G_{zx} is the shear modulus, I_y is the moment inertia of the cross section with respect to the y-axis, A is the area of the cross section, ρ is the density of the material, and κ is the shear coefficient which depends upon the shape of the cross section. Procedures for obtaining the formal solution of Timoshenko's equation have been described in the literature [11] and the frequency equation is given by:

$$2 - 2\cosh b\alpha \cos b\beta + \frac{b}{(1 - b^2 r^2 s^2)^{1/2}}[b^2 r^2(r^2 - s^2)^2 + (3r^2 - s^2)]\sinh b\alpha \sin b\beta = 0 \quad (2)$$

where the following relation holds:

$$\left.\begin{array}{c}\beta \\ \alpha\end{array}\right\} = \frac{1}{\sqrt{2}}\left\{\pm(r^2 + s^2) + \left[(r^2 - s^2)^2 + \frac{4}{b^2}\right]^{1/2}\right\}^{1/2}$$

$$b^2 = \frac{\rho A}{E_x I_y}l^4\omega^2, \quad r^2 = \frac{I_y}{Al^2}, \quad s^2 = \frac{E_x I_y}{\kappa A G_{zx} l^2} \quad (3)$$

where l is the length of the beam and ω is the natural frequency. Similar equations are obtained for the vibration in the y-direction.

These equations are highly transcendental and are numerically solved to obtain the natural frequencies of nth vibration modes, ω_{Vn} and ω_{Hn}. Note that the shear coefficient κ is a dimensionless quantity dependent on the shape of the cross section and introduced to account for the fact that shear stress and shear strain are not uniformly distributed over the cross section. A variety of numerical values are obtained for isotropic materials by a number of authors, and for a rectangular cross section, $\kappa = 2/3$ is given in Timoshenko's original paper [9], while $\kappa = 10(1 + \nu)/(12 + 11\nu)$ is given by Cowper [12] and the value of κ is almost constant irrespective of the value of ν, e.g., $\kappa = 0.8488 \sim 0.8497$ for $\nu = 0.28 \sim 0.30$.

For orthotropic material, it is difficult to obtain any relation between the shear coefficient κ and Poisson's ratios ν_{ij}, so that $\kappa = 0.8490$ will be used in the numerical computation hereafter.

Torsional Vibrations—An analysis of torsion of a rectangular bar of orthotropic material under Saint-Venant's assumption is given in the literature [13], and the equation of motion governing the torsional vibration of the specimen cut out along the x-direction is given by

$$\frac{\partial^2 \psi}{\partial t^2} = \frac{G_J}{I_p}\frac{\partial^2 \psi}{\partial x^2} \quad (4)$$

where ψ is the torsional angle and

$$\frac{G_J}{I_p} = \frac{4G_{zx}}{\rho\{1 + (\frac{h}{a})^2\}}\left[1 - \sqrt{\frac{G_{zx}}{G_{xy}}}\frac{192}{\pi^5}\frac{a}{h}\sum_{i=1,3,5,\cdots}^{\infty}\frac{1}{i^5}\tanh\frac{i\pi h}{2a}\sqrt{\frac{G_{xy}}{G_{zx}}}\right] \quad (5)$$

where a is the width, h is the height of the cross section, and $I_p = \rho(a^3 h + ah^3)/12$ is the polar moment of inertia of the cross section.

The frequency equation for torsional vibration is given by

$$\omega_{Tn} = \frac{n\pi}{l}\sqrt{\frac{G_J}{I_p}} \tag{6}$$

Calculation of Elastic Moduli by the Least Square Fit

Orthotropic elastic constants E_x, G_{zx}, and G_{xy} are calculated numerically from the measured values of natural frequencies of the flexural and torsional vibrations, ω_{Hn}, ω_{Vn}, and ω_{Tn}, by using the method of the least squares combined with the iteration technique [7].

Measurement of Elastic Constants of SiC/SiC Laminates and Damage Evaluation

The material tested is the Du Pont chemical vapor infiltration (CVI) matrix composite. The specimen blanks of 3 mm thickness were composed of eleven fabricated layers of bi-directional SiC fibers (Nicalon; Nippon Carbon Co., Ltd.) infiltrated with SiC matrix using CVI method. The mechanical and physical properties of this material published by the manufacturer (Du Pont CVI Ceramic Matrix Composites, Preliminary Engineering Data, Du Pont Composites H-28486) and those measured by the Fine Ceramics Center of Japan [14] are summarized in Table 1.

TABLE 1—Mechanical and physical properties of SiC/SiC composite.

Fiber Content %	Density, g/cm³	Porosity %	Young's Modulus, GPa	Shear Modulus, GPa	Poisson's Ratio
40	2.58	9.7	203	80	0.22

Five rectangular bar specimens were cut out by a thin diamond wheel from each of the x and y directions, i.e. , 0°/90° directions, of the as-received specimen blank as schematically shown in Fig. 3. Four surfaces of the specimen were finished using a surface grinder with a diamond wheel. The dimensions and the calculated densities of the specimens used in the present experiment are given in Table 2.

TABLE 2—Dimensions and densities of the test specimens.

Specimen	Direction	Width, mm	Height, mm	Length, mm	Density, g/cm³
a2	x	3.01	4.02	50.03	2.53
b2	y	2.99	4.02	50.08	2.54

Although the microscopic structure of this material is complicated and the published value of the porosity of the material is 9.7 % the specimens are assumed to be macroscopically homogeneous in the computations. The orthotropic elastic constants were measured at room temperature and high temperatures up to 1200°C in an oxidizing environment, i.e., air. The heating rate for the high temperature test was 20K/min and the cooling rate after experiment was 100K/min.

The measured natural frequencies and the computed orthotropic elastic constants are given in Tables 3 and 4, respectively. We conclude that the test material is almost isotropic in the xy-plane.

TABLE 3—Natural frequencies of the test specimens [kHz].

Specimen	Direction	ω_{V1}	ω_{V2}	ω_{H1}	ω_{H2}	ω_{T1}	ω_{T2}
a2	x	11.750	31.500	15.500	41.000	47.125	92.500
b2	y	11.625	31.125	15.625	41.000	49.000	96.250

TABLE 4—Orthotropic elastic constants of SiC/SiC composite.

Specimen	Direction	E_x, GPa	E_y, GPa	G_{zx}, GPa	G_{xy}, GPa	G_{yz}, GPa
a2	x	234.9	-	78.8	67.9	-
b2	y	-	235.4	-	68.3	68.3

The temperature dependence of the elastic constants, E_y, G_{zy}, and G_{xy}, of the b2 specimen is shown in Fig. 4(a). The elastic constants decreased with increasing temperature up to 1100°C. It was probable that the material suffered from damage by heat and/or oxidation. The elastic constants were also measured while holding the same specimen at 1100°C for 210 min. It was found that the values of the elastic constants recovered during the hold time as shown in Fig. 4(a). The closed symbols in Fig. 4(a) represent the elastic constants at the room temperature measured after the first heating cycle.

The same specimen was tested a second time and the elastic constants versus temperature relation is shown in Fig. 4(b). The elastic constants are almost constant irrespective of the test temperature. Similar tendencies are reported by Cutard et al. [4] and Huger et al. [5]. It is pointed out that in SiC/SiC composites the pyrocarbon interface, introduced for the achievement of good mechanical properties, makes the material sensitive to an oxidizing atmosphere at temperatures greater than 600°C.

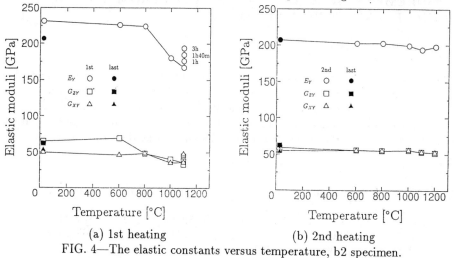

(a) 1st heating   (b) 2nd heating
FIG. 4—The elastic constants versus temperature, b2 specimen.

At temperatures greater than 800°C the formation of a silica (SiO_2) coat occurs by oxidation of silicon carbide which can act as protection against further oxidation of the interface in the core of the composites [15]. The chemical composition of the specimen surface was examined using a scanning Auger nanoprobe technique. The micrographs of the original specimen surface by the scanning secondary and/or Auger electron microscopy are shown in Fig. 5. Micrographs of the tested specimen surface after the hold time of 210 min at 1100°C in the first heating followed by the hold time of 60 min at 1200°C in the second heating are shown in Fig. 6. In the scanning Auger electron micrographs, the white parts represent the atom rich regions and the dark parts represent the atom poor regions. The chemical compositions in the atomic percent of the matrix, interface, and fiber measured by Auger electron spectroscopy before and after heating are given in Table 5. These results indicate that the pyrocarbon coatings were oxidized, and the formation of SiO_2 at the fiber/matrix interface took place during the hold time at high temperatures. We conclude in this stage that the damage as a result of oxidation can be estimated by measuring the decrease of the elastic constants.

TABLE 5—The chemical compositions of matrix, interface, and fiber before and after heating (atomic %).

Specimen	Condition	Location	Si	C	O
		matrix	46	54	<1
a2	Original	interface	10	89	<1
		fiber	38	57	5
		matrix	48	52	<1
b2	Heated	interface	53	7	39
		fiber	38	58	4

MEASUREMENT OF ELASTIC CONSTANTS FROM THE IMPACT SOUND OF RECTANGULAR PLATE

Rectangular Plate Specimens

Two rectangular plate SiC/SiC specimens were cut out by using a thin diamond wheel from another SiC/SiC specimen blank as shown in Fig. 3(b). The surfaces of the plate specimens were finished by using a surface grinder using a diamond wheel. The dimensions and densities are given in Table 6. Note that the density of the plate specimen is larger than that of the rectangular bar specimens shown in Table 2.

TABLE 6—Dimensions and densities of rectangular SiC/SiC specimens.

Specimen	Length, mm	Width, mm	Thickness, mm	Density, g/cm^3
P-1	70.00	49.99	2.80	2.65
P-2	70.00	49.99	2.81	2.67

Matrix

Interface

Fiber

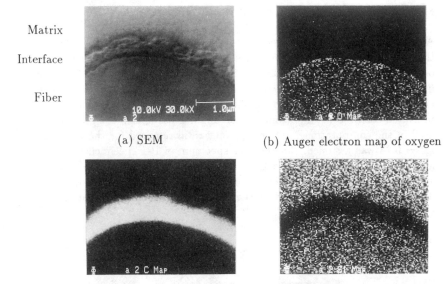

(a) SEM   (b) Auger electron map of oxygen

(c) Auger electron map of carbon   (d) Auger electron map of silicon

FIG. 5—Scanning Auger micrographs of the original specimen surface, a2 specimen.

Matrix

Interface

Fiber

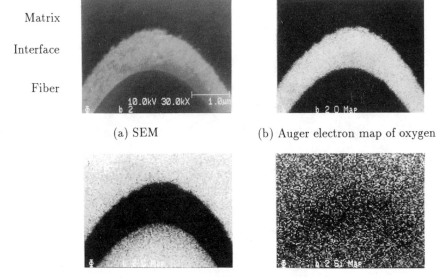

(a) SEM   (b) Auger electron map of oxygen

(c) Auger electron map of carbon   (d) Auger electron map of silicon

FIG. 6—Scanning Auger micrographs of the tested surface, b2 specimen.

Measurement of Elastic Constants at Room Temperature

A plate specimen was suspended in the place of the bar specimen shown in Fig. 1, and the natural frequencies were measured from the impact sound. The correspondence of each natural frequency to each vibration mode was determined from a preliminary finite element method (FEM) computation using ABAQUS code with eight node shell elements. The SiC/SiC composite plate was assumed to be orthotropic, therefore the measured elastic constants from the rectangular bar specimens given in Table 4 were used in the computation. As for Poisson's ratio required for the FEM computation, $\nu_{xy} = 0.28$ was assumed. The Fourier spectrum of P-1 specimen is shown in Fig. 7, and the identified natural frequencies are given in Table 7. The three elastic constants, E_x, E_y, and G_{xy}, were determined from the measured natural frequencies by using an iteration technique combined with the FEM computations [7] and are given in Table 8.

mode 1, f_1=5.15 kHz   mode 2, f_2=5.90 kHz   mode 3, f_3=11.52 kHz

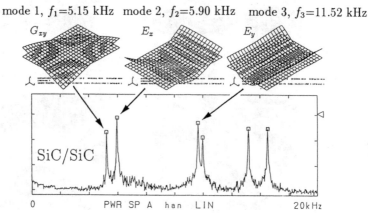

FIG. 7—Fourier spectrum and corresponding vibration modes of plate specimen.

TABLE 7—Measured and identified natural frequencies of plate specimens [kHz].

Specimen	Mode 1	Mode 2	Mode 3	Mode 4	Mode 5	Mode 6
P-1	5.150	5.900	11.526	11.850	15.025	16.400
P-2	5.200	5.950	11.650	11.975	15.175	16.525

TABLE 8—Measured elastic constants of plate specimens.

Specimen	E_x,GPa	E_y, GPa	G_{xy}, GPa
P-1	274.0	268.0	108.0
P-2	276.0	272.0	110.0

Measurement of Elastic Constants at High Temperatures

The elastic constants of the P-1 specimen at temperatures up to 1200°C were measured. The variation of elastic constants with time when held at 1200°C for 4 h was also measured. The reduction of E_x and G_{xy} as functions of test temperature is shown in Fig. 8(a), and their variation with time is shown in Fig. 8(b). The reduction of elastic constants at temperatures greater than 600°C observed in Fig. 8(a) is attributed to oxidation of the pyrocarbon layer of the SiC fiber. The recovery during the hold time is caused by the formation of SiO_2 at the previously existing pyrocarbon layer. The elastic constants versus temperature relation for the second heating stage is represented in Fig. 9. The elastic constants at room temperature after the high temperature exposure test, are represented as closed symbols in Figs. 8(a) and 9.

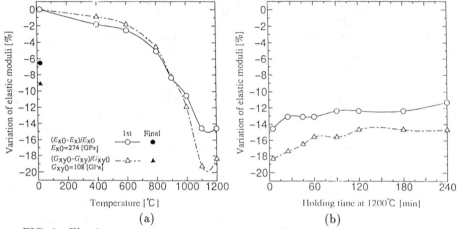

(a)   (b)

FIG. 8—Elastic constants versus temperature and time variation of elastic constants, 1st heating, specimen P-1.

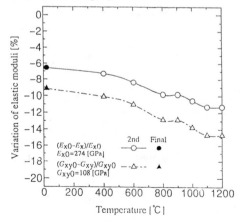

FIG. 9—Elastic constants versus temperature, 2nd heating, specimen P-1.

FIG. 10—Configuration of jet engine flap.

DAMAGE EVALUATION OF A JET ENGINE FLAP

As an example of application, the present method is extended to measure the natural frequencies of plate-like hot section components. A jet engine nozzle flap was manufactured by Ishikawajima-Harima Heavy Industries Co., Ltd. An orthogonal 3 dimensional fabric (100 by 200 by 5 mm in nominal size) woven with continuous yarns of Si-Ti-C-O fibers (Tyranno, LOX-M grade; Ube Co., Ltd.) was densified by CVI and polymer impregnation and pyrolysis (PIP) processes [16]. The nozzle flap was equipped in a demonstrator jet engine in an attempt to estimate the reliability of SiC/SiC components. The total running time was 33 h and the maximum surface temperature of the flap was 700°C. The natural frequencies of the flap before and after engine operations were measured from the impact sound, and the Young's modulus of the material was measured to estimate the damage of the flap. Since the actual nozzle flap is of a complicated configuration with bolt holes and chamfers as shown in Fig. 10, it was modeled as a rectangular plate of 190 by 112.5 by 5.0 mm. The identification of vibration modes and computation of the elastic constants were carried out by an analogous method used for the plate specimens described in the preceding section.

The measured values of the natural frequencies corresponding to the first and fifth vibration modes are given in Table 9.

TABLE 9—Natural frequencies and degradation of nozzle flap.

Vibration Mode	Mode 1	Mode 5
original flap	987.0 Hz	3375 Hz
used flap	950.0 Hz	3162 Hz
degradation D	7%	12%

The natural frequencies of bending mode vibration of a plate are expressed by

$$\omega^2 = constant \times \frac{E}{\rho} \tag{7}$$

where ω is the natural frequency, ρ is the density, E is the Young's modulus. Let the Young's moduli of the flap before and after usage be E_0 and E_d, respectively. Then, the degradation of the material in terms of the reduction of the Young's modulus is given by

$$D = 1 - \frac{E_d}{E_0} = 1 - \left(\frac{\omega_d}{\omega_0}\right)^2 \tag{8}$$

The degradation of the jet engine nozzle flap is shown in Table 9. The reduction of Young's modulus in the x-direction E_x was 7% while that in the y-direction E_y was 12% in the present case. It is thought that oxidation of the pyrocarbon is probable at the maximum test temperature, 700°C, while formation of SiO_2 does not take place.

CONCLUSIONS

The orthotropic elastic constants of SiC/SiC composites were measured from the impact sound of rectangular bar and/or plate specimens and the relation between the elastic constants and temperature was obtained up to 1200°C. When the specimens were held at high temperatures for a period of time, an increase of the elastic constants over time partially restored their observed decrease in the earlier stage. Scanning Auger electron microscopy showed that the decrease of elastic constants is attributable to the oxidation of the pyrocarbon coating of SiC fibers and formation of SiO_2. By using the present technique, the damage of a engine nozzle flap made of SiC/SiC composite was estimated as the reduction of the Young's modulus of the flap before and after engine operation. The present method is capable of measuring the orthotropic shear modulus and Young's modulus of composite materials at high temperatures by a simple and cost-effective procedure using small specimens. This method is therefore useful for material evaluation at the development and operation stages.

ACKNOWLEDGMENT

The authors gratefully acknowledge Dr. M. Mizuno of the Fine Ceramics Center of Japan for providing us with part of the specimens. The authors are also grateful to Dr. K. Sato of Nippon Steel Techno Research Co., Ltd. for help with the scanning Auger electron microscopy.

REFERENCES

[1] Stephens, J. R., Hecht, R. J., and Johnson, A. M., "Material Requirements for the High Speed Civil Transport," 11th International Symposium on Air Breathing Engines (ISABE), F. S. Billig, Ed. 1993, pp. 701-710.

[2] Williams, L. J., "NASA's High-Speed Research Program," 7th European Aerospace Conference (EAC'94) on The Supersonic Transport of Second Generation, Oct. 1994.

[3] Hiromatsu, M., et al., "Research and Development Status of Advanced Material Gas-Generator (AMG) Project," 95-GT-287, Internal Gas Turbine and Aeroengine Congress and Exposition, June 1995.

[4] Cutard, T., Huger, M., Fargeot, D., and Gault. C., "Ultrasonic Characterization at High Temperature of Damage in Ceramic Composites Subjected to Tensile Stresses," 6th European Conference on Composite Materials, High Temperature Ceramic Matrix Composites (HT-CMC1), Bordeaux, 1993, pp. 699-706.

[5] Huger, M., Fargeot, D., and Gault, C., "Ultrasonic Characterization of Oxidation Mechanism in Nicalon/C/SiC Composites," Journal of the American Ceramic Society, Vol. 77, No. 10, Oct. 1994, PP. 2554-2560.

[6] Moreau, A. and Jones, J. T., "Laser-Ultrasonic Assess High-Temperature Elastic Properties," Ceramic Industry, Mar. 1995, pp. 45-46.

[7] Sakata, M., Kimura, K., and Shimojo, J., "Measurement of Isotropic and Anisotropic Elastic Moduli from the Impact Sound of Engineering Ceramics and Composites at Elevated Temperatures," in Proceedings of the International Symposium on Impact Engineering, Vol. II, I. Maekawa, Ed., Nov. 1992, Sendai, Japan, pp 502-507.

[8] Sakata, M. and Ohnabe, H., "Measurement of Elastic Moduli from the Impact Sound of Ceramic Matrix Composites at Elevated Temperatures," in Proceedings of the American Society for Composites–Ninth Technical Conference, Newark, Delaware, Sept. 1994, pp 79-86.

[9] Timoshenko, S. P., "On the Correction for Shear of the Differential Equation for Transverse Vibrations of Prismatic Bars," Philosophical Magazine, Ser. 6, Vol. 41, 1921, pp. 744-746.

[10] Nowinski, J. L., "On the Transverse Wave Propagation in Orthotropic Timoshenko Bars," Technical Report No. 98, Deptartment of Mechanical and Aerospace Engineering, University of Delaware, 1969.

[11] Huang, T. C., "The Effect of Rotatory Inertia and of Shear Deformation on the Frequency and Normal Mode Equations of Uniform Beams with Simple End Conditions ," Journal of Applied Mechanics, 1961, pp. 579-584.

[12] Cowper, G. R., "The Shear Coefficient in Timoshenko's Beam Theory," Journal of Applied Mechanics, Vol. 33, 1966, pp. 335-340.

[13] Kobayashi, S. and Kondo, K., "Elasticity," Baifukan, Tokyo, 1987, pp. 252-254.

[14] Mizuno, M., Nagano, Y., Usami, H., Ito, T., and Kagawa, Y., "Effect of Specimen Shape on Fracture Toughness and Effective Fracture Energy in SiC-SiC Composite," in Proceedings of the 18th Annual Conference on Composites and Advanced Ceramic Materials-B, Cocoa Beach, FL, Jan. 1993, pp. 859-866.

[15] Filipuzzi, L., Camus, G., and Naslain, R., "Oxidation Mechanisms and Kinetics of 1D-SiC/C/SiC Composite Materials: I, An Experimental Approach," Journal of the American Ceramic Society, Vol. 77, No. 2, 1994, pp.456-466.

[16] Araki, T., Natsumura, T., Hayashi, M., Sugai, S., Masaki, S., Imamura, R., and Ohnabe, H., " Development of Ceramic Matrix Composite Nozzle Flaps For Jet Engines," in Proceedings of 4th Japan International SAMPE Symposium, Tokyo, Sep. 1995, pp. 374-379.

Modeling and Processing

Alexander L. Kalamkarov[1]

ON THE OPTIMAL DESIGN OF FIBER-REINFORCED LAMINATES

REFERENCE: Kalamkarov, A. L. **"On the Optimal Design of Fiber-Reinforced Laminates,"** Thermal and Mechanical Test Methods and Behavior of Continuous-Fiber Ceramic Composites, ASTM STP 1309, Michael G. Jenkins, Stephen T. Gonczy, Edgar Lara-Curzio, Noel E. Ashbaugh, and Larry P. Zawada, Eds., American Society for Testing and Materials, 1997.

ABSTRACT: The optimal design of the fiber-reinforced laminates is based on the application of the general homogenization model for the composite shell developed earlier by the author. The optimal design algorithm for the fiber-reinforced laminates with the prescribed set of effective stiffnesses is developed. The set of prescribed effective stiffnesses for which the design problem is solvable, is described, and the effective method of the design parameters calculation based on the convex analysis is developed. The sufficient number of plies required for the design of the fiber-reinforced angle-ply laminate with the prescribed set of effective stiffnesses is determined. The design problem is generalized on account of minimization of the fiber volume content. The effectiveness and advantages of the developed approach are illustrated by several design examples.

KEYWORDS: fiber-reinforced angle-ply composite laminate, homogenization, effective stiffenesses, optimal design

INTRODUCTION

A fiber-reinforced lamina based upon ceramic or metal matrices can be manufactured by various solid, liquid, or gaseous routes, for example, by diffusion bonding, extrusion and drawing, liquid infiltration, compocasting, etc. A composite laminate is fabricated by stacking and bonding together individual laminae with various orientations of principal material directions determined by the directions of fibers. Laminates may be unidirectional ($0°$), cross-ply ($0°/90°$) or angle-ply ($0°<\phi<90°$) depending on the arrangements of fibers in laminae. The general type of angle-ply laminates will be considered in the present study.

The mechanical model which allows the prediction of the behavior of multiple inhomogeneities in composite structure is provided by the sets of equations with rapidly varying coefficients that characterize the properties of the individual phases of the composite material. The resulting boundary-value problems are very complex, and it is quite natural, therefore, to seek mechanical models with some averaged coefficients.

[1]Professor, Director of the Smart Materials Centre, Mechanical Engineering Department,Technical University of Nova Scotia, Halifax, Nova Scotia, B3J 2X4 Canada.

Different averaging techniques have been adopted to estimate the effective elastic properties of composites, see e.g., [1 - 6]. Analytical averaging schemes were also utilized in [7 - 9] to provide an estimate of the overall elastic properties of inhomogeneous composite structures.

The effective properties of the composite material of a periodic structure can be calculated by means of the asymptotic homogenization method. The mathematical aspects of the asymptotic homogenization technique can be found in [10 - 13]. This method is mathematically rigorous, and it enables the prediction of both the local and overall averaged properties of the composite solid.

The rigorous general homogenization composite shell model was developed earlier by the author [12, 14 - 16] by applying a modified asymptotic homogenization technique to three-dimensional elastic problem for a thin curvilinear periodically inhomogeneous composite layer. The application of this general model to the analysis of fiber-reinforced composite shells provides an accurate analytical determination of their effective stiffnesses as well as the local stress distributions, see [12] and [16].

In the present paper, these results are taken as a basis to formulate and solve a design problem for fiber-reinforced laminates with the prescribed set of effective stiffnesses.

GENERAL HOMOGENIZATION COMPOSITE SHELL MODEL

Let us consider a three-dimensional composite layer of a periodic structure with the unit cell Ω_δ. Thickness of this layer, δ, and scale of the composite material inhomogeneity are assumed to be small as compared with the dimensions of the solid as whole. It is common practice in performing the stress analysis of a composite structural member that the inhomogeneous medium being studied is replaced with a homogeneous anisotropic medium whose response is believed to be equivalent to that of the actual composite in a certain average sense. If the composite material has a periodic structure, the averaged (or effective) properties of the equivalent anisotropic homogeneous material can be estimated by means of the asymptotic homogenization method, which also gives asymptotically correct results for the local stress field in the bulk of the composite solid. In the previous studies by the author, see [12, 14 - 16], this approach was adopted in the analysis of composite and reinforced thin-walled structural members. As a result, the general composite shell model was developed. It was shown that it is possible to calculate both the effective and local properties of this composite layer by first solving appropriate three-dimensional local problems set on the unit cell, and subsequently solving a two-dimensional boundary-value problem for a homogeneous (or quasi-homogeneous) anisotropic shell with the effective stiffness moduli obtained at the first step.

The constitutive relations of the anisotropic homogeneous shell, that is those between the stress resultants N_1, N_2, N_{12} and moment resultants M_1, M_2, M_{12} on the one hand, and the mid-surface strains ε_{11}, ε_{22} (elongation), $\varepsilon_{12}=\varepsilon_{21}=\omega/2$ (shear), τ_{11}, τ_{22} (bending), $\tau_{12}=\tau_{21}=\tau$ (torsion) on the other, can be represented as follows [12]:

$$N_\beta = \delta<b_{\beta\beta}{}^{\lambda\mu}>\varepsilon_{\lambda\mu} + \delta^2<c_{\beta\beta}{}^{\lambda\mu}>\tau_{\lambda\mu}, \qquad N_{12} = \delta<b_{12}{}^{\lambda\mu}>\varepsilon_{\lambda\mu} + \delta^2<c_{12}{}^{\lambda\mu}>\tau_{\lambda\mu} \qquad (1)$$

$$M_\beta = \delta^2<zb_{\beta\beta}{}^{\lambda\mu}>\varepsilon_{\lambda\mu} + \delta^3<zc_{\beta\beta}{}^{\lambda\mu}>\tau_{\lambda\mu}, \qquad M_{12} = \delta^2<zb_{12}{}^{\lambda\mu}>\varepsilon_{\lambda\mu} + \delta^3<zc_{12}{}^{\lambda\mu}>\tau_{\lambda\mu} \qquad (2)$$

where β assumes the values 1 and 2, and is not summed here; $\lambda,\mu = 1,2$ and are summed. The functions $b_{kl}{}^{mn}(\xi_1,\xi_2,z)$ and $c_{kl}{}^{mn}(\xi_1,\xi_2,z)$, k,l,m,n,=1,2,3 can be calculated from the solution of local problems on the unit cell [12]. They are periodic in variables

$\xi_1=\alpha_1 A_1/(\delta h_1)$ and $\xi_2=\alpha_2 A_2/(\delta h_2)$ with periods A_1 and A_2 correspondingly; α_1, α_2 and γ are the orthogonal curvilinear coordinates, such that the coordinate lines α_1 and α_2 coincide with the curvature lines of the mid-surface of the shell and coordinate lines γ are normal to the mid-surface ($\gamma=0$), and $z=\gamma/\delta$. Functions $A_1(\alpha_1,\alpha_2)$ and $A_2(\alpha_1,\alpha_2)$ are the coefficients of the first quadratic form of the mid-surface of the layer, and δh_1, δh_2 are tangential dimensions of the periodicity cell Ω_δ. The averaging symbol $<...>$ in Eqs. (1) and (2) denotes the integration over the three-dimensional unit cell of composite layer, as follows:

$$<F(\xi_1,\xi_2,z)> = \int_\Omega F(\xi_1,\xi_2,z)d\xi_1 d\xi_2 dz \tag{3}$$

Local problems having been solved, the functions $b_{kl}{}^{mn}(\xi_1,\xi_2,z)$ and $c_{kl}{}^{mn}(\xi_1,\xi_2,z)$ are averaged by application of Eq. (3), giving the effective stiffnesses of the anisotropic homogeneous shell, $<b_{\alpha\beta}{}^{\lambda\mu}>$, $<zb_{\alpha\beta}{}^{\lambda\mu}>=<c_{\alpha\beta}{}^{\lambda\mu}>$, and $<zc_{\alpha\beta}{}^{\lambda\mu}>$. One may proceed then to solution of the boundary-value problem for the homogeneous shell [12], to calculate the mid-surface strains $\varepsilon_{\lambda\mu}(\alpha_1,\alpha_2)$ and $\tau_{\lambda\mu}(\alpha_1,\alpha_2)$.

The notation for the effective stiffnesses used in Eqs. (1) and (2) is naturally related to the local problem formulation in the general homogenization composite shell model. There is the following simple correspondence between this notation and the conventional notation of classical laminated plate theory (see e.g., [8]) for the effective stiffnesses:

$$
\begin{aligned}
&A_{11} = \delta<b_{11}{}^{11}>, && B_{11} = \delta^2<zb_{11}{}^{11}> = \delta^2<c_{11}{}^{11}>, && D_{11} = \delta^3<zc_{11}{}^{11}> \\
&A_{12} = \delta<b_{11}{}^{22}>, && B_{12} = \delta^2<zb_{11}{}^{22}> = \delta^2<c_{11}{}^{22}>, && D_{12} = \delta^3<zc_{11}{}^{22}> \\
&A_{16} = \delta<b_{11}{}^{12}>, && B_{16} = \delta^2<zb_{11}{}^{12}> = \delta^2<c_{11}{}^{12}>, && D_{16} = \delta^3<zc_{11}{}^{12}> \quad (4)\\
&A_{22} = \delta<b_{22}{}^{22}>, && B_{22} = \delta^2<zb_{22}{}^{22}> = \delta^2<c_{22}{}^{22}>, && D_{22} = \delta^3<zc_{22}{}^{22}> \\
&A_{26} = \delta<b_{22}{}^{12}>, && B_{26} = \delta^2<zb_{22}{}^{12}> = \delta^2<c_{22}{}^{12}>, && D_{26} = \delta^3<zc_{22}{}^{12}> \\
&A_{66} = \delta<b_{12}{}^{12}>, && B_{66} = \delta^2<zb_{12}{}^{12}> = \delta^2<c_{12}{}^{12}>, && D_{66} = \delta^3<zc_{12}{}^{12}>
\end{aligned}
$$

Both notations related by Eq. (4) will be used in the sequel.

The general homogenization composite shell model also provides an asymptotic result for the three-dimensional local stress distribution in the composite layer. These stresses can be calculated as follows ($i,j = 1,2,3$; $\mu,\nu = 1,2$):

$$\sigma_{ij} \approx b_{ij}{}^{\mu\nu}(\xi_1,\xi_2,z)\varepsilon_{\mu\nu}(\alpha_1,\alpha_2) + \delta c_{ij}{}^{\mu\nu}(\xi_1,\xi_2,z)\tau_{\mu\nu}(\alpha_1,\alpha_2) \tag{5}$$

Analysis of local deformations and stresses was performed earlier, see [12] and [16], and it was shown, in particular, that the large local shear stresses arise in the matrix material in the case of dense placement of the fiber plies. The failure of matrix material caused by the torsion deformation occurs if the fiber volume content exceeds 60%. Torsion failure of the matrix causes the delamination of the high-stiffness fiber-reinforced laminate.

The application of the general homogenization composite shell model is limited to the case in which thickness of the laminate and the scale of periodicity, i.e., parameter δ, is much smaller than the overall dimensions of the solid. This requirement is fulfilled in a large number of applications.

FIBER-REINFORCED ANGLE-PLY LAMINATE

The fiber-reinforced angle-ply laminate is shown in Fig. 1. The laminate is formed by N layers reinforced by parallel fibers. The fiber within a jth layer, $j=1,2,...,N$, makes an angle φ_j with the coordinate line α_1. The thickness of laminate is δ, and the departure of the axis of the fiber of the jth ply from the mid-surface ($\gamma=0$) is equal to δa_j, where a_j is a dimensionless quantity equal to a departure of the axis of the fiber normalized by δ.

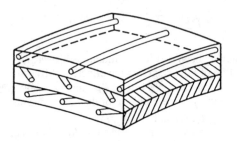

FIG. 1 -- Fiber-reinforced angle-ply laminate.

We assume that material of fibers is much stiffer than the matrix material, $E_F \gg E_M$. That is typical for the polymer matrix fiber-reinforced composites, for which E_F/E_M is of the order of 100. Local problems are much simplified, on account of the above assumption, by a decoupling in the regions of fibers and matrix.

<u>Effective Stiffnesses</u>

Local problems of the general homogenization composite shell model can be solved analytically for the elliptical cross-section of the fibers, see [14]. Having solved the local problems, we average the functions $b_{\alpha\beta}{}^{\lambda\mu}(\xi_1,\xi_2,z)$ and $c_{\alpha\beta}{}^{\lambda\mu}(\xi_1,\xi_2,z)$ and then sum them up over the all N layers to obtain the following formulas for the effective moduli of the high-stiffness fiber-reinforced angle-ply shell:

$$<b_{\alpha\beta}{}^{\lambda\mu}> = \sum_{j=1}^{N} E_j \, \mathcal{B}_j^{(\alpha\beta\lambda\mu)} \, \theta\gamma_j, \quad <zb_{\alpha\beta}{}^{\lambda\mu}> = <c_{\alpha\beta}{}^{\lambda\mu}> = \sum_{j=1}^{N} a_j \, E_j \, \mathcal{B}_j^{(\alpha\beta\lambda\mu)} \, \theta_j \quad (6)$$

$$<zc_{\alpha\beta}{}^{\lambda\mu}> = \sum_{j=1}^{N} E_j \, \theta_j \, [a_j^2 \, \mathcal{B}_j^{(\alpha\beta\lambda\mu)} + C_j^{(\alpha\beta\lambda\mu)} \, (16(1+v_j))^{-1}] \quad (7)$$

Here E_j and v_j are Young's modulus and Poisson's ratio of fibers of the jth layer; θ_j is the fiber volume content in the jth layer; and the parameters $\mathcal{B}_j^{(\alpha\beta\lambda\mu)}$ and $C_j^{(\alpha\beta\lambda\mu)}$ are determined by the following formulas for each combination of superscripts α, β, λ, $\mu=1,2$:

$$\mathcal{B}_j^{(1111)} = A_1^4 \mathcal{D}_j^{-4} \cos^4\varphi_j, \qquad \mathcal{B}_j^{(1112)} = \mathcal{B}_j^{(1211)} = A_1^3 A_2 \mathcal{D}_j^{-4} \cos^3\varphi_j \sin\varphi_j$$

$$\mathcal{B}_j^{(1122)} = \mathcal{B}_j^{(2211)} = \mathcal{B}_j^{(1212)} = A_1^2 A_2^2 \mathcal{D}_j^{-4} \cos^2\varphi_j \sin^2\varphi_j \qquad (8)$$

$$\mathcal{B}_j^{(2222)} = A_2^4 \mathcal{D}_j^{-4} \sin^4\varphi_j, \quad \mathcal{B}_j^{(1222)} = \mathcal{B}_j^{(2212)} = A_1 A_2^3 \mathcal{D}_j^{-4} \cos\varphi_j \sin^3\varphi_j$$

$$C_j^{(1111)} = A_1^4 \mathcal{D}_j^{-4} \cos^2\varphi_j \,[2A_2^4 \sin^2\varphi_j (1 - e_j^2)\Delta_j + \cos^2\varphi_j (1+v_j)]$$

$$C_j^{(2222)} = A_2^4 \mathcal{D}_j^{-4} \sin^2\varphi_j \,[2A_1^4 \cos^2\varphi_j (1 - e_j^2)\Delta_j + \sin^2\varphi_j (1+v_j)]$$

$$C_j^{(1122)} = C_j^{(2211)} = A_1^2 A_2^2 \mathcal{D}_j^{-4} \sin^2\varphi_j \cos^2\varphi_j \,[- 2A_1^2 A_2^2 (1 - e_j^2)\Delta_j + (1+v_j)] \qquad (9)$$

$$C_j^{(1112)} = C_j^{(1211)} = A_1^3 A_2 \mathcal{D}_j^{-4} \sin\varphi_j \cos\varphi_j \,[A_2^2 (A_2^2 \sin^2\varphi_j - A_1^2 \cos^2\varphi_j)(1 - e_j^2)\Delta_j + \cos^2\varphi_j (1+v_j)]$$

$$C_j^{(1222)} = C_j^{(2212)} = A_1 A_2^3 \mathcal{D}_j^{-4} \sin\varphi_j \cos\varphi_j \,[A_1^2 (A_1^2 \cos^2\varphi_j - A_2^2 \sin^2\varphi_j)(1 - e_j^2)\Delta_j + \sin^2\varphi_j (1+v_j)]$$

$$C_j^{(1212)} = 0.5 \, A_1^2 A_2^2 \mathcal{D}_j^{-4} \,[(A_1^2 \cos^2\varphi_j - A_2^2 \sin^2\varphi_j)^2 (1 - e_j^2)\Delta_j + 2\sin^2\varphi_j \cos^2\varphi_j (1+v_j)]$$

where

$$\mathcal{D}_j^2 = A_1^2 \cos^2\varphi_j + A_2^2 \sin^2\varphi_j, \qquad \Delta_j = [\mathcal{D}_j^2 + A_1^2 A_2^2 (1 - e_j^2)]^{-1} \qquad (10)$$

and e_j is the eccentricity of the elliptical cross-section of the fiber of the jth ply. In the case of circular fibers, $e_j = 0$.

It is of interest to compare expressions (6)-(10) for the high-stiffness fiber-reinforced laminates with the results that have been derived in the framework of the semi-empirical approach [6]. In this procedure, first the averaging the composite material characteristics of individual layers is performed, and then the overall stiffnesses of the composite angle-ply laminate are calculated using the orthotropic effective stiffnesses of laminae and the stacking orientation of each lamina. The comparison shows that the formulas (6) for the moduli $<b_{\alpha\beta}^{\lambda\mu}>$ and $<zb_{\alpha\beta}^{\lambda\mu}>$ coincide with the corresponding formulas for the effective stiffnesses of a laminate loaded in tension/compression or shear, and that $A_1 = A_2 =1$. However, the above flexural and torsional stiffnesses, $<zc_{\alpha\beta}^{\lambda\mu}>$, given by Eq. (7), do differ from the corresponding results of the semi-empirical approach, and can be converted to these latter by setting $e_j = 1$, $j=1,2,...,N$ (which means neglecting the shape of the cross-sections of the fibers in all plies), and, in addition to that, by replacing the factor 16 by 12 in the denominator in the last term in Eq. (7) (which means neglecting the correct calculation of the moment of inertia of the fiber cross-section). Apparently, the above Eqs. (7) - (10) derived using the general homogenization composite shell model are more rigorous than the results of the approximate approach, in terms of better accounting the microstructure of the composite material.

<u>Numerical Example</u>

To obtain an estimate of the accuracy of the solution, consider a three-layer angle-ply laminate of a thickness δ and with the fiber placement angles $\varphi_1=\pi/4$, $\varphi_2=0$, and $\varphi_3=-\pi/4$. The fibers in all three plies are made of the similar material with isotropic elastic properties E and ν, and they have a similar circular cross-section. We also assume that $\theta_1=\theta_2=\theta_3=\theta_0$, $a_1=1/3$, $a_2=0$, $a_3=-1/3$, and $A_1 = A_2 = 1$. From Eq. (7), the non-zero flexural and torsional moduli of the shell in the conventional notation, see Eq. (4), are given by

$$D_{11} = [0.15 + 0.031\,(1 + \nu)^{-1}]\,\delta^3 E\theta_0, \quad D_{12} = [0.06 + 0.031\nu\,(1 + \nu)^{-1}]\,\delta^3 E\theta_0$$

$$D_{22} = [0.09 + 0.031\,(1 + \nu)^{-1}]\,\delta^3 E\theta_0, \quad D_{66} = [0.09 + 0.016\,(1 + \nu)^{-1}]\,\delta^3 E\theta_0$$

(11)

To specify the magnitude of the correction, let us consider the graphite/polyimide angle-ply laminate with the following properties of fibers and matrix: $E_F = 300$ GPa, $E_F/E_M = 100$, and $\nu_F = 0.2$. We assume that a lamina thickness is 0.14 mm, and the fiber volume content is 60%. The magnitudes of the effective stiffnesses calculated from Eq. (11) are the following: $D_{11} = 2.34$ Nm, $D_{12} = 0.93$ Nm, $D_{22} = 1.55$ Nm, and $D_{66} = 1.37$ Nm. The corresponding values resulting from the semi-empirical approach [6] are: $D_{11} = 2.4$ Nm, and $D_{12} = D_{22} = D_{66} = 1.29$ Nm. The maximum correction of 27% is obtained for the effective stiffness D_{12}.

DESIGN OF THE FIBER-REINFORCED ANGLE-PLY LAMINATE

In many cases, design of the composite engineering structures is based on some empirical approximate formulas. But it should be understood that a satisfactory design result can be achieved only if the design procedure is based on a rigorous basic theoretical model.

The application of the general homogenization composite shell model to the analysis of the fiber-reinforced laminate shown in Fig. 1 provides the accurate calculation of its effective stiffnesses. These results are used in this section for the design of a composite laminate with the required set of effective stiffnesses. A different approach was developed earlier in [17] for the optimal design of wafer- and honeycomb-like reinforced shells.

Suppose it is required to design the fiber-reinforced angle-ply laminate with the prescribed set of effective stiffnesses. Eqs. (6) - (10) express the effective moduli of the high-stiffness fiber-reinforced laminate in terms of fiber placement angles φ_j, fiber volume content θ_j, where j is a number of the layer and some other material properties and geometrical dimensions of the laminate. Let us assume now that all fibers are of a circular cross-section, and that they are made of a similar material with Young's modulus E. We also assume that $A_1=A_2=1$, which is possible for the cylindrical shells or plates, in particular. The set of effective stiffnesses in the tangential directions to the shell surface can be then expressed as follows, cf. Eqs. (4), (6) and (8):

$$A_{11} = \delta\langle b_{11}{}^{11}\rangle = E\omega Y_1(\gamma,\varphi), \qquad A_{22} = \delta\langle b_{22}{}^{22}\rangle = E\omega Y_2(\gamma,\varphi)$$

$$A_{16} = \delta\langle b_{11}{}^{12}\rangle = E\omega Y_3(\gamma,\varphi), \qquad A_{26} = \delta\langle b_{12}{}^{22}\rangle = E\omega Y_4(\gamma,\varphi)$$

(12)

$$A_{66} = A_{12} = \delta\langle b_{12}{}^{12}\rangle = \delta\langle b_{11}{}^{22}\rangle = 0.5\,E\omega\,[1 - Y_1(\gamma,\varphi) - Y_2(\gamma,\varphi)]$$

where

$$Y_1(\gamma,\varphi) = \sum_{j=1}^{N} \gamma_j \cos^4\varphi_j, \qquad\qquad Y_2(\gamma,\varphi) = \sum_{j=1}^{N} \gamma_j \sin^4\varphi_j \qquad (13)$$

$$Y_3(\gamma,\varphi) = \sum_{j=1}^{N} \gamma_j \sin\varphi_j \cos^3\varphi_j, \qquad Y_4(\gamma,\varphi) = \sum_{j=1}^{N} \gamma_j \sin^3\varphi_j \cos\varphi_j$$

Here $\omega = \sum_{j=1}^{N} \theta_j$, $\gamma = (\gamma_1,\gamma_2,...,\gamma_N)$, and $\gamma_j = \dfrac{\theta_j}{\omega}$ is the proportion of fiber content within the jth layer, and $\varphi = (\varphi_1,\varphi_2,...,\varphi_N)$. By replacing functionals $Y_1(\gamma,\varphi)$, $Y_2(\gamma,\varphi)$, $Y_3(\gamma,\varphi)$, and $Y_4(\gamma,\varphi)$ by the variables y_1, y_2, y_3, and y_4, and using the conventional notation for the effective stiffnesses, see Eq.(12), we obtain the following algebraic system:

$$A_{11} = E\omega y_1, \qquad\qquad A_{22} = E\omega y_2, \qquad\qquad A_{16} = E\omega y_3$$

$$(14)$$

$$A_{26} = E\omega y_4, \qquad A_{66} = A_{12} = 0.5\, E\omega\, (1 - y_1 - y_2)$$

If we prescribe values of the effective stiffnesses A_{11}, A_{22}, A_{16}, A_{26}, and $A_{66} = A_{12}$, then Eq. (14) will represent the system for determining $y = (y_1, y_2, y_3, y_4)$. Since the number of equations in the system (14) exceeds a number of unknowns, the following condition (it is natural to call it a solvability condition) should be fulfilled:

$$A_{66} = A_{12} = 0.5\ (E\omega - A_{11} - A_{22}) \qquad (15)$$

The system (14) can be resolved explicitly, so that

$$y_1 = A_{11}\ (E\omega)^{-1},\ y_2 = A_{22}\ (E\omega)^{-1},\ y_3 = A_{16}\ (E\omega)^{-1},\ y_4 = A_{26}\ (E\omega)^{-1} \qquad (16)$$

The next and major step in the design problem is to determine the fiber volume fractions $\gamma = (\gamma_1,\gamma_2,...,\gamma_N)$ and the fiber placement angles $\varphi = (\varphi_1,\varphi_2,...,\varphi_N)$, such that satisfy equations:

$$Y_1(\gamma,\varphi) = y_1, \qquad Y_2(\gamma,\varphi) = y_2, \qquad Y_3(\gamma,\varphi) = y_3, \qquad Y_4(\gamma,\varphi) = y_4 \qquad (17)$$

The following natural limitations are imposed on the design parameters:

$$\sum_{j=1}^{N} \gamma_j = 1, \qquad\qquad \gamma_j \geq 0,\ j=1,2,...,N \qquad (18)$$

$$\varphi_j \in [0, \pi],\ j=1,2,...,N \qquad (19)$$

The question of a great practical importance here is the determining the minimum number of layers, N_{min}, that is required to design the fiber-reinforced shell with the prescribed set of effective stiffnesses.

Design Problem Formulation

The design problem includes the following two questions:
(1) determine if the system of equations (17) is solvable in the set of variables satisfying conditions (18) and (19), and

(2) if the answer on the question (1) is positive, then find the set of solutions of the system (17) under the conditions (18) and (19).

Design Problem Solution

To solve the design problem, we first define a following set of intervals within $[0, \pi]$ that impose the limitations on fiber placement angles φ_j: $\Phi^N = \sum_{i=1}^{N} [a_i, b_i] \subset [0, \pi]$, and consider a set

$$U_\Phi^N = \{\varphi \in \Phi^N, \gamma \in R^N, \gamma \text{ satisfies conditions (18)}\} \tag{20}$$

Problem (17) and (18) is solvable in the set of variables U_Φ^N if and only if the right-hand sides of equations (17), (y_1, y_2, y_3, y_4) belong to an image of the set U_Φ^N under the mapping $\mathbf{Y}$, given by equations (13),

$$\mathbf{Y}: (\gamma,\varphi) \in U_\Phi^N \rightarrow (Y_1(\gamma,\varphi), Y_2(\gamma,\varphi), Y_3(\gamma,\varphi), Y_4(\gamma,\varphi)) \in R^4 \tag{21}$$

Statement 1

(a) If $N \geq 5$, then image of the set U_Φ^N under the mapping $\mathbf{Y}$, given by equations (13), represents a convex hull, see [18], of the following curve Γ:

$$\Gamma = \{y \in R^4: y = (\cos^4\varphi, \sin^4\varphi, \sin\varphi \cos^3\varphi, \sin^3\varphi \cos\varphi), \varphi \in \Phi^N\} \tag{22}$$

(b) Any point that belongs to the image of the set U_Φ^N under the mapping $\mathbf{Y}$ can be obtained as a value of the function $\mathbf{Y}$ on a vector $(\gamma,\varphi) \in R^5 \times \Phi^5$.

In accordance with Statement 1, a fiber-reinforced angle-ply laminate with any prescribed effective stiffness moduli $\{A_{\alpha\beta}\}$ satisfying the solvability condition (15), can be designed by using not more than five plies of reinforcing fibers.

SKEW-SYMMETRIC FIBER-REINFORCED LAMINATES

Let us consider now a practically important type of a laminate with the skew-symmetric placement of fibers about the mid-surface of a laminate. In this case, for any ply with the fiber placement angle $+ \varphi_j$, there is a symmetric ply with the fiber placement angle $- \varphi_j$, and the fiber volume fraction γ_j is similar in these two layers. In the case of skew-symmetric reinforcement, the two last functionals in Eqs. (13) are identically equal to zero. It is also sufficient in this case to limit the fiber placement angles by the interval $[0, \pi/2]$.

Design Problem Formulation

(1) determine if the following equations (cf. Eq. (17)):

$$Y_1(\gamma,\varphi) = y_1, \qquad Y_2(\gamma,\varphi) = y_2 \tag{23}$$

are solvable in the set of variables (cf. Eq. (20))

$$V_\Phi^N = \{(\gamma,\varphi) \in U_\Phi^N, \gamma_j = \gamma_{N-j}, -\varphi_j = \varphi_{N-j} \in [0, \pi/2], j=1,2,...,N/2\} \qquad (24)$$

(2) if the answer on the question (1) is positive, then find the set of solutions of the system (23) under the conditions (18).

<u>Statement 2</u>

(a) If $N \geq 6$, then image of the set V_Φ^N under the mapping $\{Y_1(\gamma,\varphi), Y_2(\gamma,\varphi)\}$, given by two first equations (13), represents a convex hull of a curve

$$\Gamma = \{y \in R^2: y=(\cos^4\varphi, \sin^4\varphi), \varphi \in \Phi^N\} = \{y \in R^2: y=(\eta, (1- \sqrt{\eta})^2), \eta \in \cos^4\Phi^N\} \qquad (25)$$

where $\cos^4\Phi$ denotes the image of the set Φ under the mapping $(\cos)^4$.

(b) Any point that belongs to image of the set V_Φ^N under the mapping $\{Y_1(\gamma,\varphi), Y_2(\gamma,\varphi)\}$ can be obtained as a value of the function $\{Y_1(\gamma,\varphi), Y_2(\gamma,\varphi)\}$ on a vector $(\gamma,\varphi) \in U_\Phi^6$.

In accordance with Statement 2, a skew-symmetric fiber-reinforced composite shell with any prescribed effective stiffnesses $\{A_{\alpha\beta}\}$, satisfying the solvability condition (15), can be designed by using not more than three pairs of plies with fiber placement angles $+\varphi_j$ and $-\varphi_j$.

MINIMIZATION OF FIBER CONTENT

Let us consider now an optimization of the design problem concerning the minimization of the fiber content, ω. We include now the variable ω into the set of independent variables of the system of Eqs. (16), and consider the problem of minimization of ω on account the condition that the laminate has the prescribed set of effective stiffnesses. Suppose, we already solved the above design problem for some fixed ω value, e.g., $\omega = \omega_0$, so that (cf. Eq. (17))

$$Y_i(\gamma,\varphi) = y_i^0, i = 1,2,3,4 \qquad (26)$$

where $y^0 = (y_1^0, y_2^0, y_3^0, y_4^0)$ is determined from expressions (16) with $\omega = \omega_0$. It follows from the formulas (16) that $y = (\omega_0/\omega)y^0$ will represent a solution for a given ω value. Moreover, fiber volume fractions γ_i satisfy conditions (18). As a result, we arrive to a problem to find a minimum ω value, such that the point $y(\omega) = (\omega_0/\omega)y^0$ belongs to convex set, $conv\ \Gamma$. Curve Γ has been described in Statements 1 and 2. The set

$$L = \{y(\omega) = (\omega_0/\omega)y^0, \omega \in (0, \omega_0)\} \qquad (27)$$

represents a ray having an origin in the point $y^0 \in conv\ \Gamma$, and tending to infinity when $\omega \to 0$. Since the set $conv\ \Gamma$ is compact (because Γ is compact), the ray L will intersect the boundary of the convex compact set $conv\ \Gamma$ when ω equals some certain value, $\omega = \omega^*$, and they will have no other intersections when $\omega < \omega^*$. We formulate this result in form of Statement 3.

<u>Statement 3</u>

The above formulated fiber content, ω, minimization problem is solvable if the design problem with the required set of effective stiffnesses and some prescribed ω_0 value is solvable. The ω minimum value is equal to ω^* that corresponds to an intersection of the ray L with the boundary of the set *conv* Γ. A design project for the composite shell with a minimum fiber content ω^* can be found by solving problem (17), (18) or the problem (23), (18) with a right-hand side equal to $\mathbf{y} = (\omega_0/\omega^*)\mathbf{y}^0$.

DESIGN EXAMPLES

The developed theory is illustrated by the following design two examples for the fiber-reinforced angle-ply laminates.

In the first example, it is required to design a glass/epoxy laminate with a skew-symmetric placement of fibers. The laminate should have the following effective stiffnesses: $A_{11} = 25$ GPa and $A_{22} = 10$ GPa. Young's modulus of fibers is $E = 100$ GPa, and the prescribed fiber volume content is $\omega = 0.5$.

Curve Γ in the considering case is determined as follows (cf. Eq. (25)):

$$\Gamma = \{y \in R^2: \mathbf{y} = (\eta, (1 - \sqrt{\eta})^2), \eta = \cos^4\varphi \in [0, 1]\} \qquad (28)$$

Curve Γ and its convex hull (area ABCD) are shown in Fig. 2.

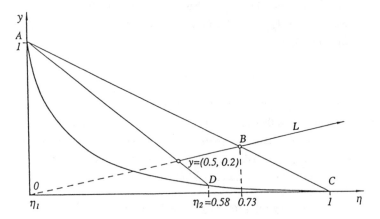

FIG. 2 -- Curve Γ and the convex hull, *conv* Γ (area ABCD).

The prescribed values $\mathbf{y}$ = (0.5, 0.2) are calculated from Eq. (16). It is seen from Fig. 2 that point $\mathbf{y}$ = (0.5, 0.2) belongs to set $conv$ Γ. Consequently, the laminate with the above prescribed effective stiffnesses can be designed. Let us calculate the design parameters of such a laminate. In fact, the problem (23), (18) can be formulated as a problem of determining the convex combinations of points on curve Γ, that produce a given point $\mathbf{y}$.

Apparently, there is an infinite number of points on curve Γ producing given point $\mathbf{y}$. For example, point $\mathbf{y}$ can be obtained as a convex combination of points A and D (see Fig. 2). Introducing subscripts 1 and 2 to coordinates of points A and D, we obtain η_1 = 0, η_2 = 0.58. Fiber placement angles φ_1 and φ_2 are expressed in terms of η_1 and η_2 by means of the formula $\varphi_i = \arccos(\eta_i)^{1/4}$, cf. Eq. (25). Using this formula, we obtain φ_1 =90° and φ_2 ≈29°. Fiber fractions γ_1 and γ_2 can be also determined from Fig. 2 as follows: γ_1=lyDl/lADl≈0.14, and γ_2=lAyl/lADl≈0.86. The resulting four-layer skew-symmetric laminate design is following: 14% reinforcing glass fibers should be placed on angles ± 90°, and 86% of fibers should be placed on angles ± 29°. Note that the obtained design parameters represent just one of the possible design solutions. However, this is a special design project in the sense that it provides the maximum values of the fiber-reinforcing angles.

Example on Fiber Volume Content Minimization

In the second example, it is required to design a skew-symmetric angle-ply laminate with the effective stiffnesses similar to the above first example, but, unlike the previous example, it is also required now to minimize the fiber content ω. As it was just shown, the design problem for ω = 0.5 was solvable. Therefore, the design problem including the minimization of ω is solvable as well. Assuming ω_0 = 0.5, and following the above theory, we look for a point of intersection of a ray (cf. Eq. (27))

$$L = \{\mathbf{y}(\omega) = \frac{\omega_0}{\omega} \mathbf{y}^0 = \frac{0.5}{\omega} (0.5, 0.2), \omega \in (0, 0.5)\} \qquad (29)$$

with a boundary of the area ABCD (see Fig. 2). This point of intersection is denoted by B in Fig. 2, and it has the coordinates (0.73, 0.28). Applying Statement 3 and using Eq. (29), we find that the minimum fiber content is equal to

$$\omega^* = \omega_0(\mathbf{y}^0/\mathbf{y})= 0.5(0.5/0.73) ≈ 0.34.$$

To calculate the design parameters, we should solve the problem (23), (18) with a right-hand side $\mathbf{y}(\omega^*)$ = (0.73, 0.28). It is seen from Fig. 2 that point B can be represented as a convex combination of points of the curve Γ in a unique way, namely, as a convex combination of points A and C. Accordingly, we obtain that η_1 = 0, η_2 = 1, and φ_1 = 90°, and φ_2 = 0°. The fiber fractions are γ_1= lBCl/lACl = 0.27 and γ_2=lABl/lACl = 0.73. The resulting design provides the minimum fiber content (ω^*= 0.34) for the above prescribed effective stiffnesses. The designed four-ply laminate is formed by two plies with fiber placement angles 90° and fiber volume fraction 27% and by two plies with fiber placement angles 0° and fiber volume fraction 73%.

CONCLUSIONS

The explicit expressions for the effective stiffnesses of the high-stiffness fiber-reinforced angle-ply laminate are obtained. Derivation is based on application of the general homogenization composite shell model. The formulas for the effective stiffnesses provide corrections to the earlier approximate effective moduli results.

The design problem for the fiber-reinforced angle-ply laminate with the prescribed values of stiffnesses is formulated and solved using the convex analysis. The set of prescribed effective stiffness values for which the design problem is solvable, is described, and the effective method of the design parameters calculation based on the convex analysis is developed. The sufficient number of reinforcing layers required for the design of the fiber-reinforced laminate with the prescribed effective stiffnesses is determined. It is shown in a general case that a laminate with any prescribed effective stiffnesses in the tangential directions that satisfy the solvability condition can be designed by using not more than five plies. In the case of a skew-symmetric fiber-reinforced laminate, the sufficient number of plies is six, so that a skew-symmetric fiber-reinforced laminate with any prescribed effective stiffnesses in the tangential directions that satisfy the solvability condition can be designed by using not more than three pairs of plies with fiber placement angles $+\varphi_j$ and $-\varphi_j$, j = 1,2,3.

The design problem is generalized on account of minimization of fiber content. It is shown that this problem is solvable for any prescribed set of effective stiffnesses for which the design problem is solvable. The effective method of the optimum design parameters calculation is developed.

The effectiveness and advantages of the developed approach are illustrated by the numerical examples.

ACKNOWLEDGMENTS

This work has been supported by the ISIS-CANADA (The Intelligent Sensing in Innovative Structures, Canadian Network of Centres of Excellence) and the Natural Sciences and Engineering Research Council of Canada.

REFERENCES

[1]   Hashin, Z., "Analysis of Composite Materials - A Survey," Transactions of the ASME. Journal of Applied Mechanics, Vol. 50, 1983, pp. 481-505.

[2]   Sendeckyj, G.P., "Elastic Behavior of Composites," Composite Materials, Vol. 2. Mechanics of Composite Materials, Academic Press, New York, 1974.

[3]   Tsai, S.W., Theory of Composites Design, Think Composites, Dayton, OH, 1992.

[4]   Christensen, R. M., Mechanics of Composite Materials, Krieger, Malabar, 1991.

[5]   Weng, G. J., Taya, M., and Abé, H., Eds., Micromechanics and Inhomogeneity - The T. Mura 65th Anniversary Volume, Springer, New York, 1990.

[6]   Vasiliev, V.V., Mechanics of Composite Structures, Taylor & Francis, Washington, DC, 1993.

[7]   Christensen, R. M ., "A Critical Evaluation for a Class of Micromechanics Models," Journal of the Mechanics and Physics of Solids, Vol. 38, 1990, pp. 379-404.

[8]   Vinson, J.R., The Behavior of Shells Composed of Isotropic and Composite Materials, Kluwer, Dordrecht, 1993.

[9]   Nemat-Nasser, S. and Hori, M., Micromechanics Overall Properties of Heterogeneous Solids, Elsevier, Amsterdam, 1993.

[10]   Bensoussan, A., Lions, J.-L., and Papanicolaou, G., Asymptotic Analysis for Periodic Structures, North-Holland, Amsterdam, 1978.

[11]   Sanchez-Palencia, E., Non-Homogeneous Media and Vibration Theory, Springer, Berlin, 1980.

[12]   Kalamkarov, A. L., Composite and Reinforced Elements of Construction, Wiley, New York, 1992.

[13]   Bakhvalov, N. S. and Panasenko, G. P., Homogenization: Averaging Processes in Periodic Media, Kluwer, Dordrecht, 1989.

[14]   Kalamkarov, A. L., "On the Determination of Effective Characteristics of Cellular Plates and Shells of Periodic Structure," Mechanics of Solids, Vol. 22, 1987, pp. 175-179.

[15]   Kalamkarov, A. L., "Thermoelastic Problem for Structurally Non-Uniform Shells of Regular Structure," Journal of Applied Mechanics and Technical Physics, Vol. 30, 1989, pp. 981-988.

[16]   Kalamkarov, A. L., "Analysis and Design of Thin-Walled Composite Structural Members," Proceedings of the Second Canadian International Conference on Composites (CANCOM'93), Ottawa, 1993, pp. 741-748.

[17]   Kalamkarov, A. L. and Kolpakov, A. G., "Numerical Design of Thin-Walled Structural Members on Account of their Strength," International Journal for Numerical Methods in Engineering, Vol. 36, 1993, pp. 3441-3449.

[18]   Rockafellar, R. T., Convex Analysis, Princeton University Press, Princeton, NJ, 1970.

Joseph R. Zuiker[1]

A MODEL FOR THE CREEP RESPONSE OF OXIDE-OXIDE CERAMIC MATRIX COMPOSITES

REFERENCE: Zuiker, J. R., "A Model for the Creep Response of Oxide-Oxide Ceramic Matrix Composites," Thermal and Mechanical Test Methods and Behavior of Continuous-Fiber Ceramic Composites, ASTM STP 1309, Michael G. Jenkins, Stephen T. Gonczy, Edgar Lara-Curzio, Noel E. Ashbaugh, and Larry P. Zawada, Eds., American Society for Testing and Materials, 1997.

ABSTRACT: A numerical model has been developed to predict the creep response of ceramic matrix composites (CMCs) to understand better the sustained load behavior of an eight-harness satin-weave Nextel™ 610[2] /aluminosilicate CMC. A two-phase system in which each phase exhibits significant creep is considered. Mori-Tanaka estimates of the overall elastic response are used in conjunction with transformation field analysis to predict the inelastic deformation in each phase and evaluate the overall CMC response. Good correlation between the model and experimental data is obtained over a wide range of temperature and stress conditions when micromechanical estimates of the matrix elastic stiffness are used. The correlation is sensitive to the matrix elastic properties and, thus, provides a method to determine in-situ matrix properties when conventional methods fail, as in this case.

KEYWORDS: creep, ceramic matrix composite, transformation field analysis

INTRODUCTION

Oxide-oxide ceramic matrix composites (CMCs) consisting of oxide fibers embedded in an oxide matrix are currently the subject of increased interest as a result of superior thermal stability at high temperature. The fibers are often woven into mats such as the eight-harness satin-weave (8HSW) architecture considered here. Recently, a system incorporating Nextel™ 610 alumina fibers into an aluminosilicate matrix has been investigated for application in turbine engine augmentor components and found to possess attractive high-temperature tensile and fatigue properties [1, 2]. Of concern, however, is the relatively high rate of creep at operating temperatures in comparison with other

---

[1] Materials Research Engineer, Wright Laboratory Materials Directorate, Wright-Patterson AFB, OH 45433.
[2] 3M Company, St. Paul, Minnesota.

CMCs. To determine optimal combinations of fiber content, ply layup, and weave architecture, it is important to develop a mechanics-based approach to creep modeling that is based on the response of the constituents.

As a first effort in this direction, a micromechanics-based model of a laminated composite has been developed that incorporates creeping fibers embedded in a creeping matrix. The model assumes a symmetric laminate subjected to in-plane loading. At the ply level, the Mori-Tanaka method (MTM) [3, 4] has been used to assess the average stress in each phase. This method has been used by several researchers to analyze the response of inelastic composites [5, 6]. Inelastic deformation at the constituent and ply level is accounted for via the transformation field analysis method [7] which treats all nonmechanical or nonelastic strains as stress-free transformation strains or eigenstrains and accounts for their interactions through a set of concentration factors.

The paper proceeds with an overview of the model and a brief description of the experimental results to be considered. Next, assumptions concerning constituent material behavior are reviewed and constants are selected based on fiber and composite testing. The predictions are then compared with experimental data and sensitivity studies are conducted on the effect of varying matrix elastic properties. Finally, results are discussed and conclusions are drawn.

Plain face uppercase and lowercase Greek or Roman characters indicate scalar quantities, while vectors and matrices are denoted by boldface lowercase Greek and boldface uppercase Roman characters, respectively.

MODEL REVIEW

The principal goal of this analysis is to account for the stress transfer between plies and between the fiber and matrix in each ply during sustained load tests. With this in mind, a relatively simple approximation to the 8HSW microstructure is invoked following the mosaic model [8] in that undulation of the fibers is neglected. It is further assumed that there are many plies stacked in such a way that regions of undulation do not lie directly upon one another, but rather are displaced in the plane of the laminate in a random pattern. Therefore, all out-of-plane warpage caused by the woven microstructure is suppressed, and each 8HSW mat is assumed to behave as a $[0/90]_s$ crossply.

Progressive cracking of both the fiber and matrix is neglected. Although the matrix is observed to contain many distributed microcracks before testing, these can be accounted for through use of reduced effective elastic matrix properties, which are assumed constant throughout the simulation. Thermal stresses are neglected because of similarity in the fiber and matrix coefficients of thermal expansion and the fact that all testing was conducted at high temperature (near the processing temperature) under isothermal conditions which quickly dissipate any thermal residual fields. Finally, note that the system under consideration has no fiber coating. No evidence of debonding has been noted at the conclusion of creep testing.[3] Thus, the fiber-matrix bond is assumed to remain intact.

---

[3] S. S. Lee, Wright Laboratory, Materials Directorate, Private Communication, 1995.

Each phase is assumed to follow a simple power law creep constitutive equation such that, in uniaxial loading, the total strain rate at any time t is defined as

$$\dot{\varepsilon}_i(t) = \dot{\sigma}(t)/E_i + A_i e^{-[Q_i/T(t)]}(\sigma(t))^{n_i} \tag{1}$$

where $\sigma(t)$ and $\dot{\sigma}(t)$ are the variable stress and stress rate, respectively, T is the temperature, E_i is Young's modulus of phase i, and A_i, Q_i, and n_i define the steadystate creep response of the ith phase.

<u>Micromechanics Relations</u>

Predicting composite strain as a function of mechanical load and time involves determining the stress and strain as a function of time in the fiber and matrix in both the $0°$ and $90°$ plies. For in-plane loading, ply stresses and strains are estimated via classical laminated plate theory using a $[0/90]_s$ layup in which each ply is composed of a two-phase composite. Transformation field analysis (TFA) [7, 9, 10] is used to account for inelastic deformation. TFA is versatile and can be immediately extended to any set of phase constitutive relations. Application of the method to laminated plates under in-plane loading has been addressed [11], as have higher order extensions for the combined stretching and bending of laminated plates [12, 13].

Using TFA, the stress vector in phase α, σ^α, of a heterogeneous body can be written in terms of the overall stress applied to the plate, σ, and a summation of the transformation strain in each phase of the body as

$$\sigma^\alpha = B^\alpha \sigma - \sum_{\beta=m,f} F^{\alpha\beta} L^\beta \mu^\beta \tag{2}$$

where B^α is a stress concentration factor matrix giving the contribution to σ^α as a result of σ, $F^{\alpha\beta}$ is a transformation concentration factor matrix, L^β is the stiffness matrix of phase β, and μ^β is the transformation strain in phase β. The matrix product $F^{\alpha\beta}L^\beta$ gives the contribution to σ^α caused by μ^β. Transformation strain μ^β represents all strains in phase β not caused by elastic mechanical loading and may include plastic and creep deformation, thermal strains, strains caused by phase transformation, and other phenomena. The forms of B^α and $F^{\alpha\beta}$ depend on the elastic properties of the phases and their microstructure. Approximate closed form solutions may be obtained by a variety of micromechanical techniques when the microstructure is relatively simple. Elastic finite element techniques are necessary for complex geometries [10]. Here, because of the simple assumptions made concerning the fiber architecture, the Mori-Tanaka method can be used to obtain closed form solutions to all of the required concentration factors. Solutions for the concentration factors via the Mori-Tanaka method can be found elsewhere [7].

The stress, total strain, and transformation strain increments in phase α of the ith ply are related as

$$\Delta\bar{\varepsilon}_i^\alpha = \overline{M}^\alpha \Delta\bar{\sigma}_i^\alpha + \Delta\bar{\mu}_i^\alpha, \quad i = 1, 2, \quad \alpha = f, m \tag{3}$$

where $\Delta\bar{\sigma}_i^\alpha$ is the stress increment in phase α of ply i, $\Delta\bar{\varepsilon}_i^\alpha$ is the total strain increment,

$\Delta\overline{\mu}_i^{\alpha}$ is the transformation strain increment, and $\overline{\mathbf{M}}^{\alpha}$ is the elastic compliance matrix for phase α. The bar over each quantity indicates that these quantities are in the local ply coordinate system in which the ply lies in the x_1x_2 plane with fibers aligned parallel to the x_1 direction. Only in-plane loading and pressure normal to the laminate surface are considered. Thus, vectors in Eq 3 are (4x1) and matrices are (4x4). Here, it is assumed that the transformation strain in each phase is caused solely by steadystate creep in the phase. Thermal strains, plasticity, apparent strain from distributed damage, and all other inelastic strains are neglected. The steadystate creep response of each phase noted in Eq 1 is generalized to matrix form and written in incremental form as

$$\Delta\overline{\mu}_i^{\alpha} = \tfrac{3}{2} A_{\alpha} e^{-Q_{\alpha}/T} (\sigma_{eff_i}^{\alpha})^{n_{\alpha}-1} \mathbf{P}\overline{\sigma}_i^{\alpha}\Delta t \tag{4}$$

where $\mathbf{P}$ is a matrix that converts the stress vector $\overline{\sigma}_i^{\alpha}$ into the deviatoric stress vector, and $\sigma_{eff_i}^{\alpha}$ is the effective stress in phase α of the ith ply.

At the ply level, stress and strain increments are related as

$$\Delta\varepsilon_i = \mathbf{M}_i\Delta\sigma_i + \Delta\mu_i \tag{5}$$

where $\Delta\sigma_i$ is the stress increment in ply i, $\Delta\varepsilon_i$ and $\Delta\mu_i$ are the total and creep strain increments, respectively, and $\mathbf{M}_i$ is the effective elastic compliance matrix for ply i. Quantities without bars overhead are defined in the global coordinate system in which the laminate lies in the x_1x_2 plane with the 0° ply fibers aligned in the x_1 direction. Equation 5 may also be written in the local coordinate system by placing bars over all quantities. Stress and strain may be converted from the global to the local coordinate system via rotation matrices as

$$\Delta\overline{\sigma}_i = \mathbf{R}_i\Delta\sigma_i, \qquad \Delta\overline{\varepsilon}_i = \mathbf{N}_i\Delta\varepsilon_i \tag{6a, b}$$

where

$$\mathbf{R}_i = \left(\mathbf{N}_i^T\right)^{-1} = \begin{bmatrix} \cos^2\theta_i & \sin^2\theta_i & 0 & \sin 2\theta_i \\ \sin^2\theta_i & \cos^2\theta_i & 0 & -\sin 2\theta_i \\ 0 & 0 & 1 & 0 \\ -\tfrac{1}{2}\sin 2\theta_i & \tfrac{1}{2}\sin 2\theta_i & 0 & \cos 2\theta_i \end{bmatrix} \tag{7}$$

and θ_i is the angle between the loading direction and the fiber direction in the ith ply. Local and global stiffness matrices in the ith ply are related as

$$\mathbf{M}_i = \mathbf{R}_i^{T}\overline{\mathbf{M}}_i\mathbf{R}_i, \quad \mathbf{L}_i = \mathbf{N}_i^{T}\overline{\mathbf{L}}_i\mathbf{N}_i \tag{8a, b}$$

The average ply creep strains can be determined from the phase creep strains as [7]

$$\Delta\overline{\mu}_i = \sum_{\alpha=m,f} c_{\alpha}\overline{\mathbf{B}}^{\alpha T}\Delta\overline{\mu}_i^{\alpha} \tag{9}$$

where c_{α} is the volume fraction of phase α. Equation 9 simplifies to Levin's rule [14] if the transformation strain increments are taken as thermal strain increments.

Incremental Solution Technique

Increments in stress, total strain, and creep strain at the phase, ply, and laminate levels are computed via a forward Euler integration scheme. The creep strain increment in each phase of each ply is calculated through Eq 4, and the average ply creep strain is calculated in the global system via Eqs 9 and 6b. Using a form of the TFA relation in Eqs 2 and 6a, the local stress increment in the ith ply is calculated from the applied stress increment, $\Delta\sigma$, and the ply creep strain increment as

$$\Delta\overline{\sigma}_i = R_i[H_i\Delta\sigma - \sum_{j=1}^{N} F_{ij}L_j\Delta\mu_j] \tag{10}$$

Here, H_i is the ply stress concentration factor matrix that provides the contribution to the stress increment in the ith ply as a result of the applied laminate stress increment $\Delta\sigma$. F_{ij} is a transformation concentration factor matrix that, when multiplied by the stiffness matrix of the jth ply, L_j, provides the contribution to the stress increment in ply i as a result of a transformation strain in ply j. Numerical evaluation of H_i and F_{ij} is relatively simple for in-plane loading.

Once ply stress increments have been determined, phase stress increments can be obtained using Eq 2 rewritten as

$$\Delta\overline{\sigma}_i^\alpha = \overline{B}^\alpha\Delta\overline{\sigma}_i - \sum_{\beta=f,m} \overline{F}^{\alpha\beta}\overline{L}^\beta\Delta\overline{\mu}_i^\beta, \quad i = 1, 2, \quad \alpha = f, m \tag{11}$$

Here $\overline{B}^\alpha$ and $\overline{F}^{\alpha\beta}$ are stress and transformation concentration factors that are determined via the Mori-Tanaka method.

The phase and ply total strain increments are calculated via Eqs 3 and 5, respectively. Equation 6b provides these quantities in both the local and global coordinate systems. In-plane stretching and shearing of the laminate are equal in each ply. Thus, the in-plane ply total strain increments equal the laminate in-plane total strain increments.

EXPERIMENTAL RESULTS

Twelve-ply 8HSW Nextel™ 610/AS composites were mounted in a horizontal fatigue machine and loaded in the warp direction. The test specimens were heated at 1.1°C/s from room temperature to a uniform gauge section temperature of 1000 - 1100°C and allowed to stabilize for 15 min, then mechanically loaded in under 100 s and held at constant loads between 50 - 135 MPa until specimens separated into two pieces. Total strain was measured over a 16-mm gauge section [1, 2, 15]. Figures 1 and 2 show experimentally measured values of total strain at temperatures of 1000 - 1100°C as a function of time for various applied stress levels. Very little primary and almost no tertiary creep is observed.

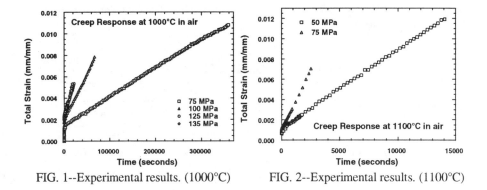

FIG. 1--Experimental results. (1000°C)   FIG. 2--Experimental results. (1100°C)

Figure 3 shows strain rate as a function of strain for each of the tests in Figs. 1 and 2. A multipoint linear regression was used to obtain strain rate estimates. In each case shown in Fig. 3, the first point was taken far enough out in time that data points from the initial mechanical loading were not included in the linear regression fit. These results indicate a short primary creep regime during which the creep rate quickly decays to a steady state value.

CONSTITUENT PHASE RESPONSE

Fiber Properties

The fiber has been well characterized in creep [16] and exhibits neither primary nor tertiary creep before failure. The creep response is accurately predicted by a simple power law of the form shown in Eq 1. A least squares fit to the experimentally measured steadystate fiber creep rates produced the fit shown in Fig. 4 which predicts the experimental creep rates within a factor of three. Data on polycrystalline alumina were used to approximate the elastic properties of the fiber at 1000 - 1100°C [17]. These are shown in Table 1 along with creep constants for Eq 1.

Matrix Properties

Because of the unique manufacturing process, it has not been possible to produce monolithic matrix samples with microstructure comparable to that observed in the composite.[4] Thus, all estimates of matrix properties are inferred from composite tests or predicted from knowledge of the matrix constituents and microstructure.

Elastic Matrix Properties--The initial estimate of the matrix elastic modulus $(E_m = 3.5 \text{ GPa})$ was inferred from tension tests on the composite. However, agreement between estimated composite response and experimental results is relatively insensitive to matrix modulus for a fiber to matrix modulus ratio on the order of 100 to 1. During the course of this analysis, the initial estimate became suspect, and an attempt was made to

---

[4] D. Carper, GE Aircraft Engines, Private Communication, 1995.

estimate the effective properties of the matrix using micromechanical techniques and a knowledge of the matrix microstructure.

TABLE 1--Properties of CMC constituents.

Property	Fiber	Al_2O_3	Glassy SiO_2	AS Matrix
E, GPa	310	310	72	58
ν	0.37	0.37	0.16	0.17
A, 1/s·Mpa^n	9.96E+12	---	---	3.75E+16
Q, K	79 500	---	---	88 700
n	2.99	---	---	3.93

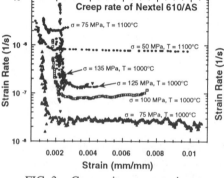

FIG. 3-- Composite creep strain rate as a function of strain.

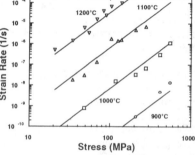

FIG. 4-- Numerical fit to fiber steady state creep rate.

The composite consists of 12-μm diameter fibers embedded in a matrix consisting of alumina particles which are in turn embedded in a porous matrix of glassy silica. Regions of macroporosity are also evident in the composite. Microscopic investigation of several samples indicated average volume fractions on the order of $c_f = 0.33$, $c_{alumina} = 0.35$, $c_{silica} = 0.09$, $c_{\mu p} = 0.12$, and $c_{Mp} = 0.11$ where $c_{\mu p}$ is the volume fraction of the microporosity which is distributed somewhat uniformly throughout the silica phase of the matrix, and c_{Mp} is the volume fraction of the macroporosity which was generally found in matrix-rich regions between fiber tows.[5] The ratios of alumina to silica to fibers are well defined in comparison with the volume of porosity and its distribution between macroporosity and microporosity.

Tuchinskii's method [18] approximates the effective properties of a continuous elastic matrix containing a continuous interpenetrating network of porosity and was used to estimate the effective elastic constants of the porous silica. The results are below the

[5] J. Staehler, Wright Laboratory, Materials Directorate, Private Communication, 1995.

Hashin-Shtrikman bounds [19] for distributed spherical pores in a silica matrix, as is expected when the pores begin to link up and form a continuous network of voids. These effective properties were then used in the next level of analysis. To estimate the effective properties of the matrix, which consists of alumina particles suspended somewhat uniformly throughout the porous silica medium, the Mori-Tanaka method was used. In this case, the MTM estimates correspond with the Hashin-Shtrikman lower bound [20]. Elastic properties for silica and alumina are shown in Table 1. The resulting effective elastic properties of the matrix are also listed in Table 1.

Creep Response of the Matrix--No experimental information is available on the creep response of the monolithic matrix. However, it is well known that both matrix constituents creep significantly at the temperatures under consideration. Alumina creeps in a steadystate manner following Eq 1 with a creep exponent of $n = 1$ up to temperatures near 1000°C. At higher temperatures, the stress exponent increases to the range of 3 to 5. The exact transition temperature is dependent on a variety of factors [21]. Silica behaves as a Newtonian fluid and creeps at a rate that is highly sensitive to small amounts of impurities [22]. Because of the variety of factors affecting the creep rate of the matrix constituents and limited information on the details of the matrix chemistry and processing history, it was considered impractical to try and attempt an estimate of the matrix creep response based on the behavior of alumina and silica.

As an alternative, the matrix was modeled using the steadystate creep model as in Eq 1. Thus, the model composite consists of two materials of different elastic and creep properties. Even though each material exhibits only steadystate creep, it is well established that the composite can exhibit primary creep as a result of stress redistribution between fiber and matrix early in the test [23]. Eventually, both fiber and matrix in each ply reach steady values of stress at which time the composite as a whole creeps at a constant rate. In the 0° ply, it is assumed that the normal stress in the loading direction is far larger than all other stress components. Thus, the fiber and matrix response are approximated by unidirectional stress states and Eq 1 holds for each. Once the fiber and matrix stresses reach constant values, Eq 1 simplifies for each as

$$\dot{\varepsilon}_f = A_f e^{-Q_f/T} (\sigma_f)^{n_f}, \qquad \dot{\varepsilon}_m = A_m e^{-Q_m/T} (\sigma_m)^{n_m} \qquad (12a, b)$$

The experimentally measured composite strain rates (Fig. 3) reach steadystate values early in the test. These steadystate creep rate data are used to obtain a fit to the matrix creep response which provides the necessary creep constants. It is assumed that the overall creep rate $\dot{\varepsilon}$ is equal to both the fiber and matrix creep rate. Given the fiber creep constants, the fiber stress is then obtained from Eq 12a. The matrix stress is then calculated from knowledge of the applied stress and the fiber and matrix volume fractions as

$$\sigma_m = \left(\sigma - c_f \sigma_f\right)/c_m \qquad (13)$$

where σ is the stress applied to the composite. A minimum of three tests covering at least two temperatures and two stresses are required to fit the matrix creep constants in Eq 12b. Test data used in the curve fit are summarized in Table 2. The resulting creep constants for the matrix are tabulated in Table 1 and are reasonable for the matrix constituents. Note, also, that the fit to the matrix creep response is independent of the elastic properties of the constituents.

TABLE 2--Experimental results for matrix creep model calibration.

Case	T, K	$\sigma_{applied}$, MPa	σ_f, MPa	σ_m, MPa	$\dot{\varepsilon}$, 1/s
1	1273	75	154.3	35.9	2.60E-08
2	1273	125	267.8	54.6	1.35E-07
3	1373	50	104.2	23.3	7.60E-07

COMPARISON WITH EXPERIMENT

Matrix Creep Fit Correlation

Figure 5 shows the experimental data for the three cases used to fit the matrix creep response (see Table 2) as well as the predicted response. Predictions are shown for two values of elastic matrix properties: E_m = 3.5 GPa, ν_m = 0.25 as inferred from composite tension tests and E_m = 58 GPa, ν_m = 0.17 as estimated above from matrix constituent properties. Both values accurately predict the steadystate creep rate of the composite. This is expected since this rate is independent of the elastic properties of the composite. However, the lower matrix stiffness (E_m = 3.5 GPa) produces a significantly larger primary creep regime in the composite during which stress redistribution occurs in the fiber and matrix. Creep predictions using the analytical estimate of matrix elastic properties (E_m = 58 GPa) show little primary creep and significantly better correlation with experiment. In all cases, a portion of the discrepancy is attributable to the fact that the matrix creep fit was based on the assumption of uniaxial stress states in both the fiber and matrix at terminal creep strain rates. Comparison with the results of the simulation described above indicate that the stress state in the 0° fiber and matrix is not uniaxial, although it is nearly so as the effective stress in each phase differs from the stress in the loading direction by no more than 5%. Nonzero average transverse stresses are predicted in both the fiber and matrix. However, they are relatively small and, as required by the micromechanical assumptions, the average ply stress through the thickness and the in-plane average plate stress perpendicular to the loading direction are zero.

Predictions of Response

Figures 6 and 7 show the predictions of total strain as a function of time for E_m = 58 GPa, ν_m = 0.17 at each of the test conditions shown in Figs. 2 and 3. Cases indicated by an asterisk were used in determining the creep response of the matrix and, thus, are not purely predictive. The remaining cases were not used in calibrating the model and serve as validation. Differences between experimental and predicted results are similar in magnitude to those between experimental results and the correlation (Fig. 5) and are within the range of accuracy of the constitutive model of the fibers as shown in Fig. 4.

Examination of the response at the end of mechanical load-up is indicative of the elastic response of the composite since little inelastic deformation has occurred (based on model predictions.) Careful examination of the data in Fig. 5 indicates that the total strain at the end of mechanical load-up is underestimated using E_m = 58 GPa, v_m = 0.17 and overestimated using E_m = 3.5 GPa, v_m = 0.25. The total strain at the end of the test is substantially overestimated using E_m = 3.5 GPa and slightly overestimated using E_m = 58 GPa.

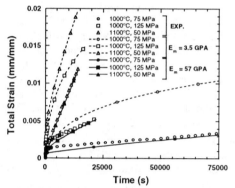

FIG. 5-- Predicted response as a function
of matrix elastic modulus.

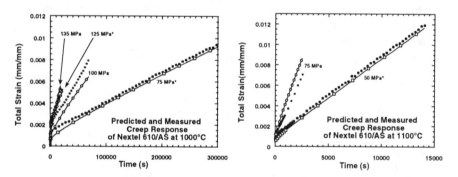

FIG. 6--Predicted results at 1000°C.   FIG. 7--Predicted results at 1100°C

Sensitivity Studies

Figure 5 indicates that the creep response of the composite is highly dependent upon the elastic properties of the matrix. Because of the large difference in fiber and matrix properties, the matrix elastic properties do not affect the overall elastic properties of the composite to the same degree. To assess the effects of matrix modulus on composite response, several analyses were performed in which the matrix elastic modulus was varied. The case of $\sigma = 75$ MPa at 1000°C was considered as a baseline case. Figure 8 shows how the response varies with matrix elastic modulus. Above a value of approximately 25 GPa, the response is relatively insensitive to further increases in matrix modulus. The region near the origin in Fig. 8 is shown in greater detail in Fig. 9 in which the time scale has been biased such that the creep test begins at $t = 0$. (That is, mechanical loading begins at $t \approx -100$ s.) The correlation in elastic response is optimized for this case when the matrix modulus lies between 10 and 25 GPa.

To determine the optimal value of matrix elastic modulus for both elastic and creep response of the composite, two evaluation criteria are used. First, the elastic response ratio is defined as the predicted strain in the composite in the direction of loading at $t = 0$ (at the end of mechanical loading) divided by the experimentally measured response at $t = 0$. The creep response ratio is defined as the total strain at the end of the test minus the total strain at $t = 0$ as determined numerically, divided by the difference in total strain at the end of the test and at $t = 0$ as measured experimentally. It must be emphasized that neither of these quantities explicitly separates elastic and creep response. However, under the conditions of interest, the elastic response ratio is dominated by the composite elastic response and the creep response ratio is dominated by the composite creep response.

. The elastic and creep response ratios are shown in Fig. 10 for the case of $\sigma = 75$ MPa, $T = 1000$°C for various values of matrix elastic modulus. At low values of matrix modulus, the elastic response is insensitive to changes in E_m, while at higher values it becomes more sensitive. The opposite holds for the creep response.

Figure 11 shows these same ratios of elastic and creep response for all six experimental cases shown in Figs. 1 and 2. The solid lines indicate the elastic response ratio, while the dashed lines show the creep response ratio. Point A indicates the initial value of E_m as inferred from elastic testing, while point B indicates the value determined from micromechanical considerations. Point C (30 GPa) indicates an optimal value of E_m that minimizes the error in elastic and creep strain over all of the cases under consideration.

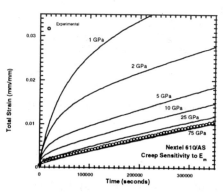

FIG. 8--Creep sensitivity to E_m.

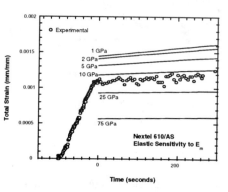

FIG. 9--Elastic sensitivity to E_m.

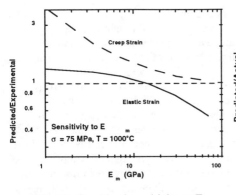

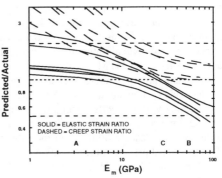

FIG. 10--Combined sensitivity to E_m for a single test.

FIG. 11--Combined sensitivity to E_m for all creep tests.

CLOSURE

Two values of matrix elastic modulus were considered: an empirical value inferred from knowledge of the fiber properties and the response of the composite under tension testing and an analytical prediction based on the matrix microstructure and constituents. Of interest is the sensitivity in overall response to the elastic properties of the matrix. The empirically determined value, while accurately characterizing the elastic response, results in poor estimates of the creep response. Although Fig. 5 shows a significant improvement in the predicted response when E_m is increased from 3.5 to 58 GPa, Fig. 11 indicates significant error in the elastic response at the higher matrix stiffness. This is easily overlooked in Fig. 5 because of the magnitude of the creep strain in comparison with the elastic strain. Based on the sensitivity study results shown in Fig. 11, correlation to and prediction of experimental results are optimized when the matrix modulus is approximately 30 GPa, an order of magnitude stiffer than the empirical estimate, yet only half the value of the analytical estimate. Note that the overall composite response using the micromechanical estimate of matrix properties is based on perfectly bonded matrix constituents with no cracking, and a [0/90] laminate in which the woven architecture is neglected. Ishikawa and Chou [24] have shown that the 8HSW architecture can have significantly lower stiffness than the cross-ply architecture. In addition, distributed microcracks, which have been observed experimentally in the matrix before testing, will act to increase composite compliance. Incorporating these effects into the analysis should result in a better correlation with experiment using E_m = 58 GPa. Thus, the results presented here using E_m = 58 GPa should serve as an upper bound on the true composite elastic stiffness.

The results presented here are based upon the Mori-Tanaka method. Work by Wang and Weng [25] indicates that this average field approach is most accurate when fibers are aligned parallel to the direction of loading and is less accurate when the fibers are perpendicular to the direction of loading. For the system under consideration, loading of the 0° fibers (parallel to the direction of loading) is expected to dominate the response. Thus, the MTM should serve as a good tool with which to make initial approximations of the creep response and gain a qualitative understanding of the interaction between various plies. More advanced micromechanical models may be invoked to improve the quantitative predictions although, at the current level of approximation, assumptions concerning laminate architecture and material response may limit accuracy more than the assumptions of the MTM.

In summary, a micromechanical approximation of the 8HSW Nextel™ 610/AS oxide-oxide composite has been developed incorporating a [0/90] cross-ply fiber architecture with perfectly bonded phases and viscoelastic material models of both the fiber and matrix. This oxide-oxide system is composed of phases with significant differences in elastic modulus. Further, the matrix elastic modulus can not be determined directly, and short, monotonic tension tests on the composite are not sufficiently sensitive to infer its magnitude. However, model predictions of the composite creep response are sensitive to the matrix elastic modulus and serve as an additional means of quantifying its value when conventional methods are not satisfactory. Such methods may be helpful in characterizing similar composite systems in the future.

ACKNOWLEDGMENTS

Thanks are due to Dr. S. S. Lee and Mr. L. P. Zawada (Wright Laboratory, Materials Directorate) for many useful discussions concerning the experimental results.

REFERENCES

[1] Zawada, L. P. and Lee, S. S., "Evaluation of Four CMCs for Aerospace Turbine Engine Divergent Flaps and Seals," Ceramic Engineering and Science Proceedings, Vol. 16, No. 4, 1995, pp. 337-339.

[2] Zawada, L. P. and Lee, S. S., "Mechanical Behavior of CMCs for Flaps and Seals," in Proceedings of ARPA Ceramic Technology Insertion Program Annual Review, Annapolis, MD, 1995.

[3] Mori, T. and Tanaka K., "Average Stress in Matrix and Average Elastic Energy of Materials with Misfitting Inclusions," Acta Metallurgica, Vol. 21, 1973, pp. 571-574.

[4] Benveniste, Y., "A New Approach to the Application of Mori-Tanaka's Theory in Composite Materials," Mechanics of Materials, Vol. 6, 1987, pp. 147-157.

[5] Zhu, Z. G. and Weng, G. J., "Creep Deformation of Particle Strengthened Metal-Matrix Composites," Journal of Engineering Materials and Technology, Vol. 111, 1989, pp. 99-105.

[6] Lagoudas, D. C., Gavazzi, A. C., and Nigam, H., "Elastoplastic Behavior of Metal Matrix Composites Based on Incremental Plasticity and the Mori-Tanaka Averaging Scheme," Computational Mechanics, Vol. 8, No. 3, 1991, pp. 193-203.

[7] Dvorak, G. J. and Benveniste, Y., "On Transformation Strains and Uniform Fields in Multiphase Elastic Media," Proceedings of the Royal Society of London A, Vol. 437, 1992, pp. 291-310.

[8] Ishikawa, T. and Chou, T.-W., "One-Dimensional Micromechanical Analysis of Woven Fabric Composites," AIAA Journal, Vol. 21, No. 12, 1983, pp. 1714-1721.

[9] Dvorak, G. J., "Transformation Field Analysis of Inelastic Composite Materials," Proceedings of the Royal Society of London A, Vol. 437, 1992, pp. 311-327.

[10] Dvorak, G. J., Bahei-El-Din, Y. A., and Wafa, A. M., "Implementation of the Transformation Field Analysis for Inelastic Composite Materials," Computational Mechanics, Vol. 14, 1994, pp. 201-228.

[11] Wafa, A. M., "Application of the Transformation Field Analysis to Inelastic Composite Materials and Structures," Ph. D. thesis, Rensselaer Polytechnic Institute, Troy, NY, 1994.

[12] Zuiker, J. R., "Elastic and Inelastic Micromechanical Analysis of Functionally Graded Materials and Laminated Structures using Transformation Field Analysis," Ph. D. thesis, Rensselaer Polytechnic Institute, Troy, NY, 1993.

[13] Zuiker, J. R. and Dvorak, G. J., " Inelastic Analysis of Laminated Plates by Transformation Field Analysis," in Titanium Metal Matrix Composites II, WL-TR-93-4105, P. R. Smith and W. C. Revelos, Eds., USAF Wright Laboratory, Wright-Patterson AFB, OH, 1993, pp. 326-343.

[14] Levin, V. M., "Thermal Expansion Coefficients of Heterogeneous Materials," Mekhanika Tverdogo Tela, Vol. 2, No. 1, 1967, pp. 88-94.

[15] Lee, S. S., Zawada, L. P., Hay, R., Staehler, J., and Carper, D. M., "High Temperature Mechanical Properties and Characterization of an Oxide/Oxide Composite," Journal of the American Ceramic Society, in press, 1996.

[16] Wilson, D. M., Lueneburg, D. C., and Lieder, S. L., "High Temperature Properties of Nextel 610 and Alumina-Based Nanocomposite Fibers," Ceramic Engineering and Science Proceedings, Vol. 14, No. 7/8, 1993, pp. 609-621.

[17] Lynch, J. F., Ruderer, C. G., and Duckworth, W. H., Engineering Properties of Ceramics, AFML-TR-66-52, Air Force Materials Laboratory, Wright-Patterson AFB, OH, 1966.

[18] Tuchinskii, L. I., "Elastic Constants of Pseudoalloys with a Skeletal Structure," Soviet Powder Metallurgy and Metal Ceramics, Vol. 22, No. 7, 1983, pp. 588-595.

[19] Hashin, Z. and Shtrikman, S., "A Variational Approach to the Theory of the Elastic Behavior of Multiphase Materials," Journal of the Mechanics and Physics of Solids, Vol. 11, 1963, pp. 127-140.

[20] Weng, G. J., "Some Elastic Properties of Reinforced Solids, with Special Reference to Isotropic Ones Containing Spherical Inclusions," International Journal of Engineering Science, Vol. 22, No. 7, 1984, pp. 845-856.

[21] Cannon, W. R. and Langdon, T. G., "Review: Creep of Ceramics Part 1 Mechanical Characteristics," Journal of Materials Science, Vol. 18, 1983, pp. 1-50.

[22] Kingery, W. D., Bowen, H. K., and Uhlmann, D. R., Introduction to Ceramics, Second Edition, John Wiley and Sons, New York, 1976.

[23] Holmes, J. W. and Wu, X., "Elevated Temperature Creep Behavior of Continuous Fiber-Reinforced Ceramics," in Elevated Temperature Mechanical Behavior of Ceramic Matrix Composites, S. V. Nair and K. Jakus, Eds., Butterworth-Heinneman, 1994.

[24] Ishikawa, T. and Chou, T.-W., "Stiffness and Strength Behaviour of Woven Fabric Composites," Journal of Materials Science, Vol. 17, 1982, pp. 3211-3220.

[25] Wang, Y. M. and Weng, G. J., "Transient Creep Strain of a Fiber-Reinforced Metal-Matrix Composite under Transverse Loading", Journal of Engineering Materials and Technology, Vol. 114, 1992, pp. 237-244.

Golam M. Newaz[1] and Nicola Bonora[2]

FATIGUE LIFE MODELING OF HYBRID CERAMIC MATRIX COMPOSITES

REFERENCE: Newaz, G. M. and Bonora, N., **"Fatigue Life Modeling of Hybrid Ceramic Matrix Composites,"** Thermal and Mechanical Test Methods and Behavior of Continuous-Fiber Ceramic Composites, ASTM STP 1309, Michael G. Jenkins, Stephen T. Gonczy, Edgar Lara-Curzio, Noel E. Ashbaugh, and Larry P. Zawada, Eds., American Society for Testing and Materials, 1997.

ABSTRACT: An investigation was undertaken to examine the fatigue characteristics of unidirectional dual fiber ceramic matrix composites made from Nicalon and SCS-6 fibers in UTRC-200 lithium aluminosilicate (LAS) glass matrix. Damage evolution was monitored as a function of fatigue cycles and stress levels via longitudinal stiffness loss. The damage consisted of matrix cracks, fiber-matrix disbonds, and broken fibers. Magnitude of damage was found to be strictly dependent on applied strain level. The consequence of damage development is manifested as stiffness loss for the composite. The stiffness degradation was monitored carefully, and a trend was observed. Based on the observed trend, a stiffness reduction model as a function of fatigue life was proposed that accounted for applied maximum strain and initial damage based on the first cycle maximum strain. The model was shown to be quite effective in predicting the damage evolution and thus fatigue life of dual fiber ceramic matrix composites (CMCs). The proposed fatigue life model is a generic one and can be applied to other CMCs exhibiting stiffness reduction as a result of multiple complex damage modes.

KEYWORDS: hybrid CMC, damage, threshold strain, critical strain, stiffness loss, fatigue life

INTRODUCTION

Fiber reinforced composites are usually notch insensitive when cracks propagate perpendicular to fibers and traditional concepts such as crack growth or fracture toughness are not as meaningful except in some particular cases, for example crack-bridging as a result of a single matrix crack in a brittle matrix composite. Because of the complex damage modes that occur in a composite material under static or cyclic loading, it is appropriate to address the complex damage states in which several basic fracture types such as matrix cracks, fiber breaks, delamination, and fiber-matrix disbonds and

[1] Professor, Mechanical Engineering Dept., Wayne State University, 505 Anthony Wayne Drive, Detroit, MI 48202, USA

[2] Assistant Professor, Industrial Engineering Dept., University of Cassino, Via G. De Biasio 43 - 03043 Cassino (FR), Italy

their mutual interactions are accounted for, particularly in developing life models. Probably, the best way to investigate fatigue effects on composite materials is to assess the degradation of the material properties such as elastic moduli, as a function of the number of cycles [1-3]. A direct consequence of damage is tensorial property change in composites.

There is an important connection between the first cycle damage and subsequent damage evolution in fatigue. Damage produced in the first cycle is similar to that of monotonic response. In order to understand clearly the implication of this initial damage, especially for hybrid composites such as Nicalon/SCS-6/lithium aluminosilicate (LAS) glass matrix composites, it is important to develop the link between monotonic damage and fatigue damage to elaborate proper fatigue life models. Monotonic response of unidirectional CMCs has been studied extensively by a number of researchers [4-12]. The proportional limit of unidirectional CMCs has been associated with matrix cracking and subsequent nonlinear behavior has been identified to be due to progressive fiber failure [9,10]. Matrix cracking in CMCs has been the subject of in-depth investigation by researchers as well [12,13]. Continuum damage mechanics models can be used to predict the stiffness loss in these composites as a result of the presence of damage which are typically microcrack entities such as matrix cracks, fiber matrix disbonds, and fiber cracks [3]. Monotonic damage evolution and modeling of attendant stiffness changes using continuum approaches have been investigated for the hybrid composite [14].

Cyclic damage has been characterized by a number of researchers for glass matrix composites, which confirms that it is a combination of damage such as matrix cracking, fiber-matrix debonding, and fiber fracture depend on the lay-up of the composite[15].

In this paper, the effect of complex damage state development in hybrid composites was examined in terms of stiffness loss as a function of the accumulated strain during cycling. This approach allows one to correlate fatigue life behavior directly to the quasi-static monotonic damage evolution law. An extensive experimental program to investigate fatigue life response of CMCs was carried out in this investigation. A phenomenological based model to predict fatigue life has been proposed. The model seems to be suitable for composite material systems that exhibit predominant brittle behavior.

EXPERIMENTAL ASPECTS

The unidirectional ceramic matrix composites were made using the slurry approach followed by hot pressing. The fibers were Nicalon and silicon carbide SCS-6 fibers in a LAS glass matrix (UTRC-200). The relative volume fractions of Nicalon, SCS-6, UTRC-200 were 20%,40% and 40%, approximately. Tensile properties of these dual fiber CMCs are given in the article by Bonora and Newaz [14]. The fatigue tests were conducted at room temperature. The unidirectional specimens were machined with taper width with a two-inch gage length in the middle. The specimen dimensions were 203 mm × 10.2 mm × 1.3 mm and they were tabbed for effective gripping. All fatigue tests were conducted at a frequency of 1 Hz under load-controlled condition. The R ratio used was 0.1. The basic purpose of the tests was to investigate thoroughly the stiffness degradation process in these composites and establish trends to develop a life assessment model.

The ultimate tensile strength of the CMC was about 690 MPa. The strain was measured using a 25.4 mm gage length extensometer for all tests. The elastic modulus was estimated from monotonic stress-strain curves using the slope of the line up to the proportional limit (onset of nonlinearity). The reduced elastic stiffness due to fatigue loading was estimated using the secant slope of each hysterisis loop.

RESULTS AND DISCUSSION

Figure 1 shows the normalized stiffness reduction data scatter (where E_D and E_0 were the current and the initial stiffness, respectively) for several fatigue tests performed at room temperature with the same R ratio, frequency and σ_{max}. To arrange experimental data in a more meaningful way, the number of cycles has been normalized by the number of cycle at failure, N_f. This representation allows us to separate the scatter relative to N_f and to underline the main feature of the fatigue damage evolution law. It is interesting to note that for the same maximum applied stress fatigue data do not show a good repeatability leading to a large scatter of possible fatigue curves. Anyway, it is possible to identify a lower bound for the degradation of the modulus as indicated in Fig.1 with the solid line.

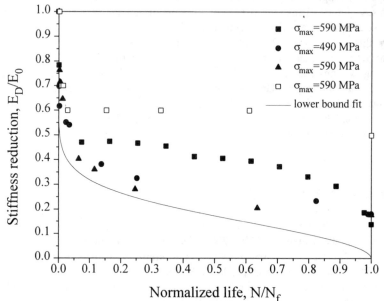

FIG. 1 -- Different stiffness loss versus number of cycle for similar maximum applied cyclic stress

The fact that brittle composites are very sensitive, in terms of accumulated damage, to the very early cycles is indicative of a high sensitivity to the applied strain.

It has been noted that, to characterize the external applied cyclic loading in terms of stress is not appropriate because when damage is generated in the material stresses are redistributed between the microstructural elements, e.g. unbroken fibers, matrix ligaments, etc. The effective stress in the damaged composite material can differ very much from the nominal applied value. In addition, because damage develops randomly along the specimen it becomes hard to define the effective stress in each region. On the other hand, strain seems to be more appropriate to identify a particular state of the material during cyclic loading for the following reasons: firstly, strain can be directly measured on the material even when damage takes place; secondly, the resistance of the composite constituents can better assessed in terms of strains at failure instead of stresses which may be to define for small scale constituents such as fibers.

If the strains applied in the first cycles are high enough to introduce damage in the microstructure, this will lead to stiffness loss. The subsequent cycles will see a progressive evolution of the initiated damage state that will develop more gradually up to the moment of final fracture. It is very difficult to develop an accurate model, defined on a micromechanical basis that is able to predict the physical evolution of complex damage states. The main features can be obtained from the fatigue tests in terms of the shape of the stiffness reduction trend. Many authors pointed out that brittle materials such as glass or glass-ceramic materials show practically no range of fatigue behavior that results in a crack of the order of an existing flaw size growing instantaneously.

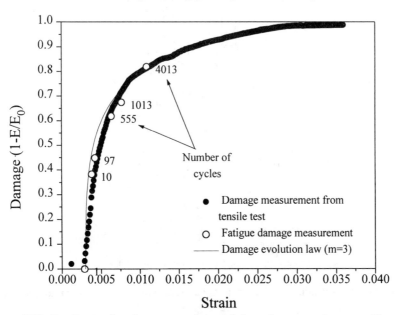

FIG. 2 -- Comparison between static and fatigue damage and proposed law.

Karandikar and Chou [15] and Evans and Fuller [16] suggested that cyclic fatigue does not lead to new damage modes in the composites.

If fatigue cycling does not introduce additional damage modes other than the growth of the already existing complex damage state, it follows that the evolution features related to the fatigue process are all contained in the shape of the distribution of the fatigue data . Furthermore, cyclic damage measurements taken at different cycles should fall on the same static damage curve shown in Fig. 2. The last observation has been verified plotting damage measurements taken at different number of cycles versus the total strain applied during the cycling. When a specimen is cycled in stress control, as a result of creation of new surfaces, the true applied strain increases with the number of cycles as shown in Fig. 3. The progressive material damage is illustrated in Fig. 4. The applied strain is partially recovered elastically in the cycle, but there is a contribution that accumulates as ratchetting, because of incomplete closure of cracked surfaces during unloading.

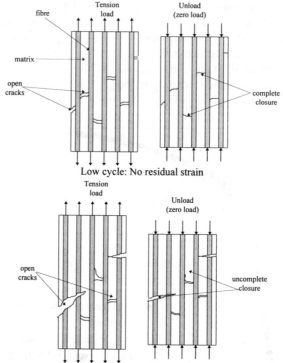

FIG. 3 -- Scheme of residual strain, due to damage, accumulation process under fatigue loading.

The relation that describes the damage evolution via modulus reduction, E_D/E_0, as a function of the number of cycles, have to be bounded between 0 and 1 for a number of cycles comprised between 1 and N_f. E_0 refers to initial modulus and E_D refers to current modulus The following relation:

$$\frac{E_D}{E_0} = B(\varepsilon, D) \cdot \left[1 - \frac{\ln(N)}{\ln(N_f)} \right]^{\frac{1}{\beta}}$$ (1)

was found to be most appropriate to describe the experimental data trend. The basis for Eqn. 1 is a phenomenological one. Stiffness reduction for various specimens appear to follow a "S" curve. In our representation, we choose a conservative lower bound, as indicated with a continuous line in Fig. 1. In Eqn. 1 $B(\varepsilon, D)$ is an appropriate function of the damage variable and cumulated strain; β is a material constant that determines the shape of the evolution law. When the number of cycle reaches N_f, i.e. the number of cycles at fracture, the ratio E_D/E_0 goes to zero. When $N=1$, then the amount of damage at the first cycle is determined by the imposed strain field in the material without any additional effect related to the cyclic nature of the loading. Only if the strain level is high enough to produce damage in the first place, then further damage will develop during cycling.

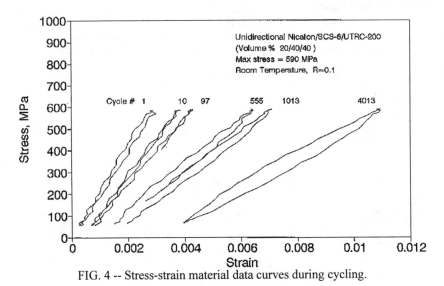

FIG. 4 -- Stress-strain material data curves during cycling.

To determine the amplitude constant B, it is sufficient to observe that the first cycle, if the strain rate is not extremely high, is similar to a static load ramp up to the imposed maximum strain. For this reason, the amount of damage produced in the first cycle has to be related to the static damage curve as suggested by Bonora and Newaz [14]:

$$B(\varepsilon) = (1 - D_0) - (D_{cr} - D_0)\left[1 - \frac{\ln(\varepsilon / \varepsilon_{th})}{\ln(\varepsilon_f / \varepsilon_{th})}\right]^{\frac{1}{m}} \qquad (2)$$

where: ε is the actual strain, ε_{th} is the strain threshold at which local damage processes start to take place, ε_f is the strain at failure, D_0 is the initial amount of damage, D_{cr} the damage at which failure takes place and m is the damage exponent values of D_{cr} can be measured in a uniaxial test while m is obtained from a best fit procedure as given in [15]. Substituting Eqn. 2 in Eqn. 1 leads to:

$$\frac{E_D}{E_0} = \left((1 - D_0) - (D_{cr} - D_0)\left[\frac{\ln(\varepsilon / \varepsilon_{th})}{\ln(\varepsilon_f / \varepsilon_{th})}\right]^{\frac{1}{m}}\right) \cdot \left[1 - \frac{\ln(N)}{\ln(N_f)}\right]^{\frac{1}{\beta}} \qquad (3)$$

Using the fatigue data available for the material under investigation, the exponent $(1/\beta)$ was found to be 0.2397 with a regression coefficient of 0.855 and a standard deviation of 0.243, (Fig.5).

As an immediate application of Eqn. 3, it is possible to draw the damage evolution curve as a function of the number of cycles for a given initial strain.

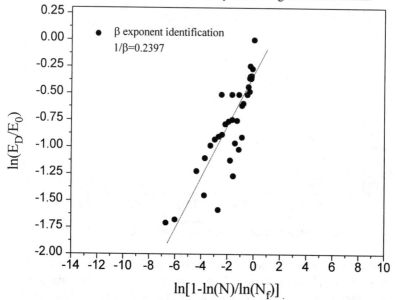

FIG. 5 -- Determination of the β exponent from fatigue experimental data.

In Fig. 6, these curves are plotted for several strain levels: it is evident how the material life is reduced by the progressive increase of the strain in the first cycle

CONCLUSIONS

Damage in hybrid CMCs is strain controlled. More particularly, magnitude of damage, as manifested by stiffness loss, is dependent on the strain experienced by the composite has been modeled. The fatigue life model presented requires the evaluation of a number of parameters such as ε_f, ε_{th} and m which can be obtained by conducting a monotonic test. Only two parameters, exponent $1/\beta$ and the number of cycles to failure N_f, have to be determined using fatigue data. Anyway, only a few fatigue tests performed at two or three different stress levels will be sufficient to identify the parameters in a proper way. The nature of damage evolution as dictated by stiffness loss during fatigue can be cast in a functional form that captures the essence of strain controlled damage. Fatigue life for a given initial reduction in stiffness can be estimated from the functional form if the nominal final life is known from limited experimental data. This modeling approach is a rational one given the complexity of the problem.

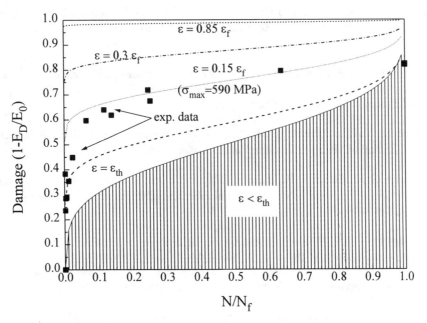

FIG. 6 -- Estimated life for different initial applied strain levels during the first cycle.

ACKNOWLEDGMENT

The authors acknowledge the funding for this research work from the IHPTET program support from the Propulsion and Materials Laboratory of Wright Laboratories. Mr. Larry Zawada of the Materials Directorate was the program monitor. Encouragement of Mr. Theodore Fecke of the Propulsion Laboratory is gratefully acknowledged. We acknowledge UTRC's Mr. Dave Jarmon and Mr. Ronald Cairo of P&W, West Palm Beach for valuable discussion during the course of the program.

REFERENCES

[1] Highsmith, A. L. and Reifsnider, K. L., "Stiffness-Reduction Mechanisms in Composite Laminates," in <u>Damage in Composite Materials, ASTM STP 775</u>, American Society for Testing and Materials, West Coshshocken, PA, 1982, p.103.

[2] Laws, N., Dvorak, G.J., and Hejazi, M., "Stiffness Changes in Unidirectional Composites Caused by Crack Systems, " <u>Journal of Mechanics of Materials</u>, vol.2, 1983, p.123.

[3] Talreja, R. , <u>Fatigue of Composite Materials,</u> Technical University of Denmark, 1985.

[4] Prewo, K. M., "Tension and Flexural Strength of Silicon Carbide Fiber-reinforced Glass Ceramics," <u>Journal of Materials Science</u>, Vol. 21, 1986, p. 3590.

[5] Prewo, K. M., " Advanced Characterization of SiC Fiber reinforced Glass Matrix Composites, " Office of Naval Research Contract N00014-81-C-0571, Interim report, June, 1983.

[6] Zawada, L. P., Butkus, L. M. and Hartman, G. A., "Room Temperature Tensile and Fatigue properties of SiC Fiber-reinforced Aluminosilicate Glass," <u>Ceramic Engineering Science Proceedings</u>, Vol. 11, 1990, p. 1592.

[7] Nardone, V. C. and Prewo, K. M., " Tensile Performance of Carbon Fiber-Reinforced Glass, " <u>Journal of Materials Science</u>, Vol. 23, 1988, p. 168.

[8] Newaz, G. M., Brust, F. W., Jarmon, D. C. and Cairo, R. R., " Deformation, Failure and Mechanical Response Modeling in Dual Fiber CMC," Presented at the Annual ACS Meeting, Cocoa beach, FL, Jan. 1994.

[9] Rousseau, C. Q., "Monotonic and Cyclic Behavior of a SiC/CAS Composite," in <u>Thermal and Mechanical Behavior of Metal Matrix and Ceramic Matrix Composites ASTM STP 1080</u>, J. M. Kennedy, H. M. Mouller, and W. S. Johnson Eds., American Society for Testing and Materials, West Corshshocken, PA, 1990, p. 136.

[10] Prewo, K. M., Johnson,B.and Starett, S., "Silicon Carbide Fiber-Reinforced Glass-Ceramics, " <u>Journal of Materials Science</u>, Vol.24, 1989, p.1373.

[11] Sbaizero, O. and Evans, A. G., "Tensile and Shear properties of Laminated Ceramic Matrix Composites, " <u>Journal of American Ceramic Society</u>, Vol. 69, n.6, 1986, p. 481.

[12] Aveston, A. and Kelly, J., " Theory of Multiple Fracture of Fibrous Composites," Journal of Materials Science, Vol.8, 1973, p. 352.

[13] Budiansky, B., Hutchinson, J. W., and Evans, A. G., "Matrix Fracture in Fiber-Reinforced Ceramics," Journal of the Mechanics and Physics of Solids, , Vol. 34., No. 2, 1986, p. 167.

[14] Bonora, N. and Newaz, G., " Modeling Damage Evolution in a Hybrid Ceramic Matrix Composite Under Static Tensile Loading," submitted to the Journal of Engineering Materials and Technology, ASME, Oct., 1995.

[15] Karandikar P. G. and Chou T. W.," Microcracking and Elastic Moduli Reductions in Unidirectional Nicalon-CAS Composites Under Cyclic Fatigue Loading", in Proceeding of the 16th Annual Conference on Composites and Advanced Ceramics, Cocoa Beach, FL, Jan., 1992.

[16] Evans A. G. and Fuller E. R.," Crack Propagation in Ceramic Materials Under Cyclic Loading Conditions", Metallurgical Transaction . Vol. 5, 1974, p.27.

M. Ramulu,[1] N. Eswara Prasad,[2] G. Malakondaiah,[2] and Z. Guo[1]

SECONDARY PROCESSING EFFECTS AND DAMAGE MECHANISMS IN CONTINUOUS-FIBER
CERAMIC COMPOSITES

REFERENCE: Ramula, M., Eswara Prasad, N., Malakondaiah, G., and Guo, Z., "**Secondary Processing Effects and Damage Mechanisms in Continuous- Fiber Ceramic Composites,**" Thermal and Mechanical Test Methods and Behavior of Continuous-Fiber Ceramic Composites, ASTM STP 1309, Michael G. Jenkins, Stephen T. Gonczy, Edgar Lara-Curzio, Noel E. Ashbaugh, and Larry P. Zawada, Eds., American Society for Testing and Materials, 1997.

ABSTRACT: Continuous-fiber ceramic composites (CFCC) are a relatively new area of composite materials in research. Therefore, the feasibility of using abrasive waterjets (AWJ) as a secondary CFCC process was explored. Continuous fiber-reinforced advanced ceramic composite materials have been machined with the AWJ piercing and cutting process. The topography and morphology of the machined surfaces were evaluated with surface profilometry and scanning electron microscopy (SEM). The surface characteristics, in terms of roughness and the micro-mechanisms of material removal, were evaluated. The AWJ surface characteristics and associated damage to the CFCC were compared with that of a conventional diamond saw cut surface. The AWJ generated surface was found to be significantly different from that of the diamond saw machining surface and the micromechanical behavior of the material removal was strongly dependent on the fiber orientation.

KEYWORDS: continuous-fiber ceramic composites, abrasive waterjets, machining, edge finishing, fiber direction, surface roughness, bending fracture, erosion, delamination

---

Recent advances in high strength and toughness materials have led to the development of a new generation of materials known as continuous-fiber ceramic composites (CFCC). These advanced composites offer not only high strength-to-weight and stiffness-to-weight ratios, but also have extremely good high-temperature properties. These materials are envisaged to be competitive for an impressive array of industrial applications ranging from piping and chemical reactors to combusters and tubes in heat-recovery systems [1-3]. Before advanced materials can be

---

[1]Professor and graduate student, respectively, Department of Mechanical Engineering, University of Washington, Seattle, WA 98195-2600.
[2]Scientists, Defence Metallurgical Research Laboratory, P.O. Kanchanbagh, Hyderabad 500058, India.

commercialized, production costs must be reduced. Net-shape manufacturing is one solution; however, for a majority of applications, tolerances will be so high that machining will still be required [1,4]. But the properties that make CFCC appealing also create a major challenge in machining as a result of their brittle behavior and hardness. The difficulties experienced in machining must be minimized to ensure their utility by a user. Since conventional machining can be costly, up to 80% of the total manufacturing cost, the improved machining processes or developing novel methods of machining are now considered to be one of the most important manufacturing science areas [1].

Current concerns of machining of composites with conventional methods include the presence of mechanical tool contact, dust and excessive noise. Mechanical tool contact can introduce stress into the workpiece. This can be compounded by extreme tool wear, especially when machining fibrous composites [5-8]. Because of excessive mechanical tool wear, it is natural to pursue the applications of cutting methods with little or no tool contact to the workpiece. Since high-temperature composites in general, and CFCC in particular, are relatively new material systems, their machinability has not been studied except for the recent work by Gonczy et al. [9]. Machining of ceramics has recently attracted large attention from the materials science community, and several nonconventional methods seem to have emerged as promising machining methods for hard to machine materials in addition to diamond grinding [3,4]. Among various machining methods, electrical discharge machining (EDM), laser machining, and AWJ are the most versatile and useful technological processes. These processes proved to machine intricate and complex shapes in various materials, including high-strength, temperature-resistant alloys [3,6].

Recently, the authors undertook the investigation of the machinability of CFCC materials by AWJ piercing and cutting processes. The purpose of this paper is to present preliminary experimental results on the secondary processing or edge-finishing characteristics of CFCC by AWJ and diamond saw-cutting methods. The results of the machining of these high-temperature composites will be discussed in terms of the surface finish for varying machining conditions and associated damage mechanisms. Based on experimental results, concluding remarks are given as to the feasibility of these machining methods.

EXPERIMENTATION AND PROCEDURE

Test Material

A commercial CFCC was obtained in a plate form of dimensions 200 x 10 x 3.7 mm for this study. The reinforcing fiber was a ceramic grade (Nicalon™) SiC fiber produced by pyrolysis of a spun polymer-derived ceramic precursor. A two-dimensional reinforced, plain woven cloth was fabricated using ~1800 denier fiber bundles (~500 fibers/bundle) by the fiber producer. The fiber preform was fabricated by the CFCC manufacturer by layering twelve plies of cloth, with the warp of the fibers aligned in the longitudinal direction. The processing of the matrix was carried out in two steps [10,11]. First a ~0.3 μm interfacial layer of pyrolytic carbon was deposited by chemical vapor infiltration (CVI) onto the fiber preform. The second and final processing step involved the decomposition of methyltrichlorosilane and the infiltration of the preforms by CVI until all the microporosity was filled, thus forming a crystalline β-SiC matrix. The remaining microporosity (~20 to 25 vol%) was primarily located within the fiber bundles. Approximate volume fractions of fibers and matrix were 35 and 40%, respectively. The optical micrograph of the material system is shown in Fig. 1. All the cutting and piercing specimens were twelve plies thick, equivalent to ~3.7 mm.

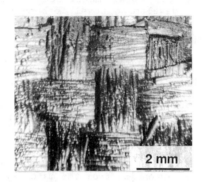

FIG. 1--Typical optical micrograph of a CFCC surface.

Procedure

Piercing and cutting experiments were performed with a waterjet (PowerJet model), which was driven by a waterje pump capable of pressures in excess of 240 MPa. A gravity feed abrasive hopper and workpiece table were both features provided with this unit. Axial feed was produced by the addition of a modified Hardinge milling machine table. Two DC motors and motor controllers were fixed to the Hardinge table to provide adjustable, reliable, and constant table feed rates. The milling table was adapted with an aluminum cutting table to support the workpiece and provided a source for clamping during the more rugged cutting modes. The primary components of the nozzle assembly consist of the sapphire jewel which transforms the high pressure water into a collimated jet, an abrasive mixing chamber, an abrasive inlet tube, two waterjet nozzle insert focusing fins, and the carbide waterjet nozzle insert. The nozzle focusing fins were provided for manual lineup of the jet emitted from the sapphire jewel of diameter 0.3 mm to the carbide nozzle insert of 1 mm diameter, which insured maximum velocity and coherency of the abrasive slurry upon exit from the nozzle insert. Extensive use of AWJ in machining of fiber-reinforced plastic materials was made, and the details of the AWJ process can be found in References 5 and 12.

The entire CFCC specimen was securely clamped on to the aluminum cutting table, with the use of a toe clamp, in a position which corresponds to the desired fiber direction. Preliminary cutting experiments were made with varying water pressure, grit size, traverse speed, and standoff distance and examined for noticeable trends in surface topography. Based on these preliminary observations, a reasonable but not necessarily optimal set of cutting conditions were chosen. Cutting conditions used for all experimental runs are listed in Table 1. Note that the abrasive size and its flow rate apply only to the AWJ cutting operations. All specimens were machined to a length of 25 mm or more to insure a constant cutting condition. Diamond saw specimens were machined with a Leematic 2000 slot machine configured with computerized motion control.   A 102 mm-diameter diamond saw of width 0.254 mm and #220 diamond grit was used for all slotting. Parameters for machining include a traverse speed of 3.15 m/min with a feed index of 76.2 μm for each pass and a spindle speed of 6000 rpm. After each slot was completed, the diamond wheel was dressed using paned glass at the aforementioned parametric levels.

TABLE 1--AWJ Experimental cutting conditions[a]

Specimen	Pressure, MPa	Abrasive Flow Rate, g/s
12	240	12
9	210	12
6	172	12
1	127	12
3	82	12
13	240	7
10	210	7
7	172	7
2	127	7
4	82	7
11	240	16
8	210	16
5	172	16

[a]Stand-off distance, 10 mm;traverse rate, 3.3 mm/s; and garnet abrasive mesh size = #100.

Data analysis and evaluation techniques used for all experiments include surface profilometry and SEM.   Surface roughness measurements were obtained with a Federal SurfAnalyzer[TM] 4000 profilometer using a 5 mm diameter probe.   The System 4000 is a stylus profilometer capable of producing the absolute profile of a surface and evaluating the associated parameters.   The surface roughness parameters were evaluated according to Surface Texture, Surface Roughness, Waviness and Lay (ANSI B46.1-1978).   A Jeol JSM-T840A Scanning Electron Microscope (SEM) was used to study the microstructural integrity of the machined specimens.

RESULTS AND DISCUSSION

Piercing

Figure 2 shows typical optical micrographs of an AWJ pierced hole, produced at a stand-off distance (SOD) of 15 mm in CFCC material.   The pierced holes were generated using a supply pressure of 172 MPa with #100-mesh garnet at an abrasive flow rate of 3.3 g/s for varying stand-off distances. Figure 2 a and b show the surface view of the hole at the top (jet entry) and bottom (jet exit) surface.   Note the random damage generated by the AWJ from the top surface as it penetrated through the thickness of the workpiece.   The severity of damage is higher near the top surface, when compared to the exit side of the hole.

Pierced hole tapers were measured with optical microscopy for varying SODs.   The degree of taper was calculated as a ratio between the upper surface hole diameter and the lower hole diameter.   The representative and limited taper results are shown in Table 2. It was observed that a linear relationship apparently exists between the SOD and the hole taper within the experimental conditions and the thickness

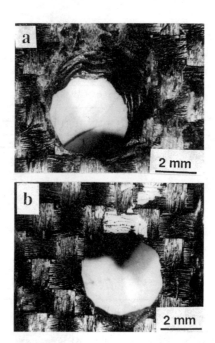

FIG. 2--Typical optical micrograph of an AWJ pierced hole in CFCC:
(a) jet entry, and (b) jet exit.

TABLE 2--Hole taper ratio[a]

Stand-off Distance, mm	Hole Taper Ratio
5	1.1
10	1.4
15	1.6
20	1.8

[a]Supply pressure, 127 MPa; garnet abrasive mesh
size = #100; and abrasive flow rate = 12 g/s.

of the work material considered in these preliminary experiments.
Piercing times associated with this series of experiments were less than
a minute.

Figures 3 and 4 show the SEM micrographs of the sectioned hole at
the jet entry and exit, respectively. Figure 3 a shows the micrograph of
the sectioned hole surface and Fig. 3 b depicts the surface features at
the jet entry. The micromechanisms associated with the hole piercing
appears to be microscopic fiber fractures and erosion shown respectively
in Fig. 3 c and d. At the jet exit, most of the matrix material was
washed out as can be seen in Fig. 4 a and b. Outer ply at the jet exit
shows the delamination is followed by severe damage (Fig. 4 c-d).
Therefore, the micromechanisms associated with AWJ hole drilling are
microfracture of fibers and matrix, delamination and fragmentation of
fiber bundles.

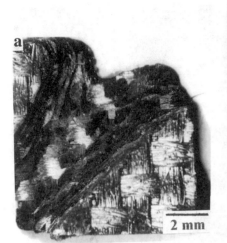

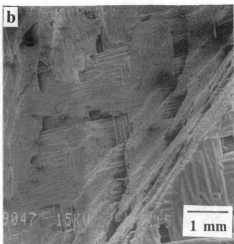

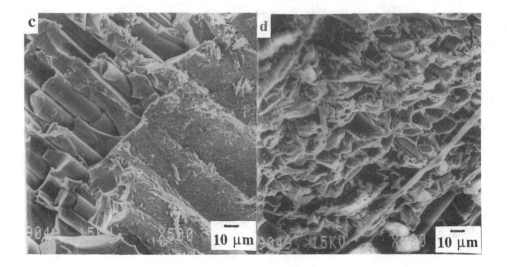

FIG. 3--Typical scanning electron micrographs of sectioned hole surface features at the jet entry. (a) Macro view of sectioned hole, (b) typical cutting zone, (c) magnified view of cutting zone, and (d) eroded zone.

FIG. 4--Typical scanning electron micrographs of sectioned hole surface features at the jet exit: (a) view of exit sectioned hole, (b) typical jet exit zone, (c) magnified view of exit zone, and (d) damaged zone at the jet exit.

Cutting

Figure 5 a and b shows the typical SEM micrographs of AWJ and a diamond machined surfaces, respectively at lower magnification. The AWJ machined surface was generated at a supply pressure of 82 MPa using a garnet abrasive flow rate of 12 g/s. The unfilled gaps or the porosity in the mid-section of the machined sample are clearly visible. This phenomenon was associated with this material in all the series of samples machined. The striations generally observed in any beam-cutting processes, were not observed because of the cutting conditions chosen based on previous modeling studies on fiber reinforced plastics [13]. The taper associated was also found to be minimal.

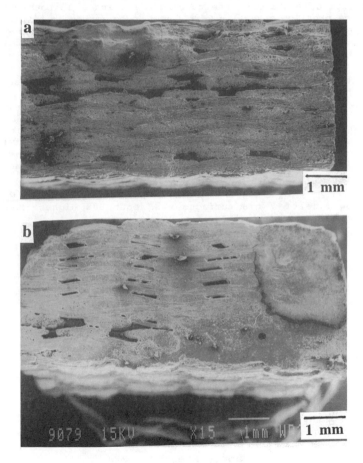

FIG. 5--Typical scanning electron micrographs of AWJ and diamond machined surface. (a) Abrasive water jet cut surface, and (b) diamond saw cut surface.

Surface quality in terms·of surface roughness was evaluated using surface profiles obtained from the Federal Surfanalyzer both for the diamond saw and the AWJ CFCC machined surfaces.   The effects of jet entry and exit were avoided by taking the surface measurements 0.5 mm below the top surface and 0.5 mm above the jet exit surface.   Surface roughness measurements were made for traverse length of 3.25 mm with a 0.8 mm cutoff length.

Under AWJ cutting conditions, all surface profiles (not shown here) exhibited irregularly spaced, and nonuniform peaks and valleys. However, these variations were not present for the surface generated by the diamond saw. The profiles recorded with the diamond saw were much more uniform, and the variance in peak-to-valley height is smaller comparatively with the AWJ cut surface profiles, regardless of the fiber orientation relative to the cutting direction.   In both cutting processes, the profiles generally were found to be random in nature.

The parameters derived from the profile analysis include the arithmetic average surface roughness (R_a), and the maximum peak-to-valley height (R_y).   The arithmetic average surface roughness, R_a, is the arithmetic average of the absolute distance of the profile from a mean line computed over a standard cut-off length.   The maximum peak-to-valley height, R_y, is the vertical distance between the top of the highest peak and the bottom of the deepest valley in one standard cut-off length.   This parameter is the most sensitive indicator of high valleys most often associated with fiber pullout and deep cracks.   In this series of experiments, R_y was always greater than R_a.   Preliminary results suggest that the low abrasive flow rate produced higher average R_y values.   Figure 6 shows only the typical surface roughness parameters R_a for varying supply pressures using garnet abrasive #100.   The average peak-to-valley surface roughness R_y (not shown here), obtained for the abrasive flow rate of 7 g/s surfaces was about 30% higher than the corresponding AWJ surface roughness for 12 g/s.

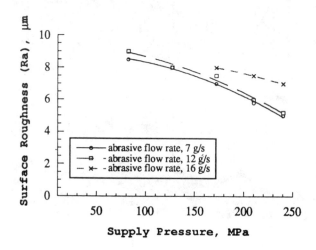

FIG. 6--Variation of average surface roughness with supply pressure.

In the diamond machining, the fiber and matrix have both been machined and the matrix was intact with the fibers. Typical micrographs of the diamond saw machined surface in Fig. 7 a-c reveal the low degree of damage to the constituents associated with material removal of this process. In general, fibers appear undisturbed on the kerf wall with minimal evidence of fiber pullout. The results are consistent with that of Gonczy et al.[9]. Interstitial matrix between adjacent fibers remains in its supportive position with only small signs of matrix smearing and no evidence of thermal degradation. Noting that parallel and perpendicular fibers were machined, and the material was remain intact on the kerf wall without indication of shear induced material removal. This suggests that the material removal occurs by low magnitudes of cutting force. Collectively, very little structural disruptions can be noted on the machined surface.

Figure 8 show the SEM micrographs of the typical AWJ generated surface in the cutting zone at a supply pressure of 240 MPa. As can be seen from Fig. 8, the surface of the 90° (or perpendicular to the jet direction plies) plies suggests that abrasive induced brittle microfractures, including shearing and abrasive micromachining, are the dominate modes of material removal. The fractured surface of the fibers and surrounding matrix appear to be machined, contrary to macrofracture induced by bending, which are the effects of sustained loading forces typical of conventional processes [14,15]. The cut surface is random in nature because of the host of abrasive attack angles at the face of the penetrating jet. Features of the postmachined fibers and interstitial matrix indicate that independent fracture of the constituents occurs during material removal. Nearly all matrix adjacent to the fibers remain intact in its supportive position after machining. Degrees of fiber pullout and fiber-matrix delamination are limited, possibly a function of the high interfacial bond strength between the constituents coupled with localized cutting forces of the AWJ. Features of the 0° or parallel plies are similar to the 90° plies and inspection of the machined surface suggests that abrasive shearing and brittle fracture account for the dominant portions of material removal. Although the surface of some exposed fibers are fractured, the matrix remains intact on the machined surface. Shallow abrasive wear tracks can be distinguished perpendicular to the fiber axis and are caused by stray abrasive particles at the exterior of the penetrating jet. This phenomena is most predominant near the jet entrance region as seen in Fig. 8b, with combinations of high supply pressure and large-size abrasives. Note the increase in wear track angle with cutting depth, which is due to an increase in jet deflection with penetration depth. Severity and depth of wear track penetration decreases with observation depth as a result of the reduction in abrasive kinetic energy. Contrary to the jet entry and the cutting zone surface, the jet exit surface damage was associated with bending fracture, delamination, and some of the matrix was washed out, as shown in Fig. 9. When AWJ machining of brittle materials, the crack nucleation and growth is much lower at greater cutting depths due to lower particle velocities. A reduction in impact energy reduces crack initiation and severely reduces ensuing crack growth. Thus on a micro level, the duration of loading is greater, because of the absence of fracture induced unloading which creates higher cutting forces.

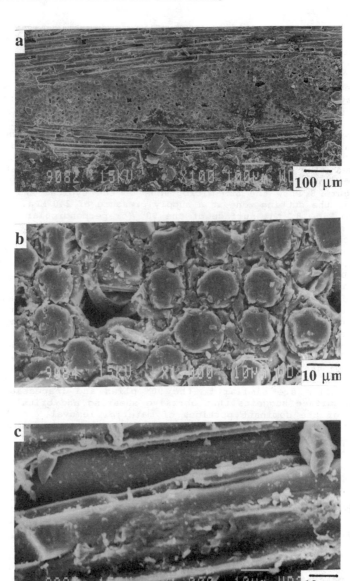

FIG. 7--Typical scanning electron micrographs of the diamond machined
surface morphology. (a) Micrograph of cut surface, (b) fiber
perpendicular to cutting direction, and (c) fiber parallel to
cutting direction.

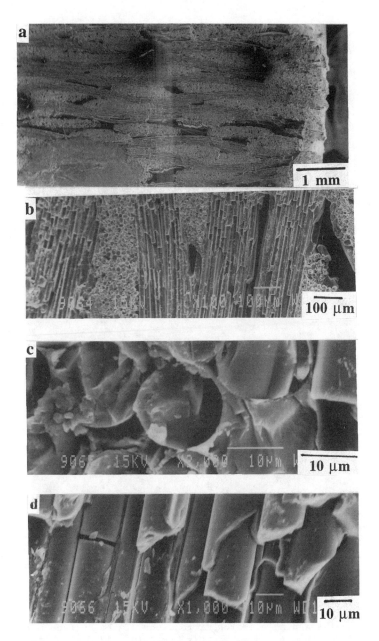

FIG. 8--Typical scanning electron micrographs of the surface morphology
of AWJ machined surface. Supply pressure, 82 MPa; abrasive flow
rate, 12 g/s; and SOD, 10 mm. (a) Macrograph of cut surface, (b)
magnified view of cutting zone, (c) fiber perpendicular to cutting
direction, and (d) fiber parallel to cutting direction.

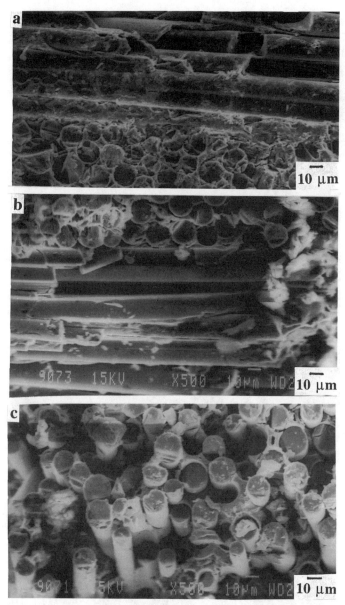

FIG. 9--Typical scanning electron micrographs of the surface morphology
of AWJ machined surface. Supply pressure, 240 MPa; abrasive flow
rate, 12 g/s; and SOD, 10 mm. (<u>a</u>) Micrograph corresponding to jet
entry, (<u>b</u>) cutting zone features, and (<u>c</u>) micrograph corresponding
to jet exit.

CONCLUSIONS

Based on these preliminary experiments on CFCC materials, the following conclusions were made:

1. AWJ cutting of CFCC consists of a combination of material removal mechanisms which include, bending, shearing, micro-machining, and erosion.

2. The micromechanisms associated with AWJ hole drilling or piercing are microfracture of fibers and matrix, delamination and fragmentation of fiber bundles. Feasibility of AWJ application to form holes in CFCC material was found to be not promising.

3. The AWJ machined surface topographic features of CFCC cut material surface are always dependent on the fiber direction or weaving pattern, with respect to the jet-cutting direction.

4. AWJ machining was found to be a feasible rough and medium cutting process for CFCC due to its material removal mechanisms and reasonable surface quality generation.

ACKNOWLEDGMENTS

The authors sincerely thank Professor M. G. Jenkins for providing the CFCC material. The first author (MR) would like to thank Mr. S. L. N. Acharyulu, Director, DMRL for providing the facilities to spend his sabbatical leave at DMRL. Thanks are also extended to Mr. S. Gupta for his help in conducting fractography.

REFERENCES

[1]   Sheppard, L. M., _Advanced Materials & Processes_, Vol. 132, No. 6, 1987, pp. 40-48.
[2]   Karnitz, M. A., Craig, D. A., and Richlen, S. L., _Ceramic Bulletin_, Vol. 70, No. 3, 1991, pp. 430-435.
[3]   Jahanmir, S., (Ed) _Machining of Advanced Materials_, NIST Special Publication 847, National Institute of Standards and Technology, Washington, DC, 1993.
[4]   Snoeys, R., Staelens, F., and Dekeysev, W., _CIRP Annals_, Vol. 35, No. 2, 1986, pp. 467-480.
[5]   Ramulu, M. and Arola, D., _Composites_ , Vol. 24, No. 4, 1993, pp. 299-308.
[6]   Hamatani, G. and Ramulu, M., _Journal of Engineering Materials and Technology_, Vol. 112, 1990, pp. 381-386.
[7]   Ramulu, M., _Advanced Ceramic Materials_, Vol. 3, No. 4, 1988, pp. 324-327.
[8]   Hashish, M., _Manufacturing Review_, Vol. 2, No. 2, 1989, pp. 142-150.
[9]   Gonczy, S. T., Lara-Curzio, E., Riester, L., Butler, E. P., Danforth, S. C., and Cannon, W. R., _Processing, Design, and Performance of Composite Materials 1994_, Bound Volume, MD- Vol. 52, ASME, 1994, pp. 217-238.
[10] Jenkins, M. G., Piccola, Jr., J. P., Mello, M. D., Lara-Curzio, E., and Wereszczak, A. A., _Ceramic Engineering and Science Proceedings_, Vol. 15, No. 4, 1994, pp. 209-218.

[11]   Piccola,   J. P., Jr., "Effects of Test Parameters on Tensile
       Mechanical Behavior of a Continuous Fiber Ceramic Composite
       (CFCC)," Master of Science thesis, University of Washington, 1994.
[12]   Arola, D., and Ramulu. M., _Processing of Advanced Materials_, Vol.
       4, 1994, pp. 37-47.
[13]   Ramulu, M., and Arola, D., _International Journal of Machine Tools
       and Manufacture_, Vol. 34, No. 3, 1994, pp. 295-313.
[14]   Wang, D. H., Ramulu, M., and Arola, D., _International Journal of
       Machine Tools and Manufacture_, Vol. 35, No. 6, 1995, pp. 1623-
       1638.
[15]   Wang, D. H., Ramulu, M., and Arola, D., _International Journal of
       Machine Tools and Manufacture_, Vol. 35, No. 6, 1995, pp. 1639-
       1648.

Testing of Tubes

W. Durell Wildman[1] and Pramod Khandelwal[2]

DESIGN, FABRICATION, AND BURNER RIG TESTING OF THREE-DIMENSIONAL WOVEN CERAMIC MATRIX COMPOSITE FLANGED HOOP SUBELEMENTS

REFERENCE: Wildman, W. D. and Khandelwal, P., **"Design, Fabrication, and Burner Rig Testing of Three-Dimensional Woven Ceramic Matrix Composite Flanged Hoop Subelements,"** Thermal and Mechanical Test Methods and Behavior of Continuous-Fiber Ceramic Composites, ASTM STP 1309, Michael G. Jenkins, Stephen T. Gonczy, Edgar Lara-Curzio, Noel E. Ashbaugh, and Larry P. Zawada, Eds., American Society for Testing and Materials, 1997.

ABSTRACT: Ceramic matrix composites (CMCs) have been identified as a key material system for improving the thrust-to-weight ratio of high-performance aircraft engines. An interturbine flow-path duct for a high-performance engine has been identified as a component with the potential for 100% reduction in active cooling air and 80% reduction in weight through the use of CMC material systems. To reduce risk prior to incorporating the interturbine duct in a high-performance engine, a CMC subelement design was conducted, parts were fabricated from two potential CMC material systems, and tests were conducted in a National Aeronautics and Space Administration (NASA) high-temperature, high-pressure burner rig with parameters representative of the high-performance engine environment. The burner rig testing verified the mechanical attachment and flow path sealing techniques as well as distinguished the oxidative stability of the two CMC material systems tested. After the burner rig testing was completed, the successful subelements were laser cut into three continuous hoop configurations and tested at room temperature for hoop retained tensile strength. The retained strength test results as well as fractography work indicated the need for regional architecture modifications as well as improved methods of infiltrating the fiber tows with oxidation inhibitors.

KEYWORDS: ceramic matrix composite, subelement, NASA burner rig, three-dimensional (3-D) weave, high-performance engine

---

[1] Program manager and development engineer, respectively, Allison Advanced Development Co., P.O. Box 7162, Indianapolis, IN 46206-7162.

[2] Senior staff engineer, Advanced Materials Department, Allison Engine Co., P.O. Box 420, Indianapolis, IN 46206-0420.

Ceramic matrix composites (CMCs) have been identified as a key enabling material technology that will assist high-performance aircraft engines in increasing thrust-to-weight ratios through the reduction of component weight and active cooling air. To reduce risk prior to their introduction into the high-performance engines, the reliability of candidate material systems must be demonstrated in environments representative of the engine parameters wherein critical issues including oxidative stability, heat flux levels, material temperatures, delta temperatures, delta pressure, attachment, flow path sealing, etc, are evaluated. The approach used for this program entailed the following:

1. Material screening resulted in evaluating test specimens fabricated for particular fiber preform architectures, matrix materials, and fabrication processes. Composite properties of interest included tensile modulus, ultimate strength, strain to failure, and thermal conductivity.

2. Flanged hoop subelement design, fabrication, and testing in a high-temperature burner rig benefited from changes of architecture and material processing based on lessons learned in the materials screening task.

The design of the flanged hoop subelement is first described, followed by a discussion of the materials and their processing. Next, the burner rig design and testing are presented. Finally, post test inspection and retained strength testing are detailed. The paper ends with conclusions about the applicability of the selected materials in high performance engines.

CMC FLANGED HOOP SUBELEMENT DESIGN

Mechanical Design

The goal of the program was to conduct the preliminary design for the interturbine transition duct of a high-performance aircraft engine as shown in Fig. 1. The design goals were to reduce the interturbine transition duct weight by 80% and the active cooling air by 100%. Detailed 3-D heat transfer and stress finite element analyses (FEA) were conducted for various engine operating cycles to determine the maximum material temperatures, stress levels, and engine cycle parameters. After completion of the preliminary design for the full size engine interturbine transition duct, a subelement was designed for testing in a NASA Lewis Research Center (LeRC) high-temperature, high-pressure burner rig. The subelement was designed with wall thicknesses, attachment, and flow-path pressure sealing methods representative of the full-size interturbine transition duct. The mechanical and thermal properties for the two material systems being developed are significantly different because of the matrix material and densification process. These differences result in significant variations in the axial and through-thickness thermal gradients as well as the operating stress levels. Room-temperature monotonic tensile tests were conducted with specimens fabricated using a proprietary 3-D angle interlock weave process. The "dog bone" tensile specimens were cut from flat panels fabricated with the same architecture and hand weaving process used for the flanged hoop subelements. The tensile specimens were 152.4 mm long, 25.4 mm wide,

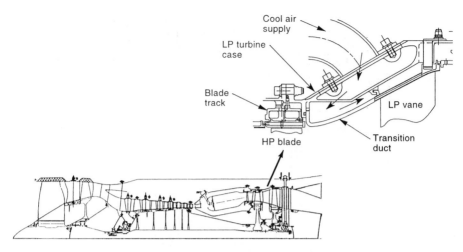

FIG. 1--The subelement design is representative of the interturbine transition duct for a high-performance aircraft engine.

and 3.8 mm thick, with a reduced gage section of 10.2 mm width and 30.5 mm length. Two clip-on extensometers were attached to either face of the specimen in the gage region for measuring strain. The specimens were loaded until failure occurred. Modulus was calculated from the stress/strain test data and ultimate strength was calculated based on load to failure and gage section cross section area. The tests were conducted using a face loaded gripping system. The thermal conductivity measurements were made using the Southern Research Institute comparative rod apparatus technique [1]. A comparison of the thermomechanical properties for the two material systems is shown in Table 1.

TABLE 1--Room temperature material property comparison.

Material system	Tensile modulus, GPa	Tensile ultimate strength, MPa	In plane thermal conductivity, W/(m·K)
HPZ/SiC (CVI)	94	160	13
HPZ/Si-N-C (PIP)	63	118	1.8

The tensile modulus and thermal conductivity combinations shown in Table 1 for the two material systems produced the stress levels and material temperatures shown in Fig. 2.

Attachment and sealing--Attaching the CMC subelement to the mating superalloy structure while maintaining adequate flow-path pressure sealing is a major challenge because of the material operating temperatures and the differential thermal expansion for

MATERIAL SYSTEM	CASE	PEAK STRESS LOCATION (NODE) MPa						SEAL LEAKAGE
		A	B-3052	C-324	D-6	D-Trφ (MPa)	T max°C	
HPZ/Si-N-C	P.D.	52	41	68	68	NA	1226	NA
	RIG TEST	20	36	24	37	6	1217	NOMINAL
	RIG TEST	22	38	24	37	6	1214	2X NOMINAL
HPZ/SiC	P.D.	102	83	135	135	NA	1184	NA
	RIG TEST	83	107	84	116	35	1178	NOMINAL
	RIG TEST	99	121	84	116	35	1170	2X NOMINAL

NOTES:
Loc A = Maximum Axial Stress   Loc D-6 = Hoop Stress
Loc B = Hoop Stress   Loc D-Trφ = Interlaminar Shear Stress
Loc C = Hoop Stress (Flange)   P.D. = Preliminary Design

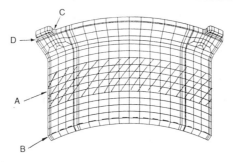

FIG. 2--Finite element model for peak stress and temperature summary for the two material systems.

the CMC and mating superalloy structure. The technique used for the subelements includes a free-floating cross-key arrangement (Fig. 3), which maintains axial, radial, and tangential retention during steady-state and transient conditions. The sealing system consists of a braided aluminum oxide cord and a high-temperature expanding gasket material.

Preform Architecture Design

The preform architecture selected was a proprietary 3-D angle interlock weave that meets the requirements for the interlaminar shear, hoop, radial, and axial strengths as well as flow-path surface finish. The preform and component design were accomplished using an integrated product design approach including the mechanical designers, meso-mechanical analysts, the preform fabricator, and the composite fabricators, as shown in Fig. 4.

Meso-mechanical preform analysis--The subelement FEA heat transfer and stress analysis were conducted using measured composite elastic and thermal properties from the material screening activity. With the material operating temperatures and stress level input, the micro- and meso-mechanical analyses were performed to define the directional fiber volume fractions required to satisfy the composite strength requirements. Several

FIG. 3--Flanged hoop subelement cross-key design addresses differential thermal expansion, axial, radial, and tangential retention and centering.

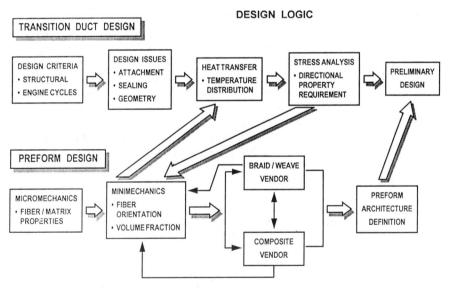

FIG. 4--Component and preform design using an integrated product design approach.

fiber architecture/fiber volume fraction systems were evaluated to determine the effect of fiber volume fraction on elastic properties, ultimate strengths, and thermal properties. The proprietary 3-D angle interlock weave architecture selected optimized the fiber volume fraction distribution to address the directional operating stress requirements as well as preform handling, preform compaction, infiltration, and surface finish issues.

CMC FLANGED HOOP SUBELEMENT FABRICATION

Fabrication

The flanged hoop subelement preforms were fabricated using the hydridopolysilazane (HPZ) fiber and the proprietary 3-D angle interlock weave process. The HPZ fiber was selected for this program based on preliminary test results reported by Jones indicating improved thermal stability for use temperatures up to 1350°C as compared to ceramic grade (CG) or HVR Nicalon fiber [2]. The architectures and fiber volume fractions for both the vertical flange and cylindrical regions were the same. The same architecture was used for both the HPZ silicon carbide (HPZ/SiC) and the HPZ silicon-nitrogen-carbon (HPZ/Si-N-C) composite systems.

The HPZ/SiC material system was fabricated using an "enhanced" SiC matrix material, a modified pyrolytic carbon interface coating, and an oxidation protection overcoat to minimize bulk oxidation using the chemical vapor infiltration (CVI) process. The vertical flange and cylinder end face surfaces were machined using a yttrium aluminum garnet (YAG) laser. The measured density of the flanged hoop subelements was 2.28 to 2.37 g/cm^3.

The HPZ/Si-N-C composites were fabricated using a proprietary interface coating. The coated preform was compressed in the closed mold and infiltrated with the preceramic polymer under vacuum using the polymer impregnation pyrolysis (PIP) process. The preform was then pyrolyzed in nitrogen, reimpregnated with the preceramic polymer, and pyrolyzed again until the target density was achieved. The measured density of the subelements was 1.93 to 2.0 g/cm^3 with 6.8 to 7.8% porosity. The vertical flange and cylinder end face surfaces were water-jet machined.

BURNER RIG TEST SECTION DESIGN

Mechanical Design

The NASA high-temperature, high-pressure burner rig facility (Fig. 5) has the capability to produce the heat flux levels, material temperatures, stress levels, and oxidizing environment required to duplicate the conditions anticipated in a high-performance aircraft engine. The original burner rig and test section were designed to test flat CMC panels. To adapt the flanged hoop subelements to the burner rig, a special test section for testing two flanged hoop subelements simultaneously was designed and fabricated to reduce testing costs. Simultaneous, yet independent, testing of two flanged

CMC subelement
test sections

CMC subelement
backside cooling
air supply/return

Combustor

Provides
CMC
Subelement
• ΔP
• ΔT
• Heat flux

• 1649°C
• 3.8 kg/s
• 1.4 MPa

FIG. 5--NASA high-temperature, high-pressure burner rig produces high-performance engine conditions.

hoop subelements required that two test section flanges be designed and fabricated with individual cooling air circuits, attachment, and pressure sealing methods, etc.

Subelement test section design--Independent test sections were designed for the two flanged hoop subelements (Fig. 6). The test sections provided the attachment, sealing, delta temperature (ΔT), and delta pressure (ΔP) control representative of a high-performance engine environment. The ΔP and ΔT were controlled by a backside preheated air circuit. The air circuit was equipped with flow meters and control valves permitting control and measurement of seal leakage, ΔP, and ΔT. In addition, each test section was equipped with instrumentation access ports allowing the flanged hoop subelements to be instrumented with thermocouples for both hot and cold side CMC material temperature measurement.

Flow-path transition and flow velocity control hardware--The NASA burner rig combustor has a 10.2 cm x 10.2 cm square cross section. The inside diameter of the flanged hoop subelement is 17.78 cm. A transition member was designed to create a flow path from the square to circular cross section. To achieve the gas stream Mach numbers for the required heat flux levels, the water-cooled centerbody member shown in Fig. 6 was designed for installation in the gas path with the requirement that all cooling water exit the centerbody downstream of the CMC flanged hoop subelements.

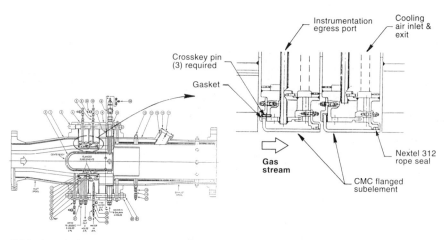

FIG. 6--Subelement test section addresses CMC attachment, sealing, delta pressure, and delta temperature.

NASA BURNER RIG TESTING

Test Procedure

Two instrumented CMC flanged hoop subelements were installed in the test flanges, and the entire test section was attached to the NASA burner rig. Instrumentation and cooling supply lines, flow meters, and flow control valves were installed. The test procedure involved flowing preheated air through the combustor until an air temperature of 611°C was achieved. Upon reaching the 611°C temperature, the combustor air/fuel mixture was ignited and the fuel and air pressure increased slowly. In parallel with the combustor temperature and pressure ramping up to the desired levels, the CMC flanged hoop subelement test section cooling air and pressure were increased to maintain the proper material temperatures and ΔP. Upon achieving the desired material temperature of 1204°C, ΔT , and ΔP, the parameters were stabilized. The typical elapsed time from combustor ignition until the parameters were stabilized was approximately 5 minutes.

The steady-state test conditions were maintained until either a rig malfunction or CMC flanged hoop subelement failure occurred. In test number one, the HPZ/Si-N-C material system flanged hoop subelement failed after 22 hrs. The failure was detected by the loss of ability to maintain ΔP across the hoop wall as well as a significant increase in test section flange material temperatures. The failed subelement was replaced with a new HPZ/SiC material system subelement and the test continued for a total of 42.5 hrs. The flanged hoop subelements test number one results are shown in Fig. 7.

The HPZ/SiC subelements shown in Fig. 7a and 7b were still intact and pressure tight but exhibited tangential cracks in the radius region. The subelement sections in Fig. 7c and 7d exhibited brittle fracture in the lower stressed composite region.

For test number two, the positions of the HPZ/SiC material and the HPZ/Si-N-C subelements were reversed to evaluate the effect of the axial location in the test sections with respect to the combustor discharge on durability. In test number two, the HPZ/SiC material system was located in the forward position nearest the combustor and the HPZ/Si-N-C material system in the aft position farthest from the combustor. Test number two was conducted in the same manner as test number one, and after only 3.5 hrs the HPZ/Si-N-C flanged hoop subelement failed. The failure again was detected by the inability to maintain the ΔP across the subelement cylinder wall as well as the significant temperature increase in the test section material temperatures. The subelement exhibited significant axial and tangential cracks through the thickness of the cylinder and flange regions. When the ceramic instrumentation lead wrapped around the cylinder region was removed, the subelement broke into segments. The HPZ/Si-N-C subelement was replaced with the HPZ/SiC subelement, which had accumulated 20.5 hrs in test number one. The test was continued and both HPZ/SiC subelements completed the balance of the testing which was stopped at 50 hrs total test time. The HPZ/SiC subelements were still intact but exhibited tangential cracks in the radius region and radial cracks in the flange region. The test two flanged hoop subelements are shown in Fig. 8. A summary of the material system test times and results for both tests one and two is shown in Table 2.

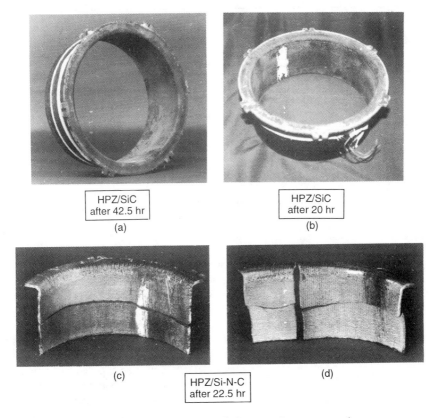

HPZ/SiC
after 42.5 hr
(a)

HPZ/SiC
after 20 hr
(b)

(c)

(d)

HPZ/Si-N-C
after 22.5 hr

FIG. 7--CMC Flanged hoop subelements from test number one.

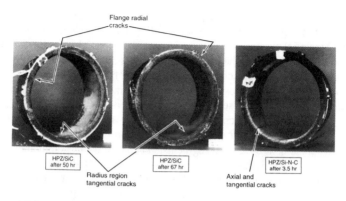

FIG. 8--CMC flanged hoop subelements from test number two.

TABLE 2--Results of NASA burner rig testing

Test No.	Forward position	Test hours	Aft position	Test hours	Comments
1	HPZ/Si-N-C	22	HPZ/SiC	42.5	HPZ/Si-N-C failed at 22 hrs
	HPZ/SiC	20.5			
2	HPZ/SiC	50	HPZ/Si-N-C	3.5	HPZ/Si-N-C failed at 3.5 hrs
			HPZ/SiC	46.5	

POST-TEST INSPECTION AND RETAINED STRENGTH TESTING

Nondestructive Evaluation (NDE)

The subelements were inspected prior to and after burner rig testing using radiography and through-transmission ultrasonics. X-radiography revealed the HPZ/Si-N-C subelements had some distorted fibers in the cylinder region, the result of preform compression in the closed mold. There were no indications of fiber distortion in the HPZ/SiC subelements. Low density areas were observed in subelements of both material systems using through-transmission ultrasonics but no cracks were detected. The density variations in the cylinder region correlated with the failure regions. Visual and radiographic inspection of the burner rig tested HPZ/SiC subelements detected cracks in the vertical flange to cylinder transition radius region on the inner surface that propagated and extended around the circumference (Fig. 9). The cracks were only partially through the wall thickness and observable only from the inside of the subelement. The cracking is believed to have been created as a result of the thermal stresses in the radius region governed by the hot cylindrical region and the much cooler flange region (ΔT ~200°C).

Retained Strength Testing

Room temperature, retained hoop strength testing was conducted using the fixturing shown schematically in Fig. 10. The test system consists of a sealed pressure vessel, a hydraulic pump, and ancillary equipment for measuring pressure and strain. The pressure vessel consists of two cover plates which are separated by precision machined spacers. The CMC hoop subelement is mounted between the two cover plates and the entire assembly is clamped together by bolts. The CMC hoop subelement is not constrained by the top or bottom plates, allowing free diametral growth when pressurized. A rubber bladder contacting the entire length of the CMC hoop subelement is installed in the inside of the CMC hoop subelement. The pressure is applied to the rubber bladder by the hydraulic pump and pressure is measured by a pressure transducer. The strain is measured by a wire wrapped around the circumference of the subelement and connected to LVDTs mounted on a fixed frame. The response to the applied pressure is recorded on an X-Y plotter as stress versus strain. Pressure is applied at the rate of 172 MPa/min until fracture occurs. Hoop tensile stress is calculated using Lame's equation.

Room-temperature hoop strength of both the HPZ/Si-N-C and the HPZ/SiC material systems was evaluated in the "as-received" condition as well as after the NASA burner rig testing. The specimens were laser machined into a cylinder region 17.77 cm inside diameter x 5.71 cm long with a wall thickness of 0.41 cm. Three hoop specimens were planned to be machined from each subelement. The specimens were to be machined from the cylindrical, vertical flange, and transition radius regions. The HPZ/Si-N-C

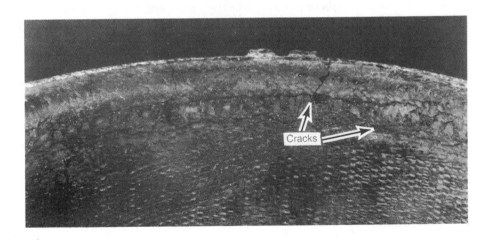

FIG. 9-- NASA burner rig testing produces cracks in the HPZ/SiC radius transition region.

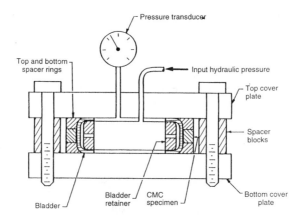

FIG. 10--Hoop test fixture measures retained tensile strength and strain to failure.

material system failed in both burner rig tests; therefore, only "as-received" properties were measured from one hoop which was not tested in the burner rig. The specimens failed in a brittle manner indicating a strong bond at the fiber/matrix interface. Microscopic analysis as shown in Fig. 11 indicated brittle fracture with extensive fiber bridging and glassy oxide layers. The "as-received" hoop strength was measured at 58.3 MPa as compared to 182 to 237 MPa reported by Chuck and Szweda for a 2-D Nicalon/Si-N-C 2-D laminate system tested at 1000°C in vacuum [3].

The three HPZ/SiC flanged hoop subelements from the NASA burner rig testing were visually and radiographically examined. The inspections revealed severe cracking in the vertical flange to cylinder transition radius region resulting from thermomechanical stresses encountered during the 1204°C testing. The retained strength hoop tensile tests for the cylinder region were conducted at room temperature. The test results and stress/strain curves are summarized in Table 3 and Fig. 12 [4]. The "as-received" room temperature hoop strength of the HPZ/SiC material system is 166.2 MPa with a fibrous composite fracture [5]. Table 3 shows a summary of hoop tensile test results and strength degradation; results do not indicate a direct strength reduction as a function of test time.

Fracture surfaces of the HPZ/SiC serial no. 003 hoop with the 3.8 MPa retained tensile strength are shown in Fig. 13 indicating fibrous failure even with low retained strength. Micrographic analysis of the fracture surfaces indicated the enhanced SiC matrix material had not adequately infiltrated the fiber tows thereby allowing oxidation paths into the modified carbon fiber interface coating.

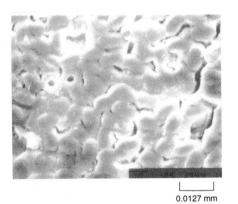
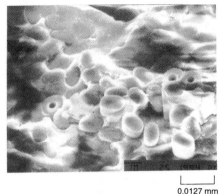

0.0127 mm   0.0127 mm

FIG. 11--Micrographs indicate brittle fracture of HPZ/Si-N-C composite after 3.5 hrs of
NASA burner rig testing at 1204°C.

TABLE 3--<u>Strength reduction due to burner rig testing of HPZ/SiC components.</u>

Serial No.	Test hours	Retained strength, MPa	Percentage retained strength*
001	42.5	93.1	56
002	67	45.3	27
003	50	3.8	2.3

* Compared to "as-received" ultimate tensile strength of 166.2 MPa [5].

CONCLUSION

The flanged hoop subelement and burner rig test section designs were
successfully demonstrated in the NASA high-temperature, high-pressure burner rig tests
at a material temperature of 1204°C with heat flux levels, ΔT, and ΔP representative of a
high-performance aircraft engine. The HPZ/SiC material system successfully completed
both tests. The HPZ/Si-N-C material system failed during both tests with brittle fracture.
The FEA stress analysis conducted for the flanged hoop subelements indicated that the
operating stress levels in the HPZ/SiC material system were significantly greater than the
HPZ/Si-N-C material system; however, the HPZ/SiC demonstrated superior performance
in both tests as a result of a superior fiber interface coating as well as an "enhanced"
matrix system for improving the oxidative stability of the material system. The as-
received hoop tensile testing of the HPZ/Si-N-C material indicated very low tensile
strengths and brittle fracture, leading to the conclusion that the interface coating was
rigidly bonded to the fiber and matrix and not an optimized system.

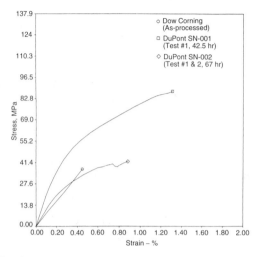

FIG. 12--Stress/strain curves for "as-received" and after NASA test subelement cylinder regions.

FIG. 13--Typical micrograph of HPZ/SiC subelement after 50 hrs of NASA burner rig testing at 1204°C demonstrates fibrous failure.

The low retained strengths for the HPZ/SiC material system were investigated via scanning electron microscope and other techniques. The investigation revealed that the enhanced matrix material had not adequately infiltrated the fiber tows thereby resulting in insufficient oxidation protection for the fiber interface.

Use of HPZ/SiC material system will be continued for optimization in Phase III. Revisions will be made to the architecture in the flange and radius region to reduce the high thermal stresses and eliminate the cracking. In addition, improved methods will be developed to infiltrate the fiber tow with the enhanced matrix material to improve the oxidative stability of the material system.

ACKNOWLEDGMENTS

This activity was sponsored by the Aero Propulsion and Power Directorate, Wright Laboratory, Air Force Systems Command (ASD), United States Air Force, Wright-Patterson AFB, Ohio 45433-6563 under contract F33615-92-C-2279. Special thanks to NASA Lewis Research Center, Cleveland, OH, Combustion Research and Advanced Sensor Technology branches for thin-film thermocouple application and burner rig testing.

REFERENCES

[1]   Southern Research Institute, 1994, *Mechanical and Thermal Evaluation of Dow Corning and DuPont Ceramic Matrix Composites for Turbine Engine Applications*, pp. 7-8.

[2]   Jones, R., et al., "A Comparison of Ceramic Fiber Properties," NASA Conference Publication 3097, Part I, pp. 47-59, January 1990.

[3]   Chuck, L., and Szweda, A., "High-Temperature Tensile Strength Testing and Failure Analysis of a Braided Nicalon/PIP Si-C-N Ceramic Matrix Composite Tube," NASA Conference Proceedings Publication No. 3307, The 18th Conference on Metal Matrix, Carbon, and Ceramic Matrix Composites, held in Cocoa Beach, FL, January 9-14, 1994, Published September 1995.

[4]   Southern Research Institute, 1994, *Hoop Evaluation of Flanged Ceramic Matrix Composite Subelements*, pp. 17-22.

[5]   Southern Research Institute, 1993, *Hoop Tensile Evaluation of DuPont 3-D Angle Interlock SiC/SiC*, pp. 10-11.

Summary

Since its establishment in 1991, ASTM Subcommittee C28.07 on Ceramic Matrix Composites has actively promoted the development of test methods for continuous-fiber ceramic composites (CFCCs) and the transfer of research results related to these materials. Indeed, a workshop organized by David C. Cranmer at the National Institute of Standards and Technology, Gaithersburg, Maryland, in February 1990, helped set the stage for the establishment of ASTM Subcommittee C28.07 and resulted in the publication, "Workshop on Assessment of Testing Methodology for Glass, Glass-Ceramic, and Ceramic Matrix Composites," by D. C. Cranmer, *Journal of Research of the National Institute of Standards and Technology,* Vol. 96, No. 4, 1991, pp. 493–501. Following the establishment of ASTM Subcommittee C28.07, a more informal workshop was organized by George D. Quinn in January 1992 at the ASTM Committee C28 meetings in Cocoa Beach, Florida. Finally, a formal workshop entitled "Thermal and Mechanical Test Methods and Behavior of Continuous Fiber Ceramic Composites (CFCCs)" organized by Michael G. Jenkins, Stephen T. Gonczy, and Edgar Lara-Curzio was held in June 1994 at the ASTM Committee C28 meetings in Montreal, Quebec.

The impetus for these workshops was that anticipated engineering applications of CFCCs in industrial, aerospace, and propulsion systems require materials to be exposed to service cycles in various aggressive environments which may include simultaneous temperature and load cycling or thermal or mechanical shock. Materials testing and characterization elucidate aspects of the unique damage-tolerant behavior ("toughness") of this class of advanced ceramics. This information can enable proper formulation of models used for component lifetime prediction and design and guide material development. It was hoped that these workshops would assist in continuing the premarket penetration standardization process required to ensure timely and rapid introduction of these emerging materials into international markets. Researchers from industry, academia, and government who participated in this workshop discussed topics in the following areas:

- development and application of novel test methods and equipment;
- application of standardized test methods;
- environmental and thermal effects;
- tensile, compressive, or shear strength behavior;
- creep/creep rupture behavior;
- cyclic fatigue including frequency, waveform, and amplitude effects;
- thermomechanical fatigue;
- deformation behavior;
- multiaxial loading as applied to test specimen coupons or components (for example, tubes);
- effects of fiber architecture including laminate, fabric, or braided reinforcements;
- specimen design, including volume and geometrical effects; and
- interfacial property measurement and effects of composite performance.

By 1996, ASTM Subcommittee C28.07 had succeeded in introducing four test methods for CFCCs. While CFCCs are said to be an enabling technology for U.S. industry, test methods are viewed as being an enabling supporting technology. Thus, without the common language and procedures of standardized test methods, CFCCs cannot be refined and improved to fill their premier role on the advanced technology. The symposium "Thermal and Mechanical Test Methods and Behavior of Continuous Fiber Ceramic Composites" was held in Cocoa Beach, Florida, 8–9 Jan. 1996, with the intent of formally introducing novel test methods for CFCCs, presenting some of the unique aspects of the thermal and mechanical behavior of CFCCs, and addressing the application of existing standarized test methods to CFCCs. The presentations and the collection of papers in this special technical publication, ASTM STP 1309, are the results of recent research and development programs for CFCCs.

The papers in this STP are a significant contribution to the development and understanding of the behavior of continuous-fiber ceramic matrix composites. Each of the papers in the five sections is briefly summarized in the following paragraphs with some perspective on the significance of the work.

Room-Temperature Test Results/Methods

"Influence of Test Mode, Test Rate, Specimen Geometry, and Bending on Tensile Mechanical Behavior of a Continuous Fiber Ceramic Composite" by Piccola, Jenkins, and Lara-Curzio—the ASTM Test Method for Monotonic Tensile Strength Testing of Continuous Fiber-Reinforced Advanced Ceramics with Solid Rectangular Cross-Section Specimens at Ambient Temperatures (C 1275) was used to investigate the effects of test mode, test rate, specimen geometry, and bending on the mechanical behavior of a CFCC. Analysis of variance showed no effect of test mode and test rate on proportional limit stress and ultimate strength but an effect of specimen geometry for ultimate strength but not proportional limit stress.

"Effect of High Strain Rate on the Tensile Behavior of Nicalon™/CAS Continuous-Fiber Ceramic Composites" by Sánchez, Puente, Elizalde, Martín, Martínez, Daniel, Fuentes, and Beesley—Tensile properties of a CFCC were measured as a function of strain rate. Novel test methods included the use of piezoelectric load cells and strain gages and showed that fracture strength and strain energy density increased with increasing strain rate. These trends were related to fracture mode and damage in the material.

"Shear Strength of Continuous Fiber Ceramic Composites" by Lara Curzio and Ferber— Two test methods for shear strength testing of CFCCs are presented: double-notched compression for interlaminar shear strength and Iosipescu shear test to determine in-plane shear strength. Experimental results are presented for two CFCCs and are related to the thickness of fiber coating.

"Unloading-Reloading Sequences and the Analysis of Mechanical Test Results for Continuous Fiber Ceramic Composites" by Steen and Vallés—Intermittent unloading-reloading cycles are shown to be a powerful tool to assist the interpretation of the mechanical response of a CFCC. A correlation between fiber-matrix interfacial phenomena and the unloading-reloading response is drawn. Implications of the technique for modeling the mechanical behavior of CFCCs are discussed.

High-Temperature Test Results/Methods

"The Effect of Hold Times on the Fatigue Behavior of an Oxide/Oxide Ceramic Matrix Composite" by Zawada and Lee—An oxide fiber-reinforced oxide matrix ceramic composite was tested under monotonic, cyclic, and constant loading. The effect of temperature, maximum stress, frequency, and hold time were examined. Increased strain accumulation occurred with decreasing frequency and increasing hold times.

"Subcritical Crack Growth in Ceramic Composites at High Temperature Measured Using Digital Image Correlation" by Mumm, Morris, Dadkhah, and Cox—An in-situ experimental technique allowed high-resolution, high-sensitivity determination of full-field strains during high-temperature testing. Creep crack growth was investigated in a CFCC at 1150°C. Crack opening displacements werr monitored for advancing bridged cracks and related to models for crack growth.

"Tensile and Fatigue Behavior of a Silicon Carbide/Silicon Carbide Composite at 1300°C" by Ünal—Monotonically and cyclically loaded response of a CFCC was studied in nitrogen at 1300°C. Fiber architecture and the interphase material contributed to failure occurring in stages. In monotonically loaded tests, failure occurred by creep of bridging fibers. In cyclically loaded tests, failure occurred by brittle fracture.

"Stress-Temperature-Lifetime Response of Nicalon Fiber-Reinforced Silicon Carbide (SiC) Composites in Air" by Lin and Becher—Time-to-failure tests were conducted in four-point flexure in ambient air at elevated temperatures to study the effects of stress level and temperature on the performance of a CFCC. A threshold stress was identified, although the thickness of the graphitic interface did not have as great an effect as oxidation inhibitors.

"Fatigue Crack Growth Behavior of a Woven HPZ/Silicon Carbide Ceramic Matrix Composite" by Kramb and John—Fatigue crack growth behavior in a CFCC was monitored using optical and scanning electron microscopy in addition to compliance techniques. Comparison of crack growth in the CFCC and the monolithic matrix was used to deduce the fiber/matrix interfacial shear stress during crack propagation. This stress was correlated to the fiber-bridging stress and the crack opening displacements.

"Creep-Rupture Behavior of a Nicalon/SiC Composite" by Verrilli, Calomino, and Brewer—High-temperature creep tests were performed on a CFCC at constant maximum stresses equal to or less than the proportional limit stress. Intermediate temperature tests in ambient air caused decreased creep lives, whereas higher temperature tests in a vacuum produced run-out lives. An oxidation-embrittlement damage mechanism was identified.

"Retained Tensile Properties and Performance of an Oxide-Matrix Continuous-Fiber Ceramic Composite After Elevated-Temperature Exposure in Ambient Air" by Munson and Jenkins—Oxide matrix CFCC specimens were exposed for 1, 24, and 100 h at 800 and 1000°C in ambient air. Retained tensile properties at room temperature showed small decreases in elastic modulus and proportional limit stress, but large decreases in ultimate tensile strength and modulus of toughness as a result of the degradation of the interphase and fibers.

Nondestructive Characterization

"Characterization of Damage Progression in Ceramic Matrix Composites Using an Integrated NDE/Mechanical Testing System" by John, Buchanan, Stubbs, and Herzog—A unique integrated nondestructive evaluation/mechanical test system was developed to characterize damage progression in CFCCs. Conventional extensometry plus ultrasonic surface and longitudinal wave transducers were used to track damage. A correlation between experimental results and the NDE method are shown.

"Infrared-Based NDE Methods for Determining Thermal Properties and Defects in Ceramic Composites" by Ahuja, Ellingson, Steckenrider, and Koch—Flashed infrared light is used to heat instantaneously CFCC components. Digital images of the temperature distribution are used to detect internal defects (for example, delamination or porosity) and are also used to determine thermal diffusivity. Correlations are shown between the nondestructive characterization technique and actual defects.

"Measurement of Orthotropic Elastic Constants of Ceramic Matrix Composites from Impact Sound" by Sakata and Ohnabe—The elastic constants of CFCCs were measured from a combination of the impact sound, natural frequencies, and finite element analysis of small specimens and a jet engine component. Damage of the component after operation of the jet engine is correlated to the reduction of the elastic modulus of the material.

Modeling and Processing

"On the Optimal Design of Fiber-Reinforced Laminates" by Kalamkarov—An optimal design algorithm is proposed for fiber-reinforced laminate CFCCs with a prescribed stiffness. The design problem is generalized to account for the minimization of the volume content of fibers. Examples are used to illustrate the effectiveness and advantages of the developed method.

"A Model for the Creep Response of Oxide-Oxide Ceramic Matrix Composites" by Zuiker—A numerical model was developed to predict the creep response of CFCCs. In the model, Mori-Tanaka estimates of overall elastic response in conjunction with transformation-filed analysis are used to predict the inelastic deformation. Good correlation is shown between the model and experimental results over a wide range of temperatures and stresses.

"Fatigue Life Modeling of Hybrid Ceramic Matrix Composites" by Newaz and Bonora—Cyclic fatigue of a hybrid glass matrix was characterized. Damage evolution was monitored as a function of fatigue cycles and stress levels via stiffness loss. The magnitude of damage was dependent on strain level. A stiffness reduction model was proposed as a function of fatigue life and was successful in predicting damage evolution/fatigue life in the hybrid CFCC.

"Secondary Processing Effects and Damage Mechanisms in Continuous-Fiber Ceramic Composites" by Ramulu, Prasad, Malakondaiah, and Guo—Comparisons are made of CFCC surfaces machined by conventional diamond-grit grinding and nonconventional abrasive water jet (AWJ) cutting. AWJ cut surfaces show a through-thickness variation of roughness and associated cutting/damage mechanisms. The increased damage of AWJ is of concern in applying this machining technique to CFCCs.

Testing of Tubes

"Design, Fabrication, and Burner Rig Testing of Three-Dimensional Woven Ceramic Matrix Composite Flanged Hoop Subelements" by Wildman and Khandelwal—Design considerations for a CFCC flow path duct for high-performance turbine engines are detailed. Test considerations and results for high-temperature testing in a burner rig to simulate the engine operating conditions are reported. Retained strengths are obtained for CFCC subelements that survived the burner rig tests.

Michael G. Jenkins
Department of Mechanical Engineering
University of Washington, Seattle, WA;
Symposium cochair and coeditor.

Edgar Lara-Curzio
Metals and Ceramics Division
Oak Ridge National Laboratory,
Oak Ridge, TN;
Symposium cochair and coeditor.

Stephen T. Gonczy
Gateway Materials Technology,
   Mt. Prospect, IL;
   Symposium cochair and coeditor.

Noel E. Ashbaugh
University of Dayton Research Institute
   University of Dayton, Dayton OH;
   Symposium cochair and coeditor.

Larry P. Zawada
Materials Directorate
   Wright Laboratory,
   Wright-Patterson AFB, OH;
   Symposium cochair and coeditor.

Author Index

Subject Index

A

Abrasive waterjets, 274
Acoustic emission, 193
Acousto-ultrasonic
    measurements, 193
Alumina, 209
Aluminosilicate matrix, 69
Analysis of variance, 3
ANOVA, 3
Applied stress, 158
ASTM standards
    C 1275, 3, 176
    C 1292, 31
    D 2344, 31
    D 3518, 31
Auger electron microscopy, 219

B

Beam method, short, 31
Beam theory, 219
Bending, 3, 176
Bridging, 102
Burner rig testing, 291

C

Calcium aluminum silicate
    matrix, 16
Coating density, 209
Coating thickness, 31
Compression, 31
Crack growth, 142
Crack growth, fatigue, 142
Crack growth, subcritical,
    102
Crack opening displacement,
    102, 142
Creep, 49, 102, 113
    deformation, 69
    rupture, 6, 158
Critical stress, 264
Cross-ply structure, 16

D

Damage accumulation, 49
Damage evaluation, 219
Damage mechanisms,
    oxidation-embrittlement,
    158
Damage modes, 264
Damage progression, 193
Damage tolerance, 142
Deformation behavior, 193
Delamination, 274
Differential image correlation,
    102
Digital filtering, 209
Displacements, 102

E

Edge finishing, 274
Elastic constants, 219
Elastic properties, 237
Engine, high performance, 291
Erosion, 274
Extensometer, conventional,
    193

F

Failure mechanisms, 16
Failure tests, time to flexure,
    128
Fast Fourier transform analyzer,
    219
Fatigue behavior, 113
Fatigue crack growth, 142
Fatigue life modeling, 264
Fatigue loading, 142
Fatigue, static, 128
Fatigue tests, 49, 69
Fiber bridging, 142
Finite element, 219
Flow path sealing technique,
    291
Fractography, 176, 291
Fracture, bending, 274
Fracture strength, 16